An Introduction to Mini & Micro Computers

by

Fabian Monds
Department of Electrical and Electronic Engineering
The Queen's University of Belfast

and
Robert McLaughlin
Computer Centre
The Queen's University of Belfast

Published by: Peter Peregrinus Ltd., London, UK.
© 1981: Peter Peregrinus Ltd.
Revised Edition 1984

British Library Cataloguing in Publication Data

Monds, Fabian
    An introduction to mini and microcomputers.
    — 2nd rev. ed.
    1. Microcomputers   2. Minicomputers
    I. Title   II. McLaughlin, Robert
    001.64'04   QA76.5

ISBN 0 86341 028 6

Printed in the United Kingdom by A. Wheaton & Co. Ltd., Exeter

<u>Dedication</u>

To Vera and Eileen

Preface

Modern minicomputer and microcomputer systems are impressively powerful and cost effective combinations of electronic technology - the hardware - and programs of instructions which define the system operation - the software. This book sets out to introduce in a balanced manner, both hardware and software aspects of today's small computers, with no assumptions made regarding the reader's background knowledge or experience. It is hoped that the interested reader will work straight through the text, perhaps returning to a later detailed study of sections of special interest. Where appropriate, a tutorial style of presentation is adopted. Computer principles are illustrated by the presentation of detail on real minicomputers, microcomputers and microprocessors, and on real software. This material may also be used for reference purposes.

Chapter 1 presents the basic concepts of a computer system and introduces fundamental terms and computer components, including programs and programming.

Chapter 2 covers conventions for the representation of instructions and data, and explains instruction formats and memory addressing principles.

Chapter 3 reviews the actual instruction formats of three minicomputers and two microprocessors, and summarises their structures. Considerable detail is included, particularly for the microprocessors.

Chapter 4 introduces basic electronic digital logic elements and shows how these are combined, in integrated circuit form, to implement real computer structures. The major large scale integrated (LSI) computer components, including the microprocessor, are described.

Chapter 5 deals with the characteristics of practical microprocessor based computer structures, including memory organisation, instruction execution and input/output procedures. An 8-bit 'standard' microcomputer is used as an example.

Chapter 6 reviews the peripheral equipment available to implement complete computer systems and describes the hardware and standard techniques adopted for interconnecting computers and peripherals.

Chapter 7 adds the software to the system, and explains the features and use of assemblers, compilers and interpreters. FORTRAN, COBOL and PASCAL languages are reviewed, with example programs.

Chapter 8 extends the software review of cover supervisors, overlaying, multiprogramming and interrupt handling, and describes supervisor functions.

Chapter 9 is a tutorial presentation of the high level interpreted language BASIC, widely used on mini and microcomputers. It is intended as a first guide to BASIC programming.

We hope that this book will help those taking their first steps into the computer world to understand the basics of both hardware and software, and to appreciate their interdependence.

Acknowledgments

This book has its origins in undergraduate and postgraduate courses in computer science and computer technology presented at the Queen's University of Belfast, in post experience courses in mini and microcomputers presented for the Low Cost Automation Centre, Queen's University and for the Institution of Electrical Engineers, and in the correspondence course 'Minicomputer Systems' made available through the Continuing Education Service of the Institution of Electrical Engineers

Our engineer and computer scientist friends have made very practical contributions to this text. In particular, we wish to thank Derek Noblett of Queen's for generous help with material included in Chapter 4, Ronnie Carse and Adib Aliabadi of the Computer Centre at Queen's for the specimen programs in Chapter 7, and Charles Moore of Medical & Scientific Computer Services Ltd., who developed the material of Chapter 9. The interest and involvement of these colleagues is greatly appreciated.

Interest and helpful comments were provided by our colleagues Jim Magowan and David Ryan, and we thank them.

Feedback from undergraduate and postgraduate students at Queen's has been a most helpful contribution.

Aisling, Niamh, Helen, Rachael, Stephen, Owen and Amos simulated a random access memory for the index preparation.

Finally we wish to thank, for all her patience, ability and industry in typing and material preparation, Anne Wilson.

Contents

Computer Concepts
Chapter 1

1.1.   INTRODUCTION

This first chapter will attempt to get across the basic concepts of a computer system and hopefully make it clear that there is nothing magical inside these machines which have become so important and essential in modern day living.

We will take an overall view of the structure of a computer system but first we need to look at and explain some of the "jargon" which is used in computer systems. A reasonable grasp of the terms involved means that explanations later become much simpler and reading other computer oriented literature is more meaningful.

1.2.   BITS

The first of the buzzwords is the bit. This is a short form of the two words binary digit and is the fundamental unit of information in a computer system. The word information itself is delightfully vague - there are many varieties of information, eg, the population of a country, a person's name, your bank balance, a medical record, laws of the land, etc. At the moment most of the information in the world is stored as sets of written or printed symbols just like the ones on the pages of this book. Hopefully by the time you finish the book you will have absorbed some of the information represented on its pages by the set of communication symbols with which we are all familiar.

1. the letters of the alphabet, a, b, c...z
2. the numerals, 0, 1, 2...9
3. punctuation marks, ;:.,?!-÷, etc.

Our brains are obviously extremely adaptable in being able to scan these funny patterns of squiggly lines on a page and make some sense of them, and not only that but to master all the variations in these symbols when our friends write to us. The brain can also group these symbols together and form images for example the pattern of letters

HOUSE

is conjuring up in your mind a rather large inanimate object with doors and windows and tiles, while the slightly different pattern

MOUSE

is generating the image of a timid little creature. If one considers letters, numerals, and punctuation marks there are probably over 100 different symbols which we can easily recognise and therefore use in conveying information from one person to another. The medium for transferring the information is either by sight (the symbol A written on a page) or by sound (we hear someone speak the letter A). The blind can also sense the letter A by touch. Fortunately or unfortunately we cannot smell the letter A or taste it.

In summary then information is stored by human beings and passed between them using a set of symbols; they normally use two of their five senses, sight and sound, to see or hear these symbols.

Unfortunately computer systems do not have the adaptability of human beings and are not as cheap to construct, so the range of symbols which they are manufactured to recognise is cost effective if it is small and cheap. These are the basic criteria which led to the use of the binary system for storing and transmitting information in a computer system. The binary system contains only two symbols

0 1

because it was easy to design computer systems which can sense these symbols. Humans normally use only two sensing techniques sight and sound but computer systems have a range of sensors. The symbols 0 and 1 can be represented and sensed using

a high voltage (1)	a low voltage (0)
a current in a wire (1)	no current (0)
a hole in a paper tape (1)	no hole (0)
a switch up (1)	down (0)
a light on (1)	off (0)
a magnet polarity one way (1)	the opposite way (0)
a high pitched tone (1)	a low pitched tone (0)

At first sight it appears to be an almost impossible task to represent information as we know it using only two symbols so let us investigate a little further.

1.3.   BINARY NUMBERS

One of the standard type of "intelligence" puzzles goes as follows:

A shopkeeper wishes to weigh groceries in units of 1 pound from 1 to 15. What is the smallest number of brass weights necessary to allow him to do this and what is the value of each? (If you fancy trying to work this out don't read the next sentence - it is assumed that the weights will only be used

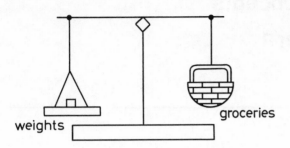

weights   groceries

An additional weight of 32 allows him to weigh
up to 63 and so on. So provided he starts wit
a one pound weight and each new weight which
he buys is twice as heavy as the previous, he
can extend his range of weighings for ever,
and the same applies to our binary numbering
system. With only one binary digit we can
represent two numbers O and 1 (zero and one),
with two digits we can represent four numbers

O O   zero
O 1   one
1 O   two
1 1   three

and with eight digits we can represent numbers
in the range O to 255, for example,

Binary	Decimal
O O O O O O O O	0
O O O O O 1 O O	4
O 1 O O O O 1 1	67
1 O O O O O O O	128
1 1 1 1 1 1 1 1	255

It can be easily shown that with n digits one
can represent numbers in the range O to
(2^n-1) so that

4 binary digits give O-15
8 binary digits give O-255
1O binary digits give O-1023
16 binary digits give O-65535

Before leaving numbers it is probably worth
pointing out that the number 1024 above, ie,
2^{10} is usually written as K, so, for example,
65536 is 64K, ie, 64 x 1024.

Numbers are stored inside a computer system
in this form which as we will see later is
convenient for carrying out arithmetic.
However when we wish to transfer information
either to another computer system at some
distance or to send information to a special
device for printing we use a slightly differen
code - ASCII.

1.4. ASCII

ASCII is the American Standard Code for
Information Interchange, and is reproduced
in the table overleaf. The table is read by
selecting the character for which a binary
code is required and writing down the three
digits at the top of the column followed by
the four digits at the left of the row. For
example, the letter A is found in the fifth
column on the second row. At the top of the
fifth column we have 1OO, at the left of the
second row we have OOO1. So in this code

similarly

          A is represented by 1000001
          B is   "   by 1000010
          + is   "   by 0101011
          = is   "   by 0111101

The symbols in the last six columns are all
familiar - the alphabet (upper and lower case)
the numerals, and punctuation marks. Those in
the first two columns are used to tell the
equipment at the other end to carry out some
operation,

eg, BEL is the code to sound a bell
     CR is the code to return the typewriter
         carriage
     LF is the code to move to the next
         line, etc.

on one side of the scales.)

The answer is four weights and their values
are one pound, two pounds, four pounds and
eight pounds. The following table gives the
distribution of the weights for each of the
15 units. A 1 in a column indicates that the
weight at the top of that column should be
placed on the scales, a zero indicates that
the weight in that column must not be used.

Eight	Four	Two	One	Total Weight
O	O	O	1	1
O	O	1	O	2
O	O	1	1	3
O	1	O	O	4
O	1	O	1	5
O	1	1	O	6
O	1	1	1	7
1	O	O	O	8
1	O	O	1	9
1	O	1	O	10
1	O	1	1	11
1	1	O	O	12
1	1	O	1	13
1	1	1	O	14
1	1	1	1	15

It is obvious that we now have a system for
representing the numbers from 1 to 15 using
only the two symbols O 1. For example

5 = O 1 O 1
9 = 1 O O 1
11 = 1 O 1 1

It is clear that if we give the shopkeeper a
weight whose value is sixteen, he can extend
his range of weighings right up to 31

16 = 1 O O O O
17 = 1 O O O 1
31 = 1 1 1 1 1

TABLE   - ASCII conversion table

HEX		O	1	2	3	4	5	6	7
	BITS	000	001	010	011	100	101	110	111
O	0000	NUL	DLE	SPACE	O	@	P	`	p
1	0001	SOH	DC1	!	1	A	Q	a	q
2	0010	STX	DC2	"	2	B	R	b	r
3	0011	ETX	DC3	#	3	C	S	c	s
4	0100	EOT	DC4	$	4	D	T	d	t
5	0101	ENQ	NAK	%	5	E	U	e	u
6	0110	ACK	SYN	&	6	F	V	f	v
7	0111	BEL	ETB		7	G	W	g	w
8	1000	BS	CAN	(	8	H	X	h	x
9	1001	HT	EM	)	9	I	Y	i	y
A	1010	LF	SUB	*	:	J	Z	j	z
B	1011	VT	ESC	+	;	K	[	k	{
C	1100	FF	FS	,	<	L	\	l	--
D	1101	CR	GS	-	=	M	]	m	}
E	1110	SO	RS	.	>	N	Λ	n	~
F	1111	SI	US	/	?	O	←	o	DEL

Note that the numerals O, 1, 2 . . . 9 are only represented in this code when they require to be printed out on the page or sent to another computer system. When they are used for arithmetic inside a computer they are represented by the standard binary code mentioned earlier. Note also that only seven bits are required to represent each of the symbols shown. In fact when sending data to another device it is usual to add an eighth bit as a check. A later chapter will go into greater detail on this point.

1.5. DATA PATHS

In most small computers today data is passed around the interior of the equipment from section to section along parallel wires. The computer is constructed of a set of individual units which perform specified functions and then pass the data on to the next unit. The data is sent as a pattern of input pulses each of which lasts (typically) for only a fraction of a millionth of a second. The diagram below shows a unit called OP sending the number 5 to a unit called LEDD (the names are unimportant).

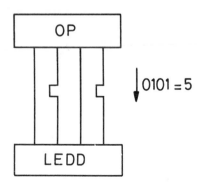

The number 5 is represented by the binary pattern 0101 and this can be physically manifested by two very short pulses travelling at exactly the same time down two of the four wires connecting OP to LEDD. When these pulses arrive at LEDD it will "realize" that it has received the number 5. Similarly the number seven will be represented in transit as -

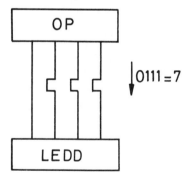

The data path is entirely passive - its only function is to convey data/information from one unit to another within the system. The units (OP and LEDD) however do perform some function on the data, as we see from the "snapshots" overleaf taken of the circuit as the number 5 passes through the LEDD.

Pulses going into the LEDD on lines b and d cause pulses to come out on lines p, q, s, u, v. Similarly a single pulse entering on line a (representing the number eight) will cause a pulse on all seven lines p, q, r, s, t, u, v.

This apparent random behaviour of the LEDD is easily understood when we realize that at the

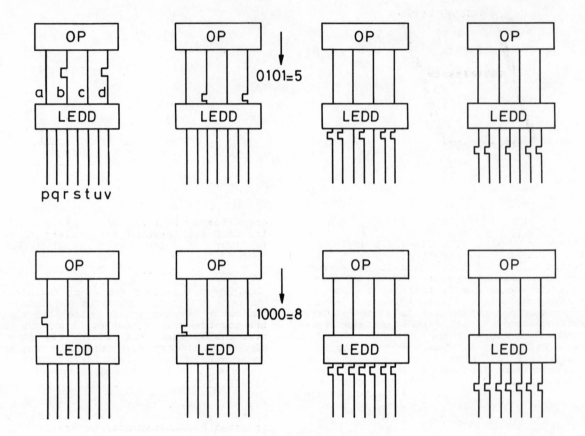

ends of the seven wires leading out of the LEDD is a seven segment display which illuminates some of the seven segments to indicate the numerals 0 to 9 (like the numerals on electronic calculators). It is constructed as follows -

Each of the seven wires p, q, r, s, t, u, v is connected to a small bar which emits a light when the wire attached to it is activated. Thus when p, q, s, u, v are activated only the following sections are lit -

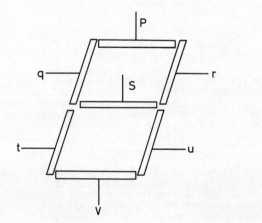

indicating the number five. Similarly when
all wires are activated as in the second
example we get the number eight.

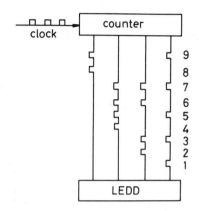

The seven individual bars are known as light
emitting diodes (LED) and the unit which converts the binary representation of the number
coming in to the appropriate pattern of pulses
to activate the diodes is the driver (LEDD).
The driver transforms a set of input pulses
to a set of output pulses as follows. Rapid
repetitive transmission of pulses produces a
continuous display.

	a	b	c	d		p	q	r	s	t	u	v
0	0	0	0	0		1	1	1	0	1	1	1
1	0	0	0	1		0	0	1	0	0	1	0
2	0	0	1	0		1	0	1	1	1	0	1
3	0	0	1	1		1	0	1	1	0	1	1
4	0	1	0	0		0	1	1	1	0	1	0
5	0	1	0	1		1	1	0	1	0	1	1
6	0	1	1	0		1	1	0	1	1	1	1
7	0	1	1	1		1	0	1	0	0	1	0
8	1	0	0	0		1	1	1	1	1	1	1
9	1	0	0	1		1	1	1	1	0	1	0

1.6. CHIPS

Example

The unit which performs the transformation of
bits for the LED display is typical of the
element of a computer system known as a chip.
Most chips will have a set of input wires and
a set of output wires. When a pattern of
pulses arrives at the chip on its input wires
a predetermined pattern of pulses is generated
at the output wires and these are passed on to
the next unit in the chain.

An example of a chip which requires no input
data (except clock pulses) is a counter. A
counter simply provides at regular intervals
the binary pattern representing 0, 1, 2, 3,
4, . . . For example the output from a four
bit counter would look something like the
following diagram.

If this pattern of pulses is fed into the LEDD
at one second intervals then we have one of the

constituents of a digital clock or watch since
the LEDD will generate the pattern of pulses
to light the segments of the unit digit of the
"seconds".

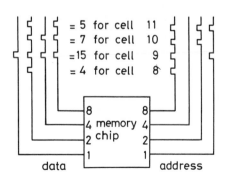

Obviously further circuitry is needed to reset
the counter when it reaches 10 and to flip
over the minutes digit after sixty seconds have
elapsed. However this chapter is not designed
to help you construct digital clocks.

Memory Chip

One of the most important sections of a computer
system is its memory and this is usually constructed from one or more memory chips. Let's
consider the simple example of a chip with 256
individual cells - each cell of which can contain a number composed of eight bits. The
chip would have eight input lines to indicate
which cell was being referenced and eight
separate lines for the data. We are then able
to instruct the chip to remember random
patterns. For example the diagram below illustrates the numbers 4, 15, 7, 5 being stored in
cells 8, 9, 10, 11 of the memory chip.

The pulses on the right indicate which of the cells the data on the left is to be stored in.

All memory chips have random access so the data does not need to be fed in in the sequence shown. We could quite easily set up 3, 13 on the address and data lines respectively followed by 7, 6 - indicating that we wished to have 13 stored in cell 3 and 6 in cell 7.

There is not much point in storing numbers in the memory chip if we cannot extract them again so there is normally a facility on the memory chip to recall data from the memory. If we imagine our memory chip to contain the data already indicated, then by placing the binary pattern for 9 on the address lines, and setting the recall pulse, the memory will reply with whatever data it has stored in cell 9 (which in our case is 15).

<u>Please produce data from cell 9</u>

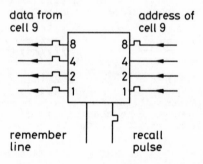

<u>Please place 11 in cell 14</u>

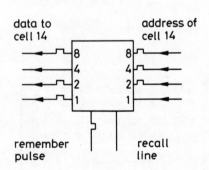

Note the essential difference between the memory chip and the LEDD chip. The LEDD always responded with the same output pattern for a given input pattern, eg, 0101, going in to the chip produced 1101011 out of the chip. However 0101 fed into the memory chip will

produce an output pattern corresponding to the data which was last stored in cell number 5, and we can overwrite this data as often as we like.

We can think of our memory chip then as a series of cells just like a street of houses. Each cell contains a number (data) and each cell is numbered (the address). After all the transactions above if we could open the chip and look into it we would see for example the binary pattern for 13 1101 in cell 3 and for 7 0111 in cell 10.

0	
1	
2	
3	13
4	
5	
6	
7	6
8	4
9	15
10	7
11	5
12	
13	
14	11

The Central Processing Unit

The most important chip in a computer system is the CPU (or central processing unit) where most of the work is done. The chips we have been describing so far are relatively standard; all memory chips behave in roughly the same fashion - given an address they will produce the data stored at that address, likewise all counters produce binary numbers in sequence. The CPU however varies significantly from one manufacturer to another. We will be looking at different CPU structures but to continue the development of the computer concept we will examine here a theoretical processor which exhibits most of the features of real devices.

Inside the CPU chip there are a number of smaller units - one of these is the accumulator. This is a special memory cell for holding totals during arithmetic operations hence its name. It features in a large number of the operations which the processor chip can perform. Like the memory chip the CPU has a datapath leading to it and an address path, but unlike memory as well as placing data on the data path we can also place a function code there.

For example,

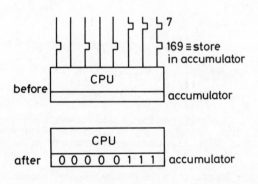

if the pattern of pulses representing 169 and 7 are fed into the CPU, the chip will store the number 7 in the accumulator. If this is followed by the binary patterns for 105 and 9 respectively, the number 9 will be added to the number 7 which is already in the accumulator, resulting in the number 16 being stored there.

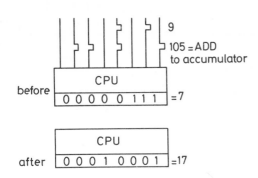

before CPU
0 0 0 0 0 1 1 1 = 7

after CPU
0 0 0 1 0 0 0 1 = 17

9
105 = ADD
to accumulator

will "pass through" the CPU on to the
address lines, a recall pulse will be sent to
the memory and the data from cell number 9
(ie, 15) will be placed on the data paths.
This pattern will be presented to the CPU
and added to the accumulator. The accumulator
will then contain the sum of the original 7
and 15, ie, 22.

So (105,9) means add 9 to the accumulator
whereas (101,9) means add whatever number is
in cell 9 to the accumulator.

The operations described above - addition
and subtraction, take place in millionths of
a second so it is obvious that we require some
automatic mechanism for feeding the instructions to the CPU. This is done by holding
the instructions themselves in memory and it
is this concept which distinguishes a computer from other electronic devices.

1.7. PROGRAM

Let us examine a typical sequence of instructions (referred to as a program of instructions). Let us assume that as well as the
numbers we have already managed to get into
our memory chip at locations 3, 7, 8, 9, 10,
11 we somehow manage to get the numbers
shown into the cells 17 to 26 inclusive. If
we examine these cells in pairs and assume
that they represent a sequence of instructions
for our central processor, the results of their
execution will be as follows -

This particular CPU has been constructed so
that when the number 169 is fed in it will
take the next number coming in on the data
path, ie, 7, and place it in the accumulator
(overwriting whatever was there already)
whereas if it gets the number 105 first it
will add the next number in the datapath to
the number already in the accumulator.
Similarly the pair (223,4) will mean - subtract the number 4 from the accumulator.
These pairs of numbers are referred to as
instructions - (they instruct the processor
what task it is to perform). The first
number is the function to be carried out (add,
subtract, etc) while the second is the operand
on which that function is to be performed.

So far we have been dealing with "immediate
operands" ie, the number present on the data
path immediately after the function code is
the number which is to be used in the
operation. But the CPU chip is always
associated with a memory chip and it is possible to extract data from the memory. So let
us attach the memory chip we discussed already
to the CPU.

Now instead of feeding the CPU with the pair
(105,9) which meant add 9 to the accumulator
we feed it the pair (101,9). Instead of
adding 9 to the accumulator the pattern for 9

(17,18) = 169,0 means put the
number zero into the accumulator.

(19,20) = 101,7 add to the
accumulator the contents of cell
7 - (ie, add 6 to 0, accumulator
now contains 6)

(21,22) = 101,8 add to the
accumulator the contents of cell
8 (ie, add 4 to the 6 already in
the accumulator, new contents
of accumulator = 10)

(23,24) = 101, 9 add to the
accumulator the contents of cell
9 (ie, add 15 to the 10 already
in the accumulator, new contents
of accumulator = 25)

(25,26) = 133,1 copy the contents of the accumulator into
cell 1. The previous contents
of cell 1 (whatever they may be)
are replaced by a copy of what
is in the accumulator, ie, 25.

0	
1	
2	
3	13
4	
5	
6	
7	6
8	4
9	15
10	7
11	5
12	
13	
14	11
15	
16	
17	169
18	0
19	101
20	7
21	101
22	8
23	101
24	9
25	133
26	1

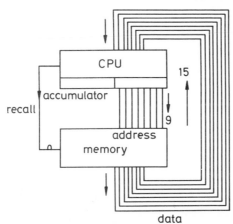

data

This program of instructions will therefore add together the numbers in cells 7, 8, 9 (ie, 6, 4, 15) and place the answer into cell 1.

There are still two problems. First looking at the contents of the memory chip there appears to be no distinction between the data and the instructions - how does the processor know that the 169 in cell 17 is a function code rather than one of the "numbers to be added"? Secondly how do we get the processor to execute these instructions in the proper sequence? Both of these problems are resolved by a special counter in the computer system called the program counter. The program counter contains a number which is always the address of the next instruction, and as each instruction is being executed 2 is added to the number in the program counter (PC). We therefore set this program counter to 17 and the computer then proceeds to execute the sequence of instructions as follows:-

PC = 17; fetch the number pair in cell 17,18
          ie, 169,0
          decode the first number to see what
          to do (copy the next data item to the
          accumulator)
          copy zero into the accumulator (A=0)
          add two to the program counter
PC = 19; fetch the number pair in cell 19,20
          (ie, 101,7)
          decode the first number to see what
          to do (add contents of cell indicated
          by next data item 7)
          get the number from cell 7 and
          add to the accumulator
          add 2 to the PC
PC = 21; etc.

So there is an automatic cycle of operations performed by the computer system as soon as it is started by having the program counter set.

1 Fetch the next instruction indicated by
   the program counter
2 Decode and obey this instruction
3 Add 2 to the program counter
4 Go back to operation 1.

The computer system when it is delivered will contain all the electronics necessary to go through the above cycle of operations. The versatility of the computer system arises from the set of numbers which we have in the memory. One set of numbers may represent a list of instructions to evaluate the payroll of a large company. They are placed in the memory of the computer and executed as above. This set of numbers may then be replaced by a completely different set which may calculate the path of a satellite around the earth.

The "art" of programming is in working out this set of numbers and getting them into memory in the correct locations.

1.8. PROGRAMMING

Knowing how the computer works at the single instruction level is one thing. Getting it to solve a particular problem is another. We have already seen that the computer will obey instructions in the memory, but these instructions are limited to arithmetic operations of the form add, subtract, copy. We will see

later that primitive instructions exist to allow us to change the program counter if particular conditions exist, but these again are limited to something of the form:-

skip the next instruction if the accumulator contains zero or go to instruction 134 if the accumulator is not zero.

Any requirement which is more complex must be broken up into a single set of instructions which the processor can "understand". The first step along this path is to write the requirement as a series of logical steps. This set of logical steps is often referred to as an algorithm.

Algorithms

Let us first consider a relatively simple problem. "A man is required by using only a 3 litre can and a 5 litre can to draw off 4 litres of water from a well". Now suppose you were sending a not too clever colleague to the well on this errand you might write out the set of instructions which he was required to execute in sequence to perform the task thus-

1. Fill 5 litre can from well
2. Fill 3 litre can from 5 litre can (leaving two litres in 5 litre can)
3. Return the 3 litres from 3 litre can to well
4. Pour the 2 litres from the 5 litre can into the 3 litre can
5. Fill the 5 litre can from the well
6. Top up the 3 litre can from the 5 litre can (leaving 4 litres in the 5 litre can)
7. Empty the 3 litre can back into the well.

What we have here is an algorithm for producing 4 litres of water from a well using only a 3 and 5 litre can. This is a fairly straightforward algorithm because no decisions require to be made by the executor at any time, he simply carries out a set of commands in sequence.

Consider a set slightly more complex (if even more unlikely) problem:

"A man is locked in a room with only two doors - a red door and a blue door. One of these doors leads to freedom and the other to certain death. Each door has a guardian, one of whom always tells the truth and the other always tells lies. The man may ask one (and only one) question of either guardian. What should he do?"

The following algorithm will cater for such unlikely situations:

1. Approach either of the two guardians and ask him the following question. "If I were to ask your friend which door led to freedom what would be his reply?"
2. If the guardian replies "the red door" proceed through the blue door.
3. If the guardian replies "the blue door" proceed through the red door.

This algorithm is a little bit more difficult for our man to follow. Firstly it required him to make a decision. "Was the response red or blue" and secondly it required a little bit of commonsense, ie, if the reply was blue not to give up but to proceed to step 3 of the algorithm.

Finally here is a section of a much more

cryptic algorithm:

A "To fit 32(34:36:38) chest.
B Length 23½(23¾:24:24¼).
C Using No. 11 cast on 110(116:122:128)
D Row 1 - K1(K4:P3,K4:K2),*P4,K4, rep from * to
        last 5(0:3:6) sts, P4, K1(0:P3:P4,K2)
E Row 2 - P1(P4:K3,P4:P2),*K4, P4, rep from *
        to last 5(0:3:6) sts, K4, P1(0:K3:K4,
        P2)
F Work 22 more rows in rib
G Change to No. 9
H Work 98 rows"

If by the time we have come to discussing assembly languages later you feel like giving up because things are too complex or cryptic, it may be sobering to reflect that dear old ladies rocking in armchairs all over the world are reading instructions like these and producing polo-necked sweaters for favoured grandchildren (not to mention keeping the cat from playing with the wool).

This algorithm is of course a knitting pattern. It is designed to produce a garment for four optional sizes (chest 32" length 23½) (chest 34",length 23¾") (chest 36", length 24") or chest 38", length 24¼").

There are two basic operations K-knit and P-purl, the number after the operation gives the number of stitches. The instructions differ slightly depending on which of these four sizes is required. Line C above indicated how many stitches are required 110 for the smallest size to 128 for the largest. The instructions for the first row are as follows:-

Size	32 x 23½	34 x 23¾	36 x 24	38 x 24¼
	K1	K4	P3,K4	K2
	P4,K4	P4,K4	P4,K4	P4,K4
	P4,K4	P4,K4	P4,K4	P4,K4
	P4,K4	P4,K4	.	.
	P4,K4	.	.	.
	P4,K4	.	.	.
	P4,K4	.	.	.
	P4,K4	.	.	.
	P4,K4	.	.	.
	P4,K4	.	.	.
	P4,K4	.	.	.
	P4,K4	.	.	.
	P4,K4	P4,K4	P4,K4	.
	P4,K1	P4,K4	P4,K4	P4,K4
			P3	P4,K4
				P4,K2
TOTAL	110	116	122	128

The instructions for the second row are effectively a mirror image of the first row. Line F then indicates that these two rows should be produced alternately for the next 22 rows, when a change of needles to size no. 9 is required.

It is evident from the foregoing examples that a series of instructions can normally be written down in some form to solve a problem, or carry out a specific task. It is usual to break the task down into simpler tasks and eventually into simple operations (like knit, purl, etc). The algorithms outlined above are to be processed by people (the drawer from the well, the knitter).

A program is an algorithm or set of instructions which is to be processed by a computer to carry out a specific task or to solve a particular problem. Just like the knitting pattern it is necessary to reduce the problem to a series of simple operations and to have some code or notation which can be understood and executed by the computer.

The knitting pattern analogy serves to dispel one other apparent paradox about the computer, ie, "if the computer operates at say 1 million instructions per second, then it requires one million instructions to keep it busy for one second and someone has to write these instructions (taking a long time), and the computer needs a large amount of storage to contain them". Techniques like those on line D

"*P4,K4 rep from* to last 5"

ie, repeat the operation P4, K4 until only 5 stitches remain and line F

"Work 22 more rows"

ie, repeat row 1 and row 2 alternately for 22 rows ensure that repetitive operations need only be explicitly stated once. In fact lines D, E, F and H obviously require very little space as a set of instructions but their execution requires that about 14,000 basic stitches have to be knit and this could well keep the processor of the instructions busy for an hour or two depending on manual dexterity.

1.9. LANGUAGES

In the early days of computing it was necessary to break each step of the algorithm down into the primitive instructions which the processor could "understand". In some cases this even meant feeding the appropriate numbers into the memory cells of the computer in binary form. This was obviously an extremely tedious and exacting task since a '1' entered where there should have been a '0' could cause the programs to completely malfunction. Such a mistake could easily result in a subtraction being performed where an addition was required.

Another disadvantage was that different manufacturers used different numbers for the same function - so a program developed on computer X would not work on computer Y because 105 meant "add" on computer X but "subtract" on computer Y. A great leap forward was made when the versatility of the computer was harnessed to alleviate this problem. A language called FORTRAN was invented and each computer manufacturer produced a translator program which converted instructions written in the FORTRAN language into the number codes required by his particular machine. Thus an instruction of the form -

CELL(1) = CELL(7)+CELL(8)+CELL(9)

when passed through the translator would result in the set of numbers 169,0,101,7,101,8,101,9,133,1 being planted in the appropriate memory cells of our computer X but which when passed through the translater on computer Y would result in -

146,0,241,7,241,8,241,9,191,1

being placed in the appropriate cells of computer Y because 241 is the code for "add" and 191 is the code for copy on computer Y.

As well as making programs transportable from one system to another, the new language made

program writing much easier and quicker because
statements of the form on previous page are
much more readable and meaningful than a set
of numbers.

The idea spread and a number of languages each
suited to a particular task emerged with names
like

ALGOL, COBOL, BASIC, PASCAL.

Each new computer that is designed is now
accompanied by a translater program for one or
more of the above languages.

The steps normally involved in using the computer to solve a given problem are

1. State the problem
2. Produce an algorithm for the solution of
    the problem
    Break each step of this algorithm down
    until eventually it can be described in
    a set of statements in a language like
    FORTRAN
3. Use the FORTRAN translater provided with
    the machine to translate each of the
    FORTRAN statements into the binary notation
    "understood" by the processor. The
    translater usually leaves this binary
    pattern of primitive instructions in the
    memory cells of the machine (or on a
    magnetic tape or disc which can easily
    be copied to the memory cells).
4. Start the machine processing the primitive
    instructions which now make up the
    solution of the problem.

1.10.   PACKAGED SYSTEMS

The final development in the chain is the
packaged system. Here the purchaser of the
system is provided not only with the processor,
memory and translater program, but also with
a special written program for his particular
application. He may have no interest whatever in the internal workings of the computer
nor in the subtleties of the languages
involved. His only interest is perhaps in
keeping track of the stock which he buys and
sells, so when he switches on his computer in
the morning, the computer greets him with a
friendly salutation, provides him with a
summary of yesterday's stock levels and waits
patiently for today's orders.

1.11.   SUMMARY

This chapter has been a very quick romp
through the basic constituents of computer
systems. The objective has been to provide an
overview of the concepts involved to set the
scene for the rest of the book which will deal
in much more detail with the components and
structure of computer systems, the mechanisms
for the input, output and storage of programs
and data, and the wide range of programs that
are necessary to make a computer system function in particular environments.

Instructions and Data
Chapter 2

2.1. INTRODUCTION

As indicated in Chapter 1, a computer manufacturer is free to design his computer system in whatever way he sees fit. The models available from different manufacturers vary widely in overall size, the number of bits in each cell, the number of different instructions which the computer understands, the speed of the processor, etc. Even models from the same manufacturer can differ widely. For example the largest manufacturer of mini-computers - Digital Equipment Corporation - produced

a PDP-8 computer with a 12 bit memory cell
a PDP-9 computer with an 18 bit memory cell
a PDP-10 computer with a 36 bit memory cell
a PDP-11 computer with a 16 bit memory cell
a VAX11/780 computer with a 32 bit memory cell.

However despite the wide variety of systems available certain conventions have emerged for the representation of instructions and data. This chapter will examine some of these conventions without reference to any specific computer system. (The next chapter looks in detail at some real implementations.)

Section 2.2. looks at the three types of instruction required (a) instructions to get our data into and out from the computer (Input/Output), (b) instructions to perform the usual arithmetic operations on the data (Arithmetic), (c) instructions to follow different paths through the program, dependent on the data (Decisions).

Section 2.3. shows how the number of operands necessary for a given instruction can vary and leads to the typical structure of the registers in a computer in Section 2.4. The availability of such registers led to the typical conventions for addressing memory outlined in 2.5.

Section 2.6. outlines the special numbering systems that are used as a shorthand for writing long binary numbers. The mathematical background for the different arithmetic schemes is included for completeness but is not essential for following the rest of the book.

Section 2.7. gives the rules for addition and subtraction showing how the simplification of these led to the complement format for storing negative numbers in 2.8.

Section 2.9. gives some of the techniques for representing non-integer values, and shows

how the range of numbers capable of being stored can be extended at the expense of accuracy (using floating point numbers).

Section 2.10. indicates how text is stored.

2.2. BASIC INSTRUCTIONS

Let us now examine what are the primitive computer instructions that are required, and how we might represent them. Our computer must obviously be capable of carrying out the basic arithmetic operations of addition, subtraction, multiplication and division. Let us consider addition - what is required is an instruction which will add two numbers stored somewhere in the computer and place the answer somewhere else in the computer. The first problem here is where are the numbers that are to be added (the operands).

The computer store is considered as a series of sequentially numbered cells or words, so that we can indicate an operand by the "address" of the cell containing that operand. (It's a little like a prison where the cells are numbered and so are the convicts inside the cells - the operand is the convict's number and the address of the operand is his cell number.) Suppose that our computer has 256 cells, then to allow for all possible combinations we will require eight bits to represent the address of each operand. (Cells numbered 0-255) Also we require eight bits to represent the address of the result of the addition. To cater for subtraction, multiplication and division as well as addition we require to distinguish four operations so two bits should be equivalent (say 00-add, 01-subtract, 10-multiply, 11-divide).

Arithmetic Instructions

A possible method of representing arithmetic instructions therefore would be to use 26 bits for each instruction as follows:-

Operation first operand second operand result

2 bits	8 bits	8 bits	8 bits

These separate sections of the instruction are usually referred to as fields.

00	00000001	00011111	11111111

could be interpreted as - add the number in cell 1 to the number in cell 31 and place the result in cell 255.

```
        OO = add
00000001 =    1
00011111 =   31
11111111 = 255
```

01	10000000	11111110	10000000

could be interpreted as subtract the number in cell 128 from the number in cell 254 and place the result in cell 128 (thus overwriting the number originally there).

Multiplication could be handled similarly but in the case of division we could enhance the system (since two results arise from this operation, ie, the quotient and the remainder) by including another result field. This would make the division instruction 34 bits long.

At first sight it might appear attractive to be able to add a list of numbers in the computer. This would require a different operation code from the straight-forward addition above, eg, increasing the operation field to 3 bits

000	00000001	00011111	11111111

100	00000001	00011111	11111111

The first of these could mean (as above) add the number in cell 1 to the number in cell 31 and place the result in cell 255, whereas the second could mean add all numbers in cells numbered 1 to 31 and place the result in cell 255.

Decisions

Instructions coded in some form like the arithmetic set above are located sequentially in the store and the computer automatically proceeds from each instruction to the following one, unless otherwise instructed. It is the facility to alter the path of instructions being obeyed which distinguishes the general purpose computer from other machines which obey a fixed program of instructions (like an automatic washing machine, dishwasher, etc.).

The decisions are usually based on a comparison of the contents of two stores in the machine (say 15 and 64). There are three possibilities

the contents of 15 are less than those of 64
the contents of 15 are equal to those of 64
the contents of 15 are greater than those of 64.

We could therefore construct our computer to obey instructions of the form:

	operation	store 1	store 2	next instruction
A	101	00001111	01000000	00011111
B	110	00001111	01000000	00011111
C	111	00001111	01000000	00011111

A means "proceed to instruction 31 if the contents of 15 are less than those of 64"
B means "proceed to instruction 31 if the contents of 15 are equal to those of 64"
C means "proceed to instruction 31 if the contents of 15 are greater than those of 64"

Although the criteria used in deciding whether to pass on to the next instruction or to some other instruction in the program are relatively

simple, an extremely versatile program can be constructed which appears to make very complex judgements (eg, programs which play chess, draughts, etc.).

Input/Output

One other group of instructions that we require our computer to understand and implement are those to take numbers from the "real world" and put them in the stores of the computer, and similarly to take numbers in the stores of the computer and transmit them to the outside world in a form that humans can read.

One mechanism for input would be to represent a number by its binary equivalent set up on a line of switches. We might have an instruction therefore (say operation 8) which would "read" the number from the switches into one store of the computer, eg,

operation	address
1000	10000001

read the number set up on switches into store 129. If a large set of numbers was required the setting up procedure would be rather long, so numbers could be punched on paper tape and read by an instruction of the form:-

Operation	number	address
1001	00010000	00100001

read the next 16 numbers from paper tape into the store beginning at cell 33. Two similar operations could be:

18 - display the contents of a cell on a set of lights
19 - punch a sequence of numbers on to paper tape

2.3.   INSTRUCTION FORMATS

The following is a brief description of the various instruction formats that have been used in computers over the years. Some of these are now defunct but are included for completeness and to demonstrate the evolution to the modern systems, and the trade-offs involved.

Four Address

In this system the instruction is made up of five fields (one operator and four operands).

F, A, B, R, N

For arithmetic instructions this is interpreted as:- perform the function F on the two cells A and B, place the result in R and proceed to the instruction in cell N. Other operations such as decisions hence could be coded as eg, F, A, B, N1, N2 interpreted as perform the test F(<, =, >) on A and B, and proceed to N1 if the test fails or N2 if the test succeeds. While such an instruction format allows very versatile instructions, this is achieved at the cost of space since each of the four operands has to have sufficient bits to address all of the cells in store. For a store containing 1024 cells this meant 10 bits for each operand and therefore each instruction requires 40+ bits.

Three Addresses

On an analysis of programs it is evident that
the majority of operations are straightforward arithmetic-type or input/output instructions where there is no decision or change in
the sequence of operations so the fourth
address could be abolished and the computer
designed to normally proceed to the next
instruction in sequence. A special cell could
be used to store the address of the next
instruction - this would be automatically
increased by one as each instruction is obeyed.
Only decision-making instructions would
explicitly state the address of the next
instruction, eg,

31	ADD	54	96	102

32	EQUAL	96	97	41

With appropriate codes for ADD and EQUAL
these instructions are interpreted as

31 add the number in cells 54 and 96, place
the result in cell 102, and proceed to the
next instruction (ie, 32)
32 compare the numbers in cells 96, 97; if
they are equal proceed to instruction 41,
otherwise (if they are unequal) proceed to
the next instruction (ie, 33).

Two Addresses

A further reduction in the length of the
instruction can be effected if we allow the
result of the arithmetic operations to overwrite one of the operands. For example

ADD	96	57

can be interpreted as add the contents of 57
to the contents of 96, and place the result
in cell 96. So that if 57 contained 5, and
96 contained 6 before execution of the
instruction, then 96 would contain 11 afterwards and 57 would remain unchanged at 5.

For a 1024 cell store our instruction now
requires only f + 10 + 10 bits where f is
the number of bits required to specify all
the different operators (or functions). We
could reduce the length further by restrict-
ing the first operand to a much smaller range
of cells, say the first 4. This means the
first operand will only require 2 bits to
specify cells 0, 1, 2 or 3.

One Address

The next logical reduction is of course to
restrict the first operand (which contains the
"accumulated" result) to only one specific
cell of the computer. So that

ADD	57

would be interpreted as "add" the contents of
cell 57 to the contents of the special cell.
This special cell conventionally does not
belong to the store of the machine and is
usually implemented as a part of the processor.
Its address is implied by the instruction
ADD and therefore we do not require any bits
to specify its address.

Zero Address

There are computers in existence which have
no operand stated explicitly. They are
sometimes referred to as stack machines

because a sequence of cells in the store is
regarded as containing a stack of operands
starting at "address" zero. When an arithmetic instruction is obeyed, the bottom two
operands are used, the result replaces the
bottom operand and the whole stack appears to
move down one place.

6				
5	f			
4	e	f		
3	d	e	f	
2	c	d	e	f
1	b	c	d	e
0	a	a+b	a+b-c	(a+b-c)xd

For example the instructions ADD, SUBTRACT,
MULTIPLY would result in the above changes
in cells "0" to "5".

2.4. SPECIAL PURPOSE REGISTERS

In the previous discussion on instruction
formats, reference was made to special 'cells'
for containing the address of the next instruction to be obeyed, and the 'accumulator' cell
in the one-address machine. There are a number
of these 'cells' in most minicomputers which,
largely because of the frequency with which
they are used, form a part of the central processing unit (CPU) rather than the memory
cells of the computer. These cells in the
processor are referred to as registers. All
of these may be explicitly used on some
machines, and many may be accessed by programs.

Program Counter

This register will always contain the address
of the next instruction to be obeyed. To
start a program executing it is necessary to
place the address of the first instruction of
that program into the program counter. The
hardware of the CPU will then fetch the
instruction whose address is in the program
counter, increase the contents of the counter,
execute the instruction, and then repeat the
cycle for the next instruction. The number by
which the program counter is increased depends
on the particular instruction and this is
'known' by the CPU. Some specific instructions cause the contents of the program counter
to be changed, again during the execution of
the instruction, eg, the EQUAL instruction in
"Three Addresses" would cause the program
counter to be changed from 33 (the next
instruction) to 41, if the result of the
comparison is true.

There are also unconditional jump instructions
on most computers, eg,

31	JUMP	93

means proceed to instruction 93, without any
decisions. (It has the same imperative tone
as that card in the game of MONOPOLY which
says "GO TO JAIL, GO DIRECTLY TO JAIL, DO NOT
PASS GO".)

The Accumulator

Most minicomputers have one such register.
It features implicitly as one of the operands
in all arithmetic operations, eg,

54	ADD	105
;

instruction 54 here requests that the contents
of cell 105 be added to the contents of the
accumulator register and that the result overwrite the previous contents of the accumulator.

Some minicomputers allow a number of accumulator registers and these are then explicitly
selected by an appropriate field in the
instruction.

eg,   <u>54</u> | ADD | 01 | 105 |

could be used to request the addition of cell
105 to accumulator 1. In this machine there
would be four accumulators numbered 0, 1, 2,
3 (or 00, 01, 10, 11 in binary).

The Accumulator Extension

If we consider the result of multiplying
numbers consisting of two decimal digits it
is clear that we will normally require more
than two digits for the product

02 x 04 =   8
11 x 09 =   99
11 x 11 =   121
12 x 99 = 1188
99 x 99 = 9801

in fact we need four digits. The same applies
to multiplying binary numbers. If we have two
16-bit numbers to multiply then the product
will require 32 bits. The extension register
provides the extra bit length required. It
is also used for <u>shift</u> operations which we
will encounter later. The extension normally
holds the least significant part of the product.

The Index Register

This register is used to optionally modify
the operand address. Normally a bit is used
to indicate whether the operand address is to
be modified. Suppose the index register contains 11 (eleven)

| ADD | 0 | 96 |

would cause the contents of cell 96 to be
added to the accumulator <u>but</u>

| ADD | 1 | 96 |

would cause the contents of cell 107 (96+11)
to be added to the accumulator.

The main purpose of this register is to allow
the same operation or sets of operations to
be performed on a sequence of cells. For
example a typical set of instructions to add
the contents of 100 cells 201, 202, 203 ...
300 might read

31	LOAD INDEX	0	100
32	ADD	1	200
33	DEC	0	35
34	JUMP	0	32
35			

31 sets the index register = 100
32 adds the contents of 300 (200+100) to the
accumulator
33 subtracts 1 from the index register (99)
and jumps to 35 if index is zero
34 goes back to 32
32 adds the contents of 299 (200+99) to the
accumulator

33 subtracts 1 from the index register (98)
and jumps to 35 if index is zero
34 goes back to 32
32 adds the contents of 298 (200+98) ...

Eventually the computer does get past 34
when all 100 numbers have been added. The
numbers were added in reverse order but the
result is not affected by the order of
addition.

The Carry Register

This is a <u>one bit</u> register which is used in
the addition of numbers which are so large
that they require more than one cell. The
addition of such numbers means that as each
pair of cells is added it may be necessary
to carry a bit into the addition of the next
pair. If this is the case the carry register
is set and is automatically included with
the next ADD instruction. The ADD instruction automatically clears the carry as soon
as it has used it, but may reset it again at
the end of the instruction, if a carry is
required into the next phase.

The Overflow Register

This is a one bit register which is used to
indicate that the result of the arithmetic
operation is too large to be held in a cell
of the store. For example in a store containing 3-bit cells, the addition of 4 and 5
is too large to be held in 3-bits.

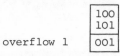

overflow 1

This one bit is used to set the overflow
register, and the result (in this case 1)
is therefore invalid. All computers have
instructions which allow the testing of the
overflow register.

For those machines with a carry register,
there are often two different add functions:-

ADDC - Add with carry (used for the lower
digits)
ADDV - Add with overflow (used for the last
pair)

The Clock

This is a register in the processor which is
incremented at a fixed interval - usually at
2^n per second where n varies from machine
to machine. Such clocks can be read accuratel
by the processor at intervals down to
1/100,000 of a second. Some machines also
allow the clock to <u>interrupt</u> the processor
at intervals which may be prescribed by the
program. An interrupt will change the program counter to some other location in store
(but before doing so will make a copy of its
contents) so that the program may be continued from this point.

Console Display

There are usually two registers which allow
basic input and output to the computer. For
output a set of lights on the console reflect
the status of the output register (where a
bit is one in the register the corresponding
light is lit). In the case of input the
setting of a row of switches at the front of
the computer cause a pattern of bits to

appear in the input register - one bit set for each switch in the down position.

2.5. ADDRESSING CONVENTIONS

Having introduced the idea of special purpose registers in the computer we now want to return to the problem of addressing the memory, and show how such registers feature in the addressing techniques. Section 2.3. outlined the various possible approaches to instruction formats, and we saw that while four address and three address systems gave considerable flexibility, this led to the disadvantage of requiring a large number of bits for each instruction. Also the more complex our computer is (ie, the greater the number of different functions like ADD, SUBTRACT etc, that it can perform) the greater the number of bits which will be required to specify these different functions. If the number of bits for each instruction is large, then the memory capacity to store programs will also need to be large and so the cost increases. To overcome these problems a number of different addressing techniques has evolved and we will consider a mythical computer to demonstrate these.

Let us assume that the memory of our computer is constructed in 16 bit words (in practice a popular minicomputer word length) and that the computer can perform 16 different basic operations coded in binary as

0 0 0 0	LOAD (ie, move data from a memory cell to the accumulator)
0 0 0 1	ADD
0 0 1 0	SUBTRACT
0 0 1 1	MULTIPLY
1 0 1 0	JUMP
1 0 1 1	JUMP IF
1 1 0 0	SKIP IF
1 1 1 1	DATA OUT (send data to a row of lights on the console)

Our computer has two accumulators 0 and 1 and one index register, so we require 1 bit to specify the accumulator and one for the index register (ie, 6 bits so far). To cater for different addressing techniques we will require two bits (often referred to as mode bits) and that leaves eight for the address of the operand. An instruction then has the following fields (don't worry about the indirect and index fields - we will come to them later).

```
BITS      0 1 2 3       4          5
         | OPERATION | ACCUMULATOR | INDEX |
      6            7     8 9 10 11 12 13 14 15
| INDIRECT | RELATIVE |         ADDRESS        |
```

Some or all of the following conventions are used in most minicomputers.

Immediate Addressing

```
        4 5 6 7
   1 0 0 1 0 0 0 0 0 0 0 1 1 1 1 1
```

This is interpreted as ADD 31 to the contents of accumulator 0 (if bit 4 were 1 then this would mean add 31 to the contents of accumulator 1). The instruction, rather than containing the address of an operand, contains

the operand itself (in this case 31). If accumulator 0 contained 28 before the operation then it would contain 59 after the operation.

Direct Addressing

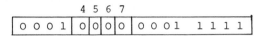
```
         4 5 6 7
   | 0 0 0 1 | 0 | 0 | 0 | 0 | 0 0 0 1   1 1 1 1 |
```

This is interpreted as ADD the contents of store 31 to the contents of accumulator 0. Thus if the contents of accumulator 0 were 28 before the operation, and store 31 contained 7, then accumulator 0 would contain 35 after the operation. The field in bits (8-15) specified here was the address of the operand. The computer distinguished the operations by recognizing the two different operation codes 0001 and 1001 and this is the usual way that immediate and direct addressing are distinguished.

This mode of addressing will allow us to access all of the stores whose address can be specified by the eight bits in the operand field, ie, stores 0-255. Minicomputers often contain memories of up to 32,768 2^{16}) stores so we need a mechanism for accessing those other stores whose address is greater than 255.

Relative Addressing

One convention in use is to regard the operand as an offset for the program counter. Consider a computer in which the program counter is increased by one just before an instruction is executed. Relative addressing is indicated by bit 7 being set equal to 1. Thus the instruction (at memory location 2641)

```
            4 5 6 7
   2641  | 0 0 0 1 | 0 | 0 | 0 | 1 | 0 0 0 1   1 1 1 1 |
```

is translated as ADD the contents of "(the program counter 2642) + (31)" to accumulator 0. That is add the contents of 2673 to accumulator 0. Thus if 2673 contained 93 and accumulator 0 contained 28 before the instruction was obeyed then accumulator 0 would be changed to 121 after the instruction. It is usual to regard the offset in bits 8-15 as a signed two's complement integer, ie,

```
0 0 0 0  0 0 0 0  =      0
1 1 1 1  1 1 1 1  =     -1
0 1 1 1  1 1 1 1  =    127
1 0 0 0  0 0 0 0  =   -128
```

This convention gives access to the stores N-127 to N+128 at instruction N (since while instruction N is being executed the program counter is at N+1). We can thus envisage an "access window" of 256 stores centred on the instruction being executed, moving down the memory as the program counter increases.

Indirect Addressing

With bit 6 set for indirect addressing and stores 31 and 127 containing 127 and 54 respectively

```
   0 0 0 1  0 0 1 0  0 0 0 1  1 1 1 1
```

is interpreted by the computer as ADD 54 to the contents of accumulator O. The computer interprets the instruction as add <u>the contents of the store specified</u> by the <u>contents of store 31</u> to accumulator O.

ie, add <u>the contents of 127</u> to accumulator O
ie, add <u>54</u>   to accumulator O

In the case of indirect addressing then, the address first calculated is not the operand for the function but is a pointer to the address of the operand. Since store 31 can contain a signed integer in the range -32,768 to +32,767 (see 2.7.) then a memory consisting of 32,768 cells labelled O to 37,767 can be accessed by indirect addressing techniques.

Indirect and relative addressing modes can be combined in one instruction. Thus if store 97 contains 181, store 181 contains 23 and store 65 contains the instruction,

```
              4 5 6 7
65   │ 0 0 0 1 │ 0 │ 0 │ 1 │ 1 │ 0 0 0 1 1 1 1 1 │
```

this instruction will be interpreted as add 23 to accumulator O. This is because the relative addressing mode (bit 7) indicates that the operand 31 in the instruction is to be used as an offset to the program counter. The program counter is 66 (65+1) so this gives an address of 97; however the indirect bit (bit 6) tells the computer that 97 is not the operand but contains the address of the operand, to wit, 181. So the "true" operand is 23. 181 is often referred to as the "effective address" of the operand to distinguish it from the "apparent address" in the instruction (ie, 31).

Indexed Addressing

In this case a special index register in the machine provides a "base address" to which the "offset" specified in the instruction is added to give the "effective address".

Thus if the index register contains 97 and store 128 contains 15 then the instruction

```
            4 5 6 7
│ 0 0 0 1 │ 0 │ 1 │ 0 │ 0 │ 0 0 0 1 1 1 1 1 │
```

would cause 15 to be added to accumulator O. The offset (31) is added to the index register (97) to give the "effective address" of the operand (128).

If bit 6 (indirect) was also set in this instruction then this would cause the <u>contents of store 15</u> to be added to accumulator. So we can have indirect indexed as well as the indirect relative combination.

Summary

To overcome the problem of specifying a function which may be up to 5 bits, the address of an operand which may require (effectively) 15 bits, and perhaps an accumulator (up to 2 bits) all in a 16 bit word a number of conventions have emerged for the address field.

Minicomputers use one or more of the above conventions in various combinations. Some have base registers in addition or instead of index registers. Some allow another level of

indirection dependent upon the first bit of the operand extracted from the effective address. When indexed and indirect are both specified in an instruction some computers do the indexing first and then the indirection while in others the order is reversed.

2.6.   NUMBER SYSTEMS - BINARY OCTAL HEXADECIMA

Let us turn now to the representation of data in a computer system. Data is always represented as a binary number. In Chapter 1 we had a short discussion of the binary number system, where the analogy was made between the weights in the balance and the "size" of the number.

We can obviously use this same technique for indicating the value of a number set up on a series of switches if we ascribe to each switch a certain "weight". Just as a weight could be either in the balance or not we must be able to indicate that the value of a particular switch is or is not to be included. This means that one of the two possible settings for each switch must mean - 'do not include the value of this switch'.

So switch 1 represents O when <u>off</u> and 1 when <u>on</u>, switch 2 represents O when <u>off</u> and 2 when <u>on</u>. When switches 2 and 1 are both <u>on</u> we have the number 3.

We can now represent the following numbers:

Number	Switch 2	Switch 1
O	OFF	OFF
1	OFF	ON
2	ON	OFF
3	ON	ON

and in so doing have exhausted all the possible combinations of positions for SWITCHES 1 and 2. It is fairly evident that the next switch we introduce should have the value 4 when <u>ON</u> and O when <u>OFF</u>. When this switch is <u>OFF</u> we have the four possibilities for switches 1 and 2 (0, 1, 2, 3) and when the switch is <u>ON</u> the value 4 is added in each of these cases giving (4, 5, 6, 7).

NUMBER	SWITCH 3	SWITCH 2	SWITCH 1
O	OFF	OFF	OFF
1	OFF	OFF	ON (=1)
2	OFF	ON (=2)	OFF
3	OFF	ON (=2)	ON (=1)
4	ON (=4)	OFF	OFF
5	ON (=4)	OFF	ON (=1)
6	ON (=4)	ON (=2)	OFF
7	ON (=4)	ON (=2)	ON (=1)

The next switch (Switch 4) should obviously have the value 8 and one can see a general principle emerging - that each switch should have a value twice as great as the previous one.

Consider now the range of numbers that can be represented by a given set of such switches:

No. of Switches	Range	
1	0 → 1	0 → (2^1-1)
2	0 → 1 2 → 3 ie 0→3	0 → (2^2-1)
3	0 → 3 4 → 7 ie 0→7	0 → (2^3-1)
4	0 → 7 8 → 15 ie 0→15	0 → (2^4-1)

The general principle holds true that if we have n switches we can represent the numbers $0 \rightarrow (2^n-1)$.

You can easily verify that if eight switches were available then the following representations give rise to the associated number:

NUMBER	SW 8	SW 7	SW 6	SW 5	SW 4	SW 3	SW 2	SW 1
63	OFF	OFF	ON	ON	ON	ON	ON	ON
28	OFF	OFF	OFF	ON	ON	ON	OFF	OFF
96	OFF	ON	ON	OFF	OFF	OFF	OFF	OFF
129	ON	OFF	OFF	OFF	OFF	OFF	OFF	ON
200	ON	ON	OFF	OFF	ON	OFF	OFF	OFF
255	ON	ON	ON	ON	ON	ON	ON	ON

This system of representing numbers by a series of switches is the binary system, which itself is one of a range of number systems based on a radix.

Once the radix (r) is chosen then any number (M) can be represented by a series of coefficients (d) such that

$$M = \cdots\cdots + d_4r^4 + d_3r^3 + d_2r^2 + d_1r^1 + d_0r^0$$

In binary notation the radix is 2, so the required coefficients for the number twenty-one are such that

$$\text{twenty-one} = \cdots\cdots + (d_5 \times 32) + (d_4 \times 16) +$$
$$(d_3 \times 8) + (d_2 \times 4) + d_1(\times 2) + (d_2 \times 1)$$

This can be represented by 1 x 16 leaving 5 (21-16), 0 x 8 leaving 5, 1 x 4 leaving 1 (21-(16+4)), 0 x 2 leaving 1, 1 x 1 leaving 0 (21-(16+4+1)) and the number twenty-one is written as 10101 (to the base 2). In order to clearly identify the base/radix it is usual to add this as a subscript. Obviously the common number system with which we are all familiar uses the radix ten and the required digits are such that

$$\text{twenty-one} = \cdots\cdots d_4 \times 10^4 + d_3 \times 10^3 + d_2 \times 10^2 +$$
$$d_1 \times 10^1 + d_0 \times 1$$
$$\text{ie, } 0 \times 10^4 + 0 \times 10^3 + 0 \times 10^2 + \underline{2} \times 10^1 + \underline{1} \times 1$$

So that twenty-one = 21_{10} = 10101_2

Any number can be chosen as a radix and the following list shows how the number two hundred and fifty-five would be represented in different systems using the radix 9, 8, 7, 6, 5, 4, 3, 2 respectively.

Base 9
$$255 = (d_3 \times 9^3) + (d_2 \times 9^2) + (d_1 \times 9^1) + (d_0 \times 9^0)$$
$$= (0 \times 729) + (3 \times 81) + (1 \times 9) + (3 \times 1) = 313_9$$

Base 8
$$255 = (d_3 \times 8^3) + (d_2 \times 8^2) + (d_1 \times 8^1) + (d_0 \times 8^0)$$
$$= (0 \times 512) + (3 \times 64) + (7 \times 8) + (7 \times 1) = 377_8$$

Base 7
$$255 = (d_3 \times 7^3) + (d_2 \times 7^2) + (d_1 \times 7^1) + (d_0 \times 7^0)$$
$$= (0 \times 343) + (5 \times 49) + (1 \times 7) + (3 \times 1) = 513_7$$

Base 6
$$255 = (d_3 \times 6^3) + (d_2 \times 6^2) + (d_1 \times 6^1) + (d_0 \times 6^0)$$
$$= (1 \times 216) + (1 \times 36) + (0 \times 6) + (3 \times 1) = 1103_6$$

Base 5
$$255 = (d_3 \times 5^3) + (d_2 \times 5^2) + (d_1 \times 5^1) + (d_0 \times 5^0)$$
$$= (2 \times 125) + (0 \times 25) + (1 \times 5) + (0 \times 1) = 2010_5$$

Base 4
$$255 = (d_3 \times 4^3) + (d_2 \times 4^2) + (d_1 \times 4^1) + (d_0 \times 4^0)$$
$$= (3 \times 64) + (3 \times 16) + (3 \times 4) + (3 \times 1) = 3333_4$$

Base 3
$$255 = (d_5 \times 3^5) + (d_4 \times 3^4) + (d_3 \times 3^3) + (d_2 \times 3^2)$$
$$+ (d_1 \times 3^1) + (d_0 \times 3^0)$$
$$= (1 \times 243) + (0 \times 81) + (0 \times 27) + (1 \times 9) +$$
$$(1 \times 3) + (0 \times 1) = 100110_3$$

Base 2
$$255 = (d_7 \times 2^7) + (d_6 \times 2^6) + (d_5 \times 2^5) + (d_4 \times 2^4)$$
$$+ (d_3 \times 2^3) + (d_2 \times 2^2) + (d_1 \times 2^1) + (d_0 \times 2^0)$$
$$= (1 \times 128) + (1 \times 64) + (1 \times 32) + (1 \times 16) +$$
$$(1 \times 8) + (1 \times 4) + (1 \times 2) + (1 \times 1) =$$
$$11111111_2$$

So we may write two hundred and fifty-five as

255_{10}
313_9
377_8
513_7
1103_6
2010_5
3333_4
100110_3
11111111_2

Of the number systems so far mentioned those most in use in computers are the systems using the base 2 and the base 8 referred to as the <u>binary</u> and <u>octal</u> systems.

There is one other system which is often used and that is the system with the radix = 16; this presents a slight problem with notation.

First it is important to note that the
coefficients or digits required to express any
number will all be less than the radix.   In
the case of the decimal system where the
radix is ten the only digits which appear are

0, 1, 2, 3, 4, 5, 6, 7, 8, 9.

Similarly in the binary system (base 2) the
only digits which occur are

0, 1

Now in the <u>hexadecimal</u> system (base 16) we
are likely to get coefficients in the range

0, 1, 2, 3, 4, 5, 6, 7, 8, 9, 10, 11, 12, 13,
14, 15.

For example $255_{10} = d_2 \times 16^2 + d_1 \times 16^1 + d_0 \times 16^0$

$$= \underline{0} \times 256 + \underline{15} \times 16 + \underline{15} \times 1$$

$$= 1515_{16}$$

This could very readily be confused with the
number

$5397_{10} = d_3 \times 16^3 + d_2 \times 16^2 + d_1 \times 16^1 + d_0 \times 16^0$

$$= \underline{1} \times 4096 + \underline{5} \times 256 + \underline{1} \times 16 + \underline{5} \times 1$$

$$= 1515_{16}$$

To avoid this confusion it is conventional to
write those coefficients of the hexadecimal
system which require two decimal digits as
the single symbols A, B, C, D, E, F.

where A = 10
      B = 11
      C = 12
      D = 13
      E = 14
      F = 15

So the number $255_{10} = \underline{15} \times 16^1 + \underline{15} \times 16^0$

$$= FF_{16}$$

Often it is necessary to print out the contents of a memory store or to communicate such
contents (say over the telephone) to someone
else so that a neater method is required than
by just representing the number as a string
of ones and zeros.   In everyday decimal numbers it is conventional to write 394631214
as 394,631,214, read as three hundred and
ninety four millions, six hundred and thirty
one thousands, two hundred and fourteen and
the decision to break the number up into
sets of three digits is purely arbitrary.

Using a 12 bit computer then the contents of
a typical store might be:-

101001111111

This could be split up in any of the following ways:

(a)   101 001 111 111
(b)   1010 0111 1111

It is clear that in the first case if one
considers all the possible combinations for
a three bit pattern that there are eight

000	0
001	1
010	2
011	3
100	4
101	5
110	6
111	7

and that if we were to use a single symbol
to represent each of these patterns then only
four such symbols would be required to
represent the contents of a word of store.
From the binary system already discussed it
is logical therefore to represent each of
these patterns by its equivalent decimal
symbol.   So the contents of the store mentioned above could be recorded as

5177_8

provided we understand that each of these
symbols is to be expanded to its 3 bit
binary pattern.

Let us now consider method (b) where each
set of four binary bits is grouped.   We
require a symbol for each possible combination
of four bits - there are 16 such combinations

0000	0	0
0001	1	1
0010	2	2
0011	3	3
0100	4	4
0101	5	5
0110	6	6
0111	7	7
1000	8	8
1001	9	9
1010	10	A
1011	11	B
1100	12	C
1101	13	D
1110	14	E
1111	15	F

So the shorthand for representing the bit
pattern in (b) is

$A \, 7 \, F_{16}$

Both of these notations are widely used in
representing bit patterns in minicomputers
and microcomputers.
Method (a) is normally used for 12 bit,
18 bit and 24 bit machines, and (b) is used
for 8 bit, 16 bit and 32 bit machines.

It is fairly clear from this example that
there is a close relation between the binary
and octal systems and between the binary and
hexadecimal systems.   Let us examine this
further by expanding the binary pattern
into its equivalent numerical value.

101001111111_2

$= \underline{(1 \times 2^{11}) + (0 \times 2^{10}) + (1 \times 2^9) + (0 \times 2^8) + (0 \times 2^7) + (1 \times 2^6)}$
$\underline{+ (1 \times 2^5) + (1 \times 2^4) + (1 \times 2^3) + (1 \times 2^2) + (1 \times 2^1) + (1 \times 2^0)}$

$= (4 \times 2^9) + (0 \times 2^9) + (1 \times 2^9) + (0 \times 2^6) + (0 \times 2^6) + (1 \times 2^6)$
$+ (4 \times 2^3) + (2 \times 2^3) + (1 \times 2^3) + (4 \times 2^0) + (2 \times 2^0) + (1 \times 2^0)$

$= (4+0+1) \times 2^9 + (0+0+1) \times 2^6 + (4+2+1) \times 2^3 + (4+2+1) \times 2^0$

$= (5 \times 2^9) + (1 \times 2^6) + (7 \times 2^3) + (7 \times 2^0)$

$= \underline{5} \times 8^3 + \underline{1} \times 8^2 + \underline{7} \times 8^1 + \underline{7} \times 8^0$

$= 5177_8$ Thus $101 \, 001 \, 111 \, 111_2 = 5 \, 1 \, 7 \, 7_8$

In a similar fashion if we group four digits together at a time we have

$$101001111111_2$$

$$= (8+0+2+0) \times 2^8 + (0+4+2+1) \times 2^4 + (8+4+2+1) \times 2^0$$

$$= (10 \times 2^8) + (7 \times 2^4) + (15 \times 2^0)$$

$$= (\underline{10} \times 16^2) + (\underline{7} \times 16) + (\underline{15} \times 16^0)$$

$$= A \times 16^2 + 7 \times 16^1 + F \times 16^0$$

$$= A \, 7 \, F_{16}$$

Thus $101001111111_2 = A \, 7 \, F_{16}$

BINARY	OCTAL	DECIMAL	HEXADECIMAL
000 000	00	0	00
000 001	01	1	01
000 010	02	2	02
000 011	03	3	03
000 100	04	4	04
000 101	05	5	05
000 110	06	6	06
000 111	07	7	07
001 000	10	8	08
001 001	11	9	09
001 010	12	10	0A
001 011	13	11	0B
001 100	14	12	0C
001 101	15	13	0D
001 100	16	14	0E
001 111	17	15	0F
010 000	20	16	10
010 001	21	17	11
010 010	22	18	12
010 011	23	19	13
010 100	24	20	14
010 101	25	21	15
010 110	26	22	16
010 111	27	23	17
011 000	30	24	18
011 001	31	25	19

Fig. 2.1.

Fig. 2.1. shows the binary, octal and hexdecimal representations for all the positive decimal integers less than 26.

2.7. ADDITION AND SUBTRACTION

Addition

After that digression into number systems let us return to our "computer". We now have a convention for representing our numbers, we have a mechanism (two series of switches) which can be used to set up the numbers. And we have a mechanism for displaying our answers (say a set of eight lamps). So to carry out the addition of ten and twelve we would set the switches on the computer in the following fashion:-

128	64	32	16	8	4	2	1	
OFF	OFF	OFF	OFF	ON	OFF	ON	OFF	= 10
OFF	OFF	OFF	OFF	ON	ON	OFF	OFF	= 12

and after reading these numbers into the computer system and executing an ADD instruction we would expect to see the result flashed on the lights as

OFF	OFF	OFF	ON	OFF	ON	ON	OFF	= 22

The binary representation of this complete operation is

```
0 0 0 0 1 0 1 0  =  10

0 0 0 0 1 1 0 0  =  12
_____

0 0 0 1 0 1 1 0  =  22
```

and the laws of addition that apply to each row are clearly:-

0 + 0 gives 0

0 + 1 gives 1

1 + 0 gives 1

1 + 1 gives 0 and carry 1

If we consider the complete addition operation for any column then we have two digits to add, each of which may be a 0 or 1 and a carry which may be 0 or 1. So the circuit to carry out the operation must be capable of obeying the following set of rules:-

bottom line	top line	previous carry	=	result	new carry
0	0	0		0	0
0	1	0		1	0
1	0	0		1	0
1	1	0		0	1
0	0	1		1	0
0	1	1		0	1
1	0	1		0	1
1	1	1		1	1

Subtraction

The laws of subtraction are easily formulated if one compares the binary system with the decimal system. They are:-

0 from 0 gives 0

0 from 1 gives 1

1 from 0 gives 1 (if we borrow 1 from next
                          column)

1 from 1 gives 0

and in the case of the borrowed 1, this
must be "paid back" to the next column. For
example subtracting on a computer with only
3 switches for input and output:-

(7 - 5) = 2   (4 - 3) = 1

   1 1 1   1 0 0

   1 0 1   0₁1₁1

  ───────   ───────

   0 1 0   0 0 1

Note however that if we were to carry out
the subtraction

(4 - 5)
   1 0 0

   1 0 1

  ───────

   1 1 1

the result looks remarkably like the number
seven. So something is amiss. In a way it
is not surprising because we have no convention for representing negative numbers
and this calculation gives us a clue as to
a reasonable strategy.

2.8. NEGATIVE NUMBERS

Let us examine a hypothetical 3 digit computer for storing numbers. The eight patterns
available as we have already seen are:

0 0 0

0 0 1

0 1 0

0 1 1

1 0 0

1 0 1

1 1 0

1 1 1

We can choose to let these patterns represent
the positive numbers 0, 1, 2, 3, 4, 5, 6, 7
respectively leaving us no "room" for negative
numbers. Alternatively we could say that
the first digit will indicate the sign, 0 for
positive and 1 for negative so that we have

0 00   +0

0 01   +1

0 10   +2

0 11   +3

1 00   -0

1 01   -1

1 10   -2

1 11   -3

If we chose this convention then the addition
circuit which we have already outlined
requires some modification since the addition
of

0 0 1   = 1

1 1 0   =-2   would give

─────────

1 1 1   =-3 rather than -1.

The way around this problem and the usual
convention is in effect to move the second
half of the range up in front of the first
half letting

1 0 0   =-4

1 0 1   =-3

1 1 0   =-2

1 1 1   =-1

0 0 0   = 0

0 0 1   = 1

0 1 0   = 2

0 1 1   = 3

and a few examples show that the laws of
addition and subtraction outlined hold true
for positive and negative numbers:-

(1 + 2) = 3	(3 + (-2)) = 1	1 - (-2) = 3
0 0 1	0 1 1	0 0 1
0 1 0	1 1 0	1 1 0
─────	─────	─────
0 1 1	0 0 1	0 1 1

Note that the first (left-most) digit
immediately indicates the sign of the number
(1 for negative; 0 for positive). This convention seems a little strange at first but
consider an analogy in the decimal system,
say the foot counter on a tape recorder.
Suppose we set the counter

(3 digits at zero)   0 0 0   (a)

(move forward thirteen stops)   0 1 3   (b)

(then move backward 15 stops)   9 9 8   (c)

This pattern must represent the numbers (-2)
if we are to consider negative numbers.

Note that if we use the normal laws of decimal addition on (b) and (c) we get eleven

0 1 1

provided we "throw away" the one thousand
carry which was too large for our three digit
counter to accommodate. So if we wanted to
represent the negative numbers from -500 to
-1 in a three digit decimal counter   the
number would be represented by its complement

with respect to one thousand (ie, the difference between the corresponding positive number and one thousand).

Thus -43 would be represented by 957
     -136 would be represented by 864, etc.

and just to check again we see that -43 and +82 would result in 39

    9 5 7

    0 8 2

1 0 3 9

In a three digit decimal system we represent the negative number -M by 10^3 - M and if we had n digits then we would represent -M by 10^n - M.

In the case of a binary number where n digits are available the number

-M is represented by 2^n - M

and this is often referred to as "two's complement".

One becomes accustomed to conversion from decimal to positive binary numbers very quickly, but negative numbers require more time. A useful trick for converting from positive to negative in binary is to invert all the bits in the positive number and add one to the result.

Thus for example in a 3 digit system the number

2 is represented by   0 1 0

invert the bits gives 1 0 1

add one to the result 1 1 0

gives the binary pattern for -2.

This follows from the fact that the number -1 is always represented by a string of one's (just as zero is represented by a string of zeros) and because of the laws of subtraction taking any number M away from -1 results in a pattern of bits which are the exact opposite to those for M.

         (-1)   1 1 1 1 1 1 1 1

Subtract 10 (ten) 0 0 0 0 1 0 1 0
                   ─────────────────
(-1 -10)   1 1 1 1 0 1 0 1

Add one gives -10 1 1 1 1 0 1 1 0

Note that ones are replaced by zeros and zeros by ones.

2.9. NON-INTEGERS

Fractions

So far we have only considered integer representation, but obviously we also require a convention for representing fractions. The system reflects the decimal system again in that just as

132.675 in decimal

represents 1 hundred 1×10^2

+ 3 tens 3×10^1

+ 2 units 2×10^0

+ 6 tenths 6×10^{-1}

+ 7 hundredths 7×10^{-2}

+ 5 thousandths 5×10^{-3}

so 101.111 in binary

represents 1×2^2 = 4

          $+ 0 \times 2^1$ = 0

          $+ 1 \times 2^0$ = 1

          $+ 1 \times 2^{-1}$ = $\frac{1}{2}$

          $+ 1 \times 2^{-2}$ = $\frac{1}{4}$

          $+ 1 \times 2^{-3}$ = $\frac{1}{8}$ ie, $5\frac{7}{8}$

shifting the decimal point one place to the left is the equivalent of dividing by 10 132.675 → 13.2675 and shifting one place to the left in binary is equivalent to division by 2.

Thus 10.1111

represents 1×2^1 = 2

          $+ 0 \times 2^0$ = 0

          $+ 1 \times 2^{-1}$ = $\frac{1}{2}$

          $+ 1 \times 2^{-2}$ = $\frac{1}{4}$

          $+ 1 \times 2^{-3}$ = $\frac{1}{8}$

          $+ 1 \times 2^{-4}$ = $1/16$ ie, $2\frac{15}{16}$

which is half of $5\frac{7}{8}$.

Similarly shifting the binary point one place to the right multiplies the number by 2, and two places to the right is equivalent to multiplication by four, three places eight and in general a shift to the right of n places is equivalent to multiplication by 2^n.

It is normal to regard the binary point as existing between the first and second digits when representing a fraction as a binary number, and the same principles apply for positive and negative fractions as for integers.

Thus in an eight bit machine:-

0 = 0.0000000

$\frac{1}{2}$ = 0.1000000

$\frac{3}{4}$ = 0.1100000

$-\frac{1}{2}$ = 1.1000000

$-\frac{3}{4}$ = 1.0100000

This allows us to represent fractions (F) in the range -1 < F < 127/128 in steps of $1/128$.

Mixed Numbers

Numbers which consist of a whole part and a fractional part can be represented using the conventions outlined above simply by deciding where the binary point is going to lie.

For example on an eight bit machine we could represent

$\qquad$ 15.875 ie, 15⅞ by 01111.111

and 7.5   ie, 7½ by 00111.100

subtraction gives   01000.011 = 8.375

This convention allows an accuracy of ⅛ and a range of values - 16 to 15⅞.

A greater range would be available by moving the point one place to the right. This would allow a range of values -32 to 31¾ with an accuracy to the nearest ¼. This trade-off between accuracy of representation and range of possible values leads to a convention for representing mixed numbers - known as floating point representations.

Figure 2.2. gives the powers of 2 and their decimal equivalent.

2^n	n	2^{-n}
1	0	1.0
2	1	0.5
4	2	0.25
8	3	0.125
16	4	0.062 5
32	5	0.031 25
64	6	0.015 625
128	7	0.007 812 5
256	8	0.003 906 25
512	9	0.001 953 125
1 024	10	0.000 976 562 5
2 048	11	0.000 488 281 25
4 096	12	0.000 244 140 625
8 192	13	0.000 122 070 312 5
16 384	14	0.000 061 035 156 25
32 768	15	0.000 030 517 578 125
65 536	16	0.000 015 258 789 062 5
131 072	17	0.000 007 629 394 531 25
262 144	18	0.000 003 814 697 265 625
524 288	19	0.000 001 907 348 632 812 5
1 048 576	20	0.000 000 953 674 316 406 25

Fig 2.2.   Powers of Two

Floating Point Numbers

When representing very large and very small numbers in the decimal system

eg, 3,567,000,000
or 0.000025

it is usually to record these as

3.567×10^9 (or 0.3567×10^{10}), and
2.5×10^{-5} respectively

so that the trailing zeros in large numbers and the leading zeros in small numbers need not take up space on the page. The same principle applies to computers except that instead of using the base 10 for the scaling factor we use the base 2.

So the binary pattern for $^{15}/_{128}$

0.0001111

could be recorded as

0.1111×2^{-3} ($^{15}/_{16} \times ⅛$) or

1111.0×2^{-7} ($15 \times ^1/_{128}$) or

11.11×2^{-5} ($3¾ \times ^1/_{32}$)

If we ignore the 2 we could represent a number N in the computer by a pair of numbers M and e

where $N = M \times 2^e$

In the example above where

$N = {}^{15}/_{128}$ M = 0.1111   e = -3

$\qquad$ or M = 1111.0   e = -7

$\qquad$ or M = 11.11   e = -5

It is conventional to choose M as a fraction where

½ ≤ M ≤ 1 for positive numbers

-½ ≤ M ≤ -1 for negative numbers

and adjust e accordingly.

For example 19 → M = 0.10011 ($^{19}/_{32}$);
e = 101 (2^5 = 32)

$\qquad$ 3 → M = 0.11 (¾);
e = 10 (2^2 = 4)

$\qquad$ -3 → M = 1.01 (-¾)
e = 10

$\qquad$ -4 → M = 1.0 (-1);
e = 10

$\qquad$ .125 → M = 0.1 (½);
e = -2 (2^{-2} = ¼)

The method for recording these two numbers M (the mantissa) and e (the exponent) varies from machine to machine. In a 16 bit machine it is conventional to use two stores ie, 32 bits using 9 for the mantissa and 23 for the exponent. The following gives some possible schemes:-

e_i means the ith digit of the exponent e

M_i means the ith digit of the mantissa M

S_M means the sign of the mantissa

S_e means the sign of the exponent.

(a) | S_M | $M_1\ M_2\ M_3\ \text{--}\ M_{22}$ | S_e | $e_1\ e_2\ e_3\ \text{--}\ e_8$ |

(b) | S_M | $S_e\ e_1\ e_2\ e_3\ \text{--}\ \ e_8$ | $M_1\ M_2\ M_3\ \text{--}\ M_{22}$ |

(c) | S_M | $128 + e$ | $M_1\ M_2\ M_3\ \text{--}\ M_{22}$ |

(d) | S | $128 + e$ | M |

In case (a) the mantissa is a conventional signed fraction, the exponent is a conventional signed integer. (b) same as (a) (c) the mantissa is a conventional signed fraction but the exponent field is always a positive integer such that it contains 128 plus true exponent.

if exponent is -128 this field is zero

if exponent is 0 this field is 128

if exponent is 127 this field is 255.

(d) the exponent here is represented as in (c) but the mantissa is always a positive fraction. The first bit is set to 1 to indicate a negative number and zero to indicate a positive number.

Note that the operations of addition, subtraction, multiplication and division are carried out in a fashion similar to the decimal system,

eg, adding $3.9\ X\ 10^7$ (39 millions)

and $2.4\ X\ 10^4$ (24 thousands)

requires that we convert both to the same exponent (say 4).

$3\ 9\ 0\ 0\ X\ 10^4$

$\quad\quad 2.4\ X\ 10^4$

_____

$3\ 9\ 0\ 2\ .\ 4\ X\ 10^4$ or

$3\ .\ 9\ 0\ 2\ 4\ X\ 10^7$ (39024 thousands)

Multiplication is performed by multiplying the mantissae and adding the exponents.

eg, multiplying $3.0\ X\ 10^2$ (3 hundreds)

by $\quad\quad 120\ X\ 10^4$ (12 thousands)

gives $\quad\quad 3.6\ X\ 10^6$ (3.6 millions)

The same rules apply to binary floating point operations for example:

		M	E
$\frac{1}{4}$	=	0.1	-1
$\frac{1}{8}$	=	0.1	-2
convert to same exponent $\frac{1}{8}$	=	0.01	-1
add $\frac{3}{8}$	=	0.11	-1

2.10 TEXT

So far we have been dealing entirely with numeric information but obviously we require some method of storing alphabetic information. The most widely used convention is the ASCII code (American Standard Code for the Interchange of Information) and Fig. 2.3. shows the codes normally available.

Symbol	Hexadecimal Code	Symbol	Hexadecimal Code
@	C0	b	A0
A	C1	!	A1
B	C2	"	A2
C	C3	#	A3
D	C4	$	A4
E	C5	%	A5
F	C6	&	A6
G	C7	'	A7
H	C8	(	A8
I	C9	)	A9
J	CA	*	AA
K	CB	+	AB
L	CC	,	AC
M	CD	-	AD
N	CE	.	AE
O	CF	/	AF
P	D0	0	B0
Q	D1	1	B1
R	D2	2	B2
S	D3	3	B3
T	D4	4	B4
U	D5	5	B5
V	D6	6	B6
W	D7	7	B7
X	D8	8	B8
Y	D9	9	B9
Z	DA	:	BA
[	DB	;	BB
\	DC	<	BC
]	DD	=	BD
↑	DE	>	BE
←	DF	?	BF
NULL	00	CR	8D
BELL	87	LF	8A
		RUBOUT	FF

Fig.2.3 ASCII

Note that in this code the first bit on the left is always a '1'. In other versions this bit may be '1' or '0', chosen to make the

total number of '1's in the 8-bit code even
(called an 'even parity' code), or odd ('odd
parity'). These parity codes provide a
measure of error detection.

Each letter of the alphabet is represented
by a pattern of eight bits (sometimes referred to as a byte).

		Hexadecimal
A is represented by	11000001	C1
B is represented by	11000010	C2
Z is represented by	11011010	DA

There are 256 possible patterns of eight bits
and the remaining possibilities are used for
representing symbols such as

%	10100101	A5
&	10100110	A6
(	10101000	A8
+	10101011	AB

lower case alphabetic characters, and certain device control characters.

Summary

We have examined a number of the conventions
for representing both data and instructions
in computer systems. Some of these conventions are almost mandatory for the manufacturer
because they are so widely used - for example
the ASCII code for text. The two's complement representation for integers is by far
the cheapest because it simplifies the
electronics for arithmetic, and is therefore
very common.

Other conventions for addressing memory,
registers, switches, etc, may be used but
the number of special registers and
accumulators and the instruction repertoire
varies considerably from one machine to
another.

The next Chapter looks in detail at the
representation of instructions in a number
of different mini and microcomputers.

Some Real Computers
Chapter 3

So far we have been talking in general terms about how a computer might be constructed and the possible formats of instructions. We will now examine the structure and instruction formats of some actual computers, and select a few features from each to demonstrate the variety of approach. Details of the electronic implementation of the computers are not considered at this stage. Later chapters examine the electronic technology involved.

3.1. DIGITAL PDP-8

Structure

The Digital Equipment Corporation manufactures a range of minicomputers with the code name PDP. The PDP-8 was introduced in 1965 and was updated several times. This is a one accumulator 12-bit computer with a memory access time of 1.5 microseconds. The memory addressing technique is novel in that the memory is considered as a number of pages, where each page contains 128 words. An instruction may reference directly a word in page 0 or a word in the same page as the instruction (the current page); references to any other word must be performed indirectly using a word in one of these two pages.

Auto-indexing

The PDP-8 has eight special registers-words (8-15) of page 0. Whenever these locations are accessed indirectly by a memory reference instruction, the content of the register is increased by one before it is used as an operand.

Example: if location 8 contained 74 and the instruction

0 0 1	1	0	0 0 0 1 0 0 0

"add the contents of word 8 to the accumulator" was executed then; the accumulator would in fact have 75 added to it. Another execution of the same instruction would add 76, etc., as word 8 is automatically increased by one, every time it is indirectly referenced.

Memory Reference Instructions (Operation Codes 0-5)

The format for memory reference instructions is -

BIT	11 10 9	8	7	6 5 4 3 2 1 0
	OPERATION CODE			WORD ADDRESS WITHIN PAGE

ADDRESS MODE   PAGE BIT

0 = DIRECT   0 = PAGE 0

1 = INDIRECT   1 = CURRENT PAGE

Example: Suppose word 31 contains 97
                   word 543 contains 153
                   word 97 contains 22
                   word 153 contains 81
          the accumulator contains 100

and 512, 513, 514, 515 contain the following instructions -

512	0 0 1	0	0	0 0 1 1 1 1 1
513	0 0 1	0	1	0 0 1 1 1 1 1
514	0 0 1	1	0	0 0 1 1 1 1 1
515	0 0 1	1	1	0 0 1 1 1 1 1

These instructions are in page 4 of the memory

page 0	0 - 127
page 1	128 - 255
page 2	256 - 383
page 3	384 - 511
page 4	512 - 639

and all have the same operation code 001 meaning "add contents of memory to accumulator" and the same "address" (31).

(i)   512 is a direct reference to page 0, so it is executed as add contents of store 31 to the accumulator. Accumulator changes from 100 to 197 (AC = AC + 97).

(ii)   513 is a direct reference to the current page, so it is executed as "add word 31 of the current page (word 543) to accumulator. Accumulator changes from 197 to 350 (AC = AC + 153).

(iii) 514 is an indirect reference to page 0, so it is executed as "add the contents of the store whose address is in word 31 of page 0 to the accumulator", ie, add the contents of word 97 to the accumulator, ie, add 22 to the accumulator. Accumulator changes from 350 to 372 (AC = AC + 22).

(iv)   515 is an indirect reference to page 4 (the current page), so it is translated as "add the contents of the store whose address is in word 31 of the current page to the accumulator". Accumulator changes from 372 to 453 (AC = AC + 81).

This format is used for instructions with operation codes O-5. These are:-

OOO - Replace the contents of the accumulator by the logical AND of the accumulator and the address specified.

OO1 - Add the contents of the address specified to the accumulator.

O1O - Add one to the contents of the memory address specified and skip the next instruction if the result is zero.

O11 - Copy the contents of the accumulator into the memory location specified and "clear" the accumulator (ie, store zero in AC).

1OO - Jump to subroutine. The contents of PC are copied to the memory address specified and the next instruction executed is the one immediately after that address.

Example:-

324 | 1 O O | O | O | O O 1 1 1 1 O |

would store 325 in word 30 and the computer would proceed to execute instructions beginning at 31. We will be dealing in more detail with subroutines in later sections, but in essence the programmer wishes to break the normal sequence (in this case at 324) perform a number of instructions elsewhere (in this case 31, 32, 33, etc) and eventually return to the point at which he left the "main-line" of instructions (at 325). Store 30 contains the "link" address.

1O1 - Jump to the address specified.

324 | 1 O 1 | O | O | O O 1 1 1 1 O |

The computer would proceed after 324 to execute instructions beginning at 30.

Peripheral Instructions (Operation Code 6)

Since all input/output is to or from the accumulator, instructions which transfer information to peripherals do not need to address memory; bits 6-O are no longer required for a memory address, nor are bits 8, 7 for page specification and indirect mode. The format of I/O instructions is:-

11	10	9	8 7 6 5 4 3	2 1 0
1	1	O	DEVICE	FUNCTION

This allows up to 64 different devices to be referenced. The function field (bits 2-O) is in fact merely used to send a pulse to the appropriate device at 1 microsecond intervals. When

bit O is set to 1, a pulse is transmitted after 1 microsecond,
bit 1 is set to 1, a pulse is transmitted after 2 microseconds,
bit 2 is set to 1, a pulse is transmitted after 3 microseconds.

The devices attached to the processor are constructed to respond to these pulses.

Example:

| 1 1 O | O O O O 1 1 | 1 O O |

causes a transfer from device 3 (teletype

keyboard) of a character (8-bits) into bits 7-O of the accumulator, while

| 1 1 O | O O O 1 O O | 1 O O |

causes bits 7-O of the accumulator to be transferred out to the teletype printer.

Other Instructions (Operation Code 7)

There are a number of other instructions which reference memory or peripherals; in this case bits 8-O are used as an extension of the operation code.

Examples: AC is the accumulator

11 10 9 8 7 6 5 4 3 2 1 O

1 1 1	O O O	O O O	O O 1	add 1 to the contents of AC.
1 1 1	O 1 O	O O O	O O O	set AC to zero.
1 1 1	O 1 O	O O O	O O 1	set AC = 1
1 1 1	1 O O	O O O	O 1 O	stop the computer after this instruction.
1 1 1	O 1 O	1 O O	O O O	set AC = 1
1 1 1	1 O O	1 O O	O O O	skip next instruction if AC = O.
1 1 1	1 O 1	O 1 O	O O O	skip if AC < O.
1 1 1	1 O 1	1 O 1	O O O	skip if AC > O.

Some PDP-8 computers may have a special unit added to allow for multiplication and division. This is called the Extended Arithmetic Element, and other variations of operation code 7 are used to drive this unit.

3.2.   DATA GENERAL NOVA

Structure

The Data General Corporation manufactures a range of minicomputers with the trade name Nova. These differ mainly in memory speeds but there are also other significant feature differences. All are 16-bit computers with cycle times of 1.2 micro-seconds (for the Nova 1200), 800 nano-seconds (for the Nova 800) and as fast as 300 nano-seconds (for some Super Nova options).

The processor uses a 15-bit program counter (PC) which is automatically incremented by one before the appropriate instruction is executed. There are four 16-bit accumulators (ACO, AC1, AC2, AC3). Data can be transferred between accumulators and memory, but all arithmetic and logical operations must have both operands in accumulators. There is also a one bit carry register used in arithmetic operations, and this can be combined with any of the accumulators, giving a 17-bit word which can be rotated right or left. The contents of an accumulator can be considered as 2 eight bit fields which can be swapped. Two of the accumulators AC2 and AC3 can be used as index registers (for indexed addressing).

Auto-increment and decrement

Locations 16 to 23 provide 8 auto-increment words. When one of these stores is specified by an indirect address, it is automatically increased by one before being used. This is a similar function to words 8-15 on the PDP-8; in addition the Nova provides 8 auto-decrement words (24-31) which are decremented by one, when addressed indirectly.

Memory Reference Instructions

There are two types of memory reference instructions:-

(a) Jump Instructions

Bits	15	14	13	12	11	10	9 8 7	- 0
A:	O	O	O	O	O	I	X	D
B:	O	O	O	O	1	I	X	D

A: Jump to address specified
B: Store PC in AC3 and jump to address specified

	15	14	13	12	11	10	9 8 7	- 0
C:	O	O	O	1	O	I	X	D
D:	O	O	O	1	1	I	X	D

C: Add 1 to store; skip next instruction if store zero.
D: Subtract 1 from store; skip next instruction if store zero.

D is a displacement (or offset) in the range 0-255.
X is a two bit code indicating relative or indexed addressing.
I is a one-bit indicator for indirect addressing.

Notes

1. The first two are <u>unconditional jumps</u>; the last two require a decision to be made and may or may not cause a jump over the next instruction (these are <u>conditional jumps</u>).

2. The second instruction (00001) is the equivalent of the jump to subroutine instruction (100) on the PDP-8. The essential difference is that here the "link" address for return is stored in an accumulator and not in a memory location.

3. Bit 10 is used for indirect addressing; if bit 10 is zero the address calculated from D and X (see below) contains the operand; if bit 10 = 1 it contains the <u>address</u> of the operand.

4. If X = 0 (ie, bits 9 and 8 = 00) then D gives an absolute address referencing words 0-255 of the memory.

5. If X = 1 (bit 9 = 0, bit 8 = 1) then D is treated as a signed integer in the range -128 to +127 which is added to PC to give relative address mode.

6. If X = 2 (bit 9 = 1, bit 8 = 0) then the contents of AC2 are added to the signed integer D (-128 to +127) to give indexed address mode.

7. If X = 3 (bit 9 = 1, bit 8 = 1). This gives indexed addressing using AC3.

(b) Move Data Instructions

These transfer information between an accumulator and memory.

Bits	15 13	12 11	10	9 8 7	- 0
E:	O O 1	A	I	X	D
F:	O 1 O	A	I	X	D

E: Transfer from store to accumulator
F: Transfer from accumulator to store.

Notes

1. The I, X, D fields have the same interpretation as above and together give the address of a store in memory.

2. Bits 3 and 4 reference an accumulator

O O indicates AC0
O 1 indicates AC1
1 O indicates AC2
1 1 indicates AC3

Input/Output Instructions

These have the following format, with bits 0-2 always set to 011.

15	14	13	12 11	10 9 8	7 6	5 - 0
O	1	1	A	TRANSFER	CONTROL	DEVICE

In theory this allows 64 different devices (ie, all the options in bits 5-0) to be connected, but 0 and 63 are reserved for special functions. Each device has a special decoder built-into it so that it will only respond to instructions containing its own address in bits 5-0. For example the teletype keyboard responds to 8 and the printer is device number 9.

Each device has a "Busy" and "Done" register. The busy register is set while the device is occupied, ie; a teletype operates at 10 characters per second, so while a character is being printed the busy register will be set for almost 100,000 microseconds. When the device finishes an operation it clears "Busy" and sets "Done" to indicate that it is ready to receive new data for output.

Bits 7 and 6 (the CONTROL field) of an I/O instruction are normally used to manipulate these registers (or flags as they are more commonly called) as follows

O O   No action
O 1   Start device, clear "Done" and set "Busy"
1 O   Clear "Busy" and "Done".
1 1   Special pulse.

Bits 10-8 specify the transfer which is to take place.

Bits	15 14 13	12 11	10 9 8	7 6	5 - 0
G:	O 1 1	A	O O 1	F	D
H:	O 1 1	A	O 1 O	F	D
I:	O 1 1	OO	O O O	F	D

G: Read data from device (D) to accumulator (A) and perform function (F).
H: Send data from accumulator (A) to device (D) and perform function (F).
I: No data is transferred but function (F) is performed.

Because of the length of time that I/O operations take (100,000 microseconds to print one character on a teletype), it is likely that the computer will be in a position to write the next character long before the previous one has been completed. The computer needs some instructions therefore to test the states of the "Busy" and "Done" flags. These are provided by setting the

TRANSFER field = 7 (ie, Bits 10, 9, 8 = 111).

Bits	15 11	10 9 8	7 6	5 - 0
J:	0 1 1 0 0	1 1 1	0 0	D
K:	0 1 1 0 0	1 1 1	0 1	D
L:	0 1 1 0 0	1 1 1	1 0	D
M:	0 1 1 0 0	1 1 1	1 1	D

J: Skip the next instruction if "Busy"
K: Skip the next instruction if "not Busy"
L: Skip the next instruction if "Done"
M: Skip the next instruction if "not Done" for device (D).

Arithmetic and Logic Instructions

These always have bit 15 set = 1 and the format is

15	14 13	12 11	10 9 8	7	6	5 4 3	2 1 0
1	SOURCE AC	DESTINATION AC	OPERATION	SHIFT	CARRY	NO LOAD	SKIP

SECONDARY FUNCTIONS (bits 7-0)

Bits 14-8 indicate the primary function to be performed on the two accumulators S (bits 14, 13) and D (bits 12, 11).

Example

1	1 0	1 1	1 1 0	0 0 0 0 0 0 0 0
	AC2	AC3	ADD	

would add the number in accumulator 2 to the number in accumulator 3 and place the result in accumulator 3.

However by specifying one or more secondary functions (in bits 7-0) a single instruction can be made to perform a very complex sequence of operations.

Example: in the operation above if the SKIP field (bits 2-0) were set to 4, ie,

1	1 0	1 1	1 1 0	0 0 0 0 0	1 0 0

then after adding AC2 and AC3, and placing the result in AC3, the computer would skip the next instruction if the result was zero.

In addition setting the NO LOAD (bit 3) in this instruction would cause the computer to add AC2 and AC3, and skip if the result is zero. In this case AC3 would be unchanged (ie, not loaded) after the operation.

The other fields allow for the 17 bit result (ie, with carry) to be shifted left or right, for the two halves to be swapped, and for the previous state of the CARRY to be included or not included in the operation.

The full range of options for the secondary function is indicated below to give some idea of the powerful nature of the arithmetic and logic operations on the Nova.

CARRY

Bits 5,4	Value of carry bit to be added
0 0	current state of carry bit
0 1	zero
1 0	one
1 1	complement of current state of carry bit

SHIFT

Result of arithmetic operation is a seventeen bit number (including the CARRY).

C	-	Result bits 15-0

Bits 7,6	Shift Operation
0 0	None
0 1	Left rotate; bit 0→1, bit 1→2 ... bit 15→carry, carry→bit 0
1 0	Right rotate, bit 15→14, bit 14→13... bit 1→0, bit 0→carry, carry→bit 15
1 1	Swap halves; bits (15-8)→bits (7-0); bits (7-0)→bits (15-8)

SKIP (ie, skip next instruction)

Bits 2, 1, 0	When to Skip Next Instruction
0 0 0	Never Skip
0 0 1	Always Skip
0 1 0	Skip if CARRY zero
0 1 1	Skip if CARRY non-zero
1 0 0	Skip if Result zero
1 0 1	Skip if Result non-zero
1 1 0	Skip if carry or result zero
1 1 1	Skip if both carry and result zer

NO LOAD

Bit 3	
0	Place result in destination accumulator (bits 12, 11)
1	Discard result; ie, both accumulators will be unchanged after the instruction is executed

The primary functions are:

Bits 10,9,8	Primary Function
0 0 0	Place the complement of the source AC in the destination AC
0 0 1	Place the negative of the source AC in the destination AC
0 1 0	Transfer the contents of the source AC to the destination AC
0 1 1	Increment source AC by 1 and place in the destination AC
1 0 0	Complement the source AC and ADD to the destination AC
1 0 1	Subtract the source AC from the destination AC

1 1 0	Add the source AC to the destination AC
1 1 1	AND the source AC and the destination AC

Notes:

1. In all cases the destination AC will be overwritten only if the NO LOAD bit (bit 3) is zero.

2. The complement of a bit pattern is achieved by changing all the ones to zeros and all the zeros to ones.

3. The AND operation on two bit patterns results in a one appearing in those positions where <u>both</u> the corresponding positions in the original patterns contained 1. Bits in all other positions are zero.

3.3. CAI-ALPHA

Computer Automation Inc. manufactures a range of minicomputers which are sold under the range name ALPHA.

Structure

Like the Nova range, the Alpha is a 16-bit computer. Typical memory speeds are 1600, 1200, 980 nano-seconds. There is only one accumulator A and one index register X (compared to 4 and 2 respectively on the Nova). The X-register can however act as an extension to the accumulator, and unlike the Nova, the basic machine includes hardware multiply and divide operations. There are no auto-increment <u>or</u> decrement stores but the Alpha range does have two novel features <u>byte mode addressing</u> and <u>automatic memory scan</u>. The first of these allows the memory to be referenced as a sequence of half-words (<u>or</u> eight bit bytes) as well as the conventional full 16-bit word addressing. The second provides an instruction which can search a section of memory for a given bit pattern. Also some instructions on the ALPHA are two words long, rather than the usual one word.

Memory Reference Instructions

(a) <u>Single Word Instructions</u> have the following format

```
15 14 - 11 10 9 8 7 - 0
┌─┬───────────┬─┬─┬─────┐
│1│ OPERATION │M│I│  D  │
└─┴───────────┴─┴─┴─────┘
```

Notes:

1. M is a two bit indicator for address mode
if M = 00 D is an absolute address in the range 0 - 255
   M = 01 D is a forward relative address, giving access to the 256 locations immediately after the instruction.
   M = 10 D is an offset which is added to the contents of X giving indexed addressing.
   M = 11 D is a backward relative address, giving access to the 256 locations immediately before the current instruction.

2. I = 1 indicates indirect addressing. If bit 15 is set = 1 when the eventual address is retrieved, then this is regarded as a further indirect address. The processor continues to fetch addresses until eventually one is accessed with bit 15 = 0.

This last address is then accessed to give the operand for the instruction.

3. When the computer is operating in byte mode, then the address calculated is the address of one byte as follows:-

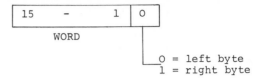

```
┌──────────────┬─┐
│  15    -   1 │0│
└──────────────┴─┘
      WORD       └── 0 = left byte
                     1 = right byte
```

bits 15-1 reference a location
bit 0 references either the first 8 bits or the second 8 bits in that word. Since bit 15 is used as part of the address in byte mode, only one level of indirection is possible.

4. The following is the list of possible operations for this format:-

OPERATION	
0 0 0 0	AND contents of specified address with the accumulator
0 0 0 1	ADD contents of specified address to the accumulator
0 0 1 0	SUBTRACT contents of specified address from the accumulator
0 0 1 1	STORE the contents of the accumulator in the specified address
0 1 0 0	Inclusive OR the contents of specified address with accumulator
0 1 0 1	Exclusive OR the contents of specified address with accumulator
0 1 1 0	LOAD the contents of the address specified into the accumulator
0 1 1 1	Compare the contents of specified address with the accumulator < A skip one instruction
1 0 1 0	Compare contents of specified address with accumulator; = A skip two instructions
1 0 1 1	Add one to contents of specified address; skip one instruction if result = 0
1 1 0 0	LOAD contents of specified address into the X-register
1 1 0 1	STORE the contents of the X-register in the address specified
1 1 1 0	JUMP to specified address
1 1 1 1	Store the contents of P-register at effective address; jump to the instruction immediately following that.

(b) <u>Double Word Instructions</u> have the format:

```
15 - 12  11 - 8   7 6 5 4  3 2 1 0
┌─────────┬─────────┬─┬─────────┬───┐
│ 0 0 0 1 │ 1 0 0 1 │0│OPERATION│   │
│         │         │ │  CODE   │   │
├─┬───────┴─────────┴─┴─────────┴───┤
│I│           ADDRESS               │
└─┴─────────────────────────────────┘
```

where ADDRESS is the 15 bit address of the operand if Bit 15 = 0 (I=0) or a pointer to the address of the address of the operand if Bit 15 = 1 (I=1).

Note 1. When operation code = 110, the contents of the specified address are multiplied by the contents of the X-register and the contents of the A register are added to the

product. The 30-bit result is placed in the
A and X register.

Note 2. When operation code = 111, the double
length number in A and X is divided by the
contents of the specified address. The
quotient is returned in the X-register and
the remainder in the A-register.

Byte Immediate Instructions have the format:

```
15  -  11  10 9 8   7 - 0
+----------+-----------+------+
| 1 1 0 0 0| OPERATION |  D   |
+----------+-----------+------+
```

and D is usually one of the operands of the
operation (rather than an address). The
following operations are available:

O O O	Skip one instruction if D is not equal to the right byte of A (the accumulator)
O O 1	Skip one instruction if D is not equal to the right byte of X (the index register)
O 1 O	Add D to the contents of X-register
O 1 1	Subtract D from the contents of X-register
1 O O	Put D into the X-register
1 O 1	Put -D into the X-register
1 1 O	Put D into the accumulator
1 1 1	Put -D into the accumulator

Conditional Jump Instruction

The ALPHA detects a conditional jump by having
the settings of bits 15, 14, 13 = O O 1
respectively. The rest of the instruction has
the following format:

```
15 14 13 12  11 10 9 8 7   6   5 - 0
+-----+--+-----------+---+-------+
|O O 1| G| CONDITIONS| R |   D   |
+-----+--+-----------+---+-------+
```

D is the jump distance (a positive number in
the range O-63).

R indicates whether the jump should be forward (to a higher address) or backward (to a
lower address). O indicates a forward jump
and 1 a backward jump.

G selects one of two sets of conditions to be
tested. If G = O then the possible conditions
are:-

bit 11 set tests if X = O
bit 10 set tests if sense indicator off
bit 9 set tests if overflow register is set
bit 8 set tests if A = O
bit 7 set tests if A is negative

and if any of the conditions specified is
true the jump takes place otherwise the computer proceeds to the next instruction.

If G = 1 then the possible tests are:-

bit 11 set tests if X = O
bit 10 set tests if sense indicator is on
bit 9 set tests if overflow register is set
bit 8 set tests if A ≠ O
bit 7 set tests if A is positive

and the jump takes place only if all of the
conditions specified are found to be true.

Examples:

	15-13	12	11 - 7	6	5 - 0
A:	O O 1	O	1 O O O O	O	O O O 1 1 1
B:	O O 1	O	1 O O O O	1	O O O 1 1 1
C:	O O 1	O	1 O O 1 O	O	O O O O 1 1
D:	O O 1	O	1 O O 1 1	O	O O O 1 O O
E:	O O 1	1	1 O O O O	O	O O O 1 1 1
F:	O O 1	1	1 O O O 1	O	O O O O 1 1
G:	O O 1	1	1 O 1 1 O	1	O O O 1 O O

A: jump forward 7 locations if X = O
B: jump back 7 locations if X = O
C: jump forward 3 locations if X=O or if A=O
D: jump forward 4 locations if X = O or A = O or if A < O
E: jump forward 7 locations if X ≠ O
F: jump forward 3 locations if both X≠O and A>O
G: jump back 4 locations if X≠O and overflow is set and A≠O

The first 4 only need any of the selected
conditions to be true for the jump to take
place whereas the last 3 require all of the
selected conditions to be true before the jump
takes place.

Register Manipulation

Instructions which allow operations on one
register or between registers take the form:

```
15  -  11  10  -  3  2 1 0
+----------+----------+------+
|O O O O O | FUNCTION |O O O |
+----------+----------+------+
```

A wide set of operations on both the A and
X registers is available, eg,

store zero, +1, or -1 in either or both
registers;
add or subtract 1 from either and place in
the other;
the logical AND, OR, NOR, complement and
negate functions;

Examples:

H:	O O O O O	O O O O O O 1 1	O O O
I:	O O O O O	O O O 1 1 O O 1	O O O
J:	O O O O O	O O 1 O O O 1 O	O O O
K:	O O O O O	O O 1 O O 1 O 1	O O O
L:	O O O O O	1 O 1 O O 1 O 1	O O O

H: Set A and X to -1
I: Set X to (the contents of A) -1
J: Clear the A register ie, set A = O
K: Add 1 to the X register
L: Set X register to +1

Input/Output Instructions

There are two types of I/O instruction. The
first type transfers one byte (8-bits) or
one word (16-bits) from a peripheral to a
specified register, or from a register to a
peripheral. The format is:

```
15 14 13  -  8   7  -  3  2  -  0
+---+----------+--------+----------+
|O 1| OPERATION| DEVICE | FUNCTION |
+---+----------+--------+----------+
```

This allows for up to 32 devices to be addressed.

Examples:

	15 14	13 - 8	7 - 3	2 - 0
M:	0 1	0 0 0 0 0 0	0 0 0 0 0	1 1 1
N:	0 1	0 1 1 0 0 0	0 0 1 1 1	0 0 0
O:	0 1	0 1 1 0 1 0	0 0 1 1 1	0 0 0
P:	0 1	1 0 1 1 0 0	0 0 0 1 1	0 0 0
Q:	0 1	1 1 1 0 0 0	0 0 0 1 1	0 0 0
R:	0 1	1 1 1 1 0 0	0 0 0 1 1	0 0 0

M: Transmits the function Code (Bits 2-0) to the peripheral

N: Copy 16-bits from peripheral 7 into the A-register

O: Copy 16-bits from peripheral 7 into the X-register

P: Copy 16-bits from the A-register to peripheral 3

Q: Copy 8-bits from peripheral 3 into the A-register

R: Take 8-bits from peripheral 3, perform the logical AND of this with the last 8-bits of the A-register, and place the result in the A-register.

The full range of operations allows transfers to or from the A or X registers in 8 or 16 bit units and in all cases the previous content of the register can be used as a "mask" to select only specified bits from the input.

The second type of I/O instruction occupies a number of sequential locations and is used for direct memory access (DMA) peripherals, where the data is transferred directly between memory and the peripheral without passing through the registers. Normally these are high speed devices and a number of bytes (8-bit units) or words (16-bit units) is transferred as the result of one instruction. In the first type of I/O instruction above, the options were sufficiently small to be coded into the operation; there were only two options for the size of transfer (8 or 16 bits) and two options for the destination (the A or X registers). With DMA devices however the destination may be any location in memory and the size of transfer may also be large. The following format is used:

	15 14	13 12	11 10	9 8	7 - 3	2 - 0
P	0 1	OPERATION	O B	O O	DEVICE	FUNCTION
P+1	-N					
P+2	ADDRESS - 1					
P+3	END OF BLOCK EXIT					
P+4	INSTRUCTION PER TRANSFER					

Notes:-

1. The OPERATION CODE (Bits 13,12) is 01 for INPUT/READ and 10 for OUTPUT/WRITE.

2. The Byte indicator B (bit 10) is 0 if one word is to be transferred and 1 if one byte is to be transferred.

3. N is the number of words or bytes to be transferred.

4. ADDRESS is the address of the first word/byte in the transfer. The contents of P+1 and P+2 are increased by 1 before each unit transfer (byte/word) ie, every time instruction P is executed. After the transfer of each unit, the contents of P+1 are examined; if non-zero then P+4 is executed next; if zero then P+3 if executed next.

Example: The following instructions would cause 16 words to be read from device 6 into memory locations 80-95.

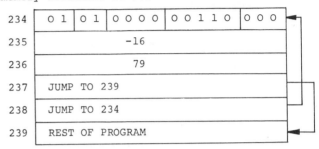

234	0 1	0 1	0 0 0 0	0 0 1 1 0	0 0 0
235	-16
236	79
237	JUMP TO 239
238	JUMP TO 234
239	REST OF PROGRAM

The sequence of instructions executed would be:-

234 add one to 235 (-15) and 236 (80) and read word into address in 236 (word 80) if contents of 235 zero go to 237 otherwise 238 - so we go to 238

238 go to instruction 234

234 add one to 235 (-14) and 236 (81) and read word into address in 236 (word 81) since 235 is non-zero go to 238

238 go to 234.

So we continue to execute alternately instructions 234 and 238 until eventually we get to

234 add one to 235 (0) and 236 (95), read one word into address in 236 (95) if contents of 235 = zero go to instruction 237

237 go to 239

239 ....

240 ....

and we continue with the rest of the program having transferred the 16 (16-bit) words into 80-95.

3.4. COMPUTER WORD LENGTH

The three computers introduced so far are classed as minicomputers and they are representative of small computers designed in the late 1960s and the early 1970s.

The way in which bits are organised and grouped in a computer is an important feature and is defined in terms of the computer's word size or word length. The PDP-8 is thus referred to as a 12-bit machine because data is accessed and processed in 12-bit words and each memory cell (location) contains a 12-bit word. The Nova and Alpha are both 16-bit minicomputers.

16 bits is the most common word length for a minicomputer, but many 12, 18, 24 and 32 bit machines have been manufactured and used. The term minicomputer has become imprecise,

with the division between powerful 16 or 32 bit machines and 'large' computers difficult to define meaningfully. It is also difficult to differentiate between minicomputers and <u>microcomputers</u>. The latter are commonly identified by their use of a microprocessor as the CPU - that is the CPU is contained within a single silicon-based, microelectronic, integrated circuit 'chip'. Electronic aspects of minicomputers and microcomputers are covered in Chapters 4 and 5.

Most microcomputers today are 8-bit machines, but 16-bit microprocessors are now available. Word length is thus a poor parameter to use for classification of 'minis' and 'micros' and indeed some computers based on 8-bit microprocessors have 'minicomputer' performance. At the present time however a minicomputer may be taken as a small computer with a 16 or 32 bit word length (18 and 24 bits are rather less popular), and a microcomputer is likely to be based on an 8-bit microprocessor.

In the remainder of this chapter we will examine two 8-bit <u>microprocessors</u> - the MOS 6502 and the Intel 8080. You should note that memory must be added to a microprocessor to make a computer, and in the treatment of the microprocessors it is assumed that memory organised in 8-bit words is accessible by the devices. Processor-memory configurations are examined in Chapter 5.

To give as comprehensive and accurate a picture as possible, considerable detail is included and this will be useful for future reference. You should be able to see, in the computer features discussed, illustration of the practical application of the computer principles already introduced.

3.5.   THE MOS 6502

This modern microprocessor is used in two of the most popular 'personal' computers (micro-computers) - the Apple and the PET.

Structure

Most of the 6502's internal registers are 8-bits wide, and memory is accessed as 8-bit words. To achieve an absolute addressing range of 64 K, two memory words are needed, and a 16 bit program counter is used. The program counter is implemented as two separate registers PCH and PCL. PCH contains the 8 high order bits of the address and PCL contains the 8 low order bits. Thus for example if PCH contains 3 and PCL contains 15 as shown,

0 0 0 0 0 0 1 1	0 0 0 0 1 1 1 1
PCH	PCL

the PC value is 783.

The memory may thus be regarded as a series of 256 word pages. (8 bits gives an address-ing range 0-255.) PCH selects the page and PCL selects the cell (location) within that page. Page 1 (memory locations 256 to 511) is used as a '<u>stack</u>'. Special instructions are available to transfer the contents of the accumulator or the status register (discussed later) on the stack.

The accumulator is 8 bits wide and is used by the standard copy, compare, add and subtract instructions.

The status register (P register) contains a set of one bit flags which usually record the status of the accumulator after an operation.

There are 2 conventional 8-bit index registers which allow an offset of up to 255. These registers are designated X and Y.

There is a stack front pointer (SP) which span the range 256-511.

Memory Addressing

The memory is considered as 256 pages each of which contains 256 bytes or words (1 byte = 8 bits). To refer to an absolute address in memory therefore will require 16 bits ie, 2 bytes (see discussion of program counter above). An instruction using absolute addressing will occupy 3 bytes - one for the operation code and 2 for the address

OPCODE	LOW	HIGH

and rather unconventionally the low 8 bits of the address precede the high 8 bits. The HIGH bits indicate which page of memory is being accessed and the LOW bits indicate which byte within the page. When page 0 is being assessed it is not necessary to include the third byte. So an instruction accessing page 0 for its operand is only 2 bytes long.

OPCODE	LOW

The X and Y registers may be used to modify the effective address. Since they are 8 bits wide, this allows access to tables of up to 256 variables.

There is also an indirect mode of addressing. This allows a pointer to be placed in page 0 of memory. Using the address of this pointer in an indirect mode instruction produces the operand from the address indicated by the pointer.

Memory Reference Instructions

Instructions which pick up an operand from memory or which deposit an operand in memory are 2 or 3 bytes long. The first byte is the OPCODE and is of the form

F F F	M M M	0 1

where the 3 bits FFF indicate the function to be performed, the 3 bits MMM indicate the addressing mode

FFF = 000   OR memory with accumulator
FFF = 001   AND memory with accumulator
FFF = 010   EOR (exclusive OR) memory with
                     accumulator
FFF = 011   ADC add memory to accumulator
                     with carry
FFF = 100   STA store accumulator in memory
FFF = 101   LDA load accumulator with memory
FFF = 110   CMP compare memory to accumulator
FFF = 111   SBC subtract memory from
                     accumulator with carry

Note there is no add without carry. This usually means the carry has to be cleared before the first addition.

Each of the above functions has 8 possible address modes for fetching the operand from memory.

```
MMM = 011 ⎫ the next 2 bytes are regarded as
MMM = 111 ⎬ LOW, HIGH indicating an absolute
MMM = 110 ⎭ address in memory
```

MMM = 111   this address is augmented by the
            contents of X.
MMM = 110   this address is augmented by the
            contents of Y.

```
MMM = 001 ⎫ the next byte gives a location
MMM = 101 ⎭ in page 0
```

MMM = 001   this is the final address
MMM = 101   this address is augmented by the
            X register

MMM = 010   the next byte contains the operand
            (immediate addressing)

```
MMM = 000 ⎫ give  indirect
MMM = 100 ⎭ address mode
```

MMM = 000   the next byte gives an offset in
            page 0. To this is added the X
            register. This address points to
            a cell whose contents give the
            address of the operand.
MMM = 100   the next byte gives an address in
            page 0. This points to an absolute
            address in memory. The contents
            of this address are augmented by
            Y to give the final address.

MMM = 000   is an indexed indirect mode whereas
MMM = 100   is an indirect indexed mode

Note: Obviously the STA (store accumulator)
function is meaningless in immediate address
mode and results in a NOP (no operation).

Register-Memory Transfers

Those memory reference instructions which use
one of the index registers as an operand
cannot also use the same register for indexing so there are fewer address modes. For
example STX (store X register in memory) has
only 3 possible address modes.

```
FFFMM110
10000110 MM=00 next byte indicates location
10010110        of result on page 0
10001110 MM=10 next byte is added to the Y
                register to give address for
                result
         MM=01 next 2 bytes give absolute
                address.
```

Register-Register Transfers

No explicit memory address is required so
these operations require only one byte - the
source and destination operands are implied.
For example.

```
10101010  TAX Transfer contents of accumulator
              to X register
10001010  TXA Transfer contents of X register
              to accumulator
11001010  DEX Subtract one from X register
10001010  DEY Subtract one from Y register
11101000  INX Add one to X register
11001000  INY Add one to Y register
10101000  TAY Transfer contents of A to Y
              register
10011000  TYA Transfer contents of Y register
              to accumulator
10111010  TSX Transfer stack pointer to X
              register
10011010  TXS Transfer X register to stack
              pointer.
```

Status Register (P)

The status register is a collection of flags
which are available in the processor to indicate
certain conditions.

Bit   7 6 5 4 3 2 1 0

P-register | N | V | - | B | D | I | Z | C |

N - sign   It is set when the result of an
              operation is negative.
V - overflow The overflow flag is set if the
              result of an operation is too
              large to be held as an eight
              bit quantity.
B - break   The BRK instruction allows the
              program to simulate an interrupt.
              This flag is set by the BRK
              instruction to allow the program
              to distinguish between a hard-
              ware and a software interrupt.
D - decimal   When D is set any arithmetic
              operations are carried out in
              'BCD-mode' ie, each 8 bit
              operand is considered as 2
              binary coded decimal digits
              (each occupying 4 bits).
I - interrupt When this flag is set no
              interrupts are permitted.
Z - zero   Indicates the result of an opera-
              tion is zero. It is tested by
              the compare instruction CMP.
C - carry   When performing multiple word
              arithmetic in either BCD or
              two's complement the carry bit
              is used to indicate that a bit
              needs to be "carried" into the
              next phase of the operation.

Bit 5 of the P register is not used. The P
register is automatically stored in the stack
when an external interrupt occurs.

The Stack

Cells 256-511 (ie, page one of the memory) are
regarded as a <u>stack</u> - information deposited
there just keeps piling up. At any time one
can only normally extract the last byte of
information sent to the stack. The top of
the stack is indicated by a special 9 bit
register - the stack pointer (SP) - the most
significant bit of the 9 is always set. This
restricts the stack pointer to the range 256-
511. The following instructions use the stack
explicitly.

PHA - 01001000 Push the contents of the
                accumulator (A) on to the
                stack
PHP - 00001000 Push the contents of the status
                register (P) on to the stack
PLA - 01101000 Pull the contents of the
                accumulator off the top of the
                stack
PLP - 00101000 Pull the contents of the
                status register off the top
                of the stack.

Pushing A or P on the stack automatically
decrements the stack pointer (SP) whereas
pulling A or P will increment the stack
pointer. Assuming that the stack pointer
starts at 511 - then 4 push instructions
followed by 4 pull instructions will access
the following cells:

```
Fourth PUSH → 508  [        ]  First PULL
Third PUSH  → 509  [        ]  Second PULL
Second PUSH → 510  [        ]  Third PULL
First PUSH  → 511  [        ]  Fourth PULL
```

Subroutines

One of the main functions of the stack is to hold the address from which a subroutine was called. The "first in – last out" nature of the stack makes it extremely suitable for nested subroutine CALLS. A subroutine call is implemented by the opcode

O O 1 O O O O O   JSR   jump to subroutine

This instruction always uses an absolute address so the whole instruction is always 3 bytes long. The contents of the program counter (+2) are stored on the stack and the processor jumps to the instruction specified in the address field. If for example an instruction to jump to the subroutine at location 2050 occurred at location 1039 and the stack was empty at the time (ie, stack pointer = 511), the instruction would

(i) cause the next address (ie, 1042) to be placed on the stack. 1042 = 4 x 256 + 18 so 4 goes to 511 and 18 goes to 510.
(ii) the stack pointer would be "updated" from 511 to 509.
(iii) the program counter would be set to 2050.
(iv) processing continues from 2050.

Address	Contents	
509		SP ←after
510	LOW=18	
511	HIGH=4	SP ←before
1039	JSR=32	
1040	LOW=2	
1041	HIGH=8	
1042		
2050	.	
2051	.	
	.	
	.	
2900	RTS=96	

The set of instructions comprising the subroutine (in this case 2050–2900) is executed. The last of these instructions at 2900 is

O11OOOOO RTS return from subroutine

This instruction is the "reverse" of the JSR. The program counter is set equal to the value at the top of the stack (in this case the two locations 511 and 510 which contain 4 x 256 + 18 = 1042 so PC is set equal to 1042) and the stack pointer is increased by 2 (to 511). The result of this is to restart processing at the instruction immediately following the JSR instruction.

Interrupts

It is possible to 'interrupt' the execution of a program to 'deal with' a situation – perhaps a device connected to the processor needs attention. There are 3 external interrupts available on the 6502. The most usual for input/output is the interrupt request or IRQ. When an interrupt of this type occurs the 6502 will automatically store the program counter (PCH and PCL) and the status register (P) in the next 3 available locations on the stack and update the stack pointer. Cells 65535 and 65534 are considered to contain a 16 bit address which in turn contains the address of the subroutine which will service the interrupt. This latter address is automatically copied into the program counter and processing continues from there. This interrupt vector technique is extremely flexible because the address of the interrupt handling routine can be changed at will. When the interrupt has been serviced the service routine may return to the main program at the point at which the interrupt occurred by using the instruction

RTI   O1OOOOOO   Return from interrupt

This instruction restores the status register from the copy which was saved in the stack, resets the program counter from the stack and updates the stack pointer. Use of the stack in this fashion avoids the programmer having to explicitly reset the registers, and speeds up the process of interrupt entry and exit.

When an interrupt occurs the I flag is automatically set to indicate that an interrupt is being processed. The IRQ will only interrupt the processor if the I flag is not set. There are two other types of interrupt the NMI or non-maskable interrupt and the power RESET. Both of these ignore the setting of the I flag but otherwise operate in a similar manner to the IRQ. The interrupt vector addresses are held in (65531, 65530) and (65533, 65532) respectively.

65530	low 8	NMI address
65531	high 8	
65532	low 8	RESET address
65533	high 8	
65534	low 8	IRQ address
65535	high 8	

There are instructions available to specifically set and unset the I-flag if required.

O1111OOO   SET   Set interrupt disable, ie, I = 1

O1O11OOO   CLI   Enable interrupts, ie, I = O

Branch Instructions

All conditional branch instructions use relative addressing. They are 2 bytes long. The first byte is the opcode and the second is regarded as a signed integer in the range –128 to +127. This offset is added to the contents of the Program Counter to give the alternate address. The instruction obeyed after the branch instruction will be either the

next highest in memory   – indicated by the program counter
or the alternate address   – indicated by the program counter and offset.

Instructions are available to Branch if

the carry flag is clear	1OO1OOOO	BCC
the carry flag is set	1OOOOOOO	BCS
the result of the last operation is zero	1111OOOO	BEQ
the result of the last operation is minus	OO11OOOO	BMI
the result of the last operation is not zero	11O1OOOO	BNE
the result of the last operation is plus	OOO1OOOO	BPL
the overflow flag is clear	O1O1OOOO	BVC
the overflow flag is set	O111OOOO	BVS

Branch instructions would normally be preceded by a compare instruction which sets the appropriate flags. There are 3 possible comparisons.

```
Compare memory with accumulator CMP 110MMM01
    "       "       "   X-register CPX 1110MM00
    "       "       "   Y-register CPY 1100MM00
```

All 3 will set the N, Z and C registers as follows

C is set if the contents of the register are greater than the contents of the specified memory location.

C and Z are set if the contents of the register are equal to the contents of the specified memory location.

N is set if the contents of the register are less than the contents of the specified memory location.

Note that the CMP instruction may use all eight of the address modes discussed earlier but the CPX and CPY are restricted to only 3 modes: absolute, immediate and zero page.

Sundry Other Instructions

Decimal Mode. As indicated earlier the addition and subtraction on the 6502 operates in one of 2 modes. In normal binary arithmetic the contents of the accumulator and memory location are considered as binary numbers in standard two's complement representation. This allows numbers in the range

-128 to +127

In decimal mode however individual decimal digits are stored as 4 bits. Thus

```
33 = 00100001 in binary
33 = 00110011 in binary coded decimal:- BCD
89 = 10001001 in BCD
90 = 10010000 in BCD
```

In the case of BCD the hardware recognizes that a carry is required into bit 4 when the least significant digit passes 9. Two special instructions are available to switch between binary addition and BCD addition.

11111000 SED - (Set decimal mode) switches the processor to perform BCD arithmetic.
11011000 CLD - (Clear decimal mode) sets the processor to perform binary arithmetic.

SED sets the decimal flag = 1, CLD sets the decimal flag = 0.

Increment Memory. The opcode 11XM110 INC - increment memory will add one to the contents of the specified memory location. XM indicates address mode. With M = 0 the instruction is 2 bytes long and the address in the second byte refers to page 0. With M = 1 the instruction is 3 bytes long and the 16 bit address refers to an absolute memory location. In both cases if X = 1 then the contents of the index register X are added to the stated address to give the effective address whose contents are to be incremented.

110XM110 DEC - decrement memory will subtract one from the contents of the specified location. The same address modes are used as for INC.

Jump. The unconditional jump instruction

01M01100 JMP (jump to specified location)

has 2 address modes indicated by M. The instruction is always 3 bytes long. When M = 0 the 16 bit address in bytes 2 and 3 is considered as an absolute address and is copied into the PC. When M = 1 the contents of the 16 bit address specified in the last 2 bytes are transferred to the Program Counter.

Thus the instruction at 768, 769, 770 will cause the processor to execute as its next instruction the instruction in cell 1027. However if 768 contained the bit pattern 01101100 then the instruction at 768, 769, 770 will cause the processor to pick up its next instruction at 2051.

```
768  01001100  JMP
769  00000011 } 1027
770  00000100



1027 00000011 } 2051
1028 00001000
```

Shift Instructions

Four shift instructions are available in which the carry register is considered as a ninth bit for the accumulator as follows

```
AC =     7   6   5   4   3   2   1   0   Carry

Before - B7  B6  B5  B4  B3  B2  B1  B0    C
```

After 01001010 LSR - Shift Right

```
0   B7  B6  B5  B4  B3  B2  B1    B0
```

After 00001010 ASL - Shift left

```
B6  B5  B4  B3  B2  B1  B0  C    0
```

After 01101010 ROR - Rotate Right

```
C   B7  B6  B5  B4  B3  B2  B1    B0
```

After 00101010 ROL - Rotate left

```
B6  B5  B4  B3  B2  B1  B0  C    B7
```

There are 4 other modes for these instructions which allow them to perform similar operations on a memory cell.

```
01XM1010  LSR - Shift Right
00XM1010  ASL - Shift Left
011XM010  ROR - Rotate Right
001XM010  ROL - Rotate Left
```

X,M have the same significance as in the Increment Register instruction.

Input/Output

There are no specific input/output instructions on the 6502. Instead a section of the memory address space is reserved to reference peripherals rather than memory cells. For example on the Apple computer system which is based on the 6502, addresses between 48 K and 52 K are reserved for peripherals. Any of the standard memory reference instructions which result in an address in this range being referenced can accept data from a device or send data to a device. How this is done will be clearer after you have read Chapters 4 and 5.

3.6.   THE INTEL 8080

Structure

The Intel 8080 resembles the 6502 in basic
structure. Each memory cell contains one
8 bit byte. The OPCODE occupies one cell.
An instruction may be one, 2 or 3 bytes long
depending on the address mode. The accumulator
(A) is 8 bits wide.

There are however a number of significant
differences.

(a) The program counter is a single 16 bit
register.
(b) The stack pointer is a 16 bit register.
This means that the stack can reside anywhere in memory and in theory be up to 64K
cells long. On the 6502 it is restricted to
page 1 with a maximum size of 256 cells.
(c) There are 6 8-bit registers which may
be referenced either individually or in pairs.
They are designated (B,C) (D,E) (H,L) and are
normally used instead of indexing.
(d) The 5 one bit flags available are:-
zero (Z), carry (CY), sign (S), parity (P),
auxiliary carry (AC).

There is no decimal mode arithmetic as such
but an instruction is available to convert
an 8 bit binary number into 2 BCD digits.

Memory Addressing

The most usual method of addressing memory
is through the register pair (H,L). H is
set to contain the most significant 8 bits of
the address and L the least significant.
H effectively specifies a page of 256 cells
and L the cell within that page. Some
instructions may use another pair of registers
in a similar way. Only the instructions
which copy data between memory and the
accumulator may use absolute addressing.
Most arithmetic instructions permit immediate
mode addressing, ie, where the data for the
instruction is contained in the last 2 bytes
of the instruction. The significance of
these 2 bytes is reversed as on the 6502 so
that when referring to either an absolute
address or when containing the data for the
instruction, byte 2 always contains the low
order 8 bits and byte 3 the high order 8 bits.

There is no short addressing (ie, page 0) or
indexed addressing as such but judicious use
of the H and L registers provide the same
capability. For example, page 0 addressing
is simply achieved by setting H to zero and
using (H,L) as a register pair as above.

Memory Reference Instructions

Data may be transferred from memory to the
accumulator using one of 2 instructions.

00111010 LDA (load absolute) is 3 bytes long;
         the second 2 bytes of the instruction
         contain the address of the data to
         be transferred.

00RR1010 LDAX (load indirect) is a one byte
         instruction. The address of the
         data is contained in a pair of
         registers specified by RR.
         If RR = 00 register pair (B,C) con-
         tains the address.
         If RR = 01 register pair (D,E) con-
         tains the address.

00110010 STA ⎫operate in a similar fashion
00RR0010 STAX ⎭to move data from the accumulator
              to memory.

The add instruction has 2 modes - immediate
or (H,L) addressing.

11000110 ADI (add immediate) is two bytes
              long and adds the contents of the
              second byte to the accumulator.
10000110 ADDM is one byte long. H and L
              are assumed to contain the address
              of a cell in memory. The contents
              of this cell are added to the
              accumulator.

11001110 ACI ⎫operate in similar fashion
10001110 ADCM ⎭except that the carry register
               is also added to the result.

There is a similar set of 4 instructions
for subtraction.

Transfers between Registers

These follow the general format

$$\boxed{01DDDSSS}$$

where SSS specifies a source register and
DDD specifies a destination register using
the addressing codes below

DDD	or SSS	Register
000		B
001		C
010		D
011		E
100		H
101		L
110		the source or des- tination is a cell in memory indicated by (H,L)
111		A

Thus 01111011 means move contents of register
E to the accumulator (A),

whereas 01011111 means move the contents of
the accumulator to register E.

When SSS is equal to 110 the source of the
transfer is the cell in memory indicated
by the registers (H,L). Similarly if DDD =
110 the destination is the memory location
indicated by the register pair (H,L).

Adding and subtracting one from a specified
register is achieved by

00DDD100 Increment register
00DDD101 Decrement register

and as above if DDD = 110 the memory cell
indicated by (H,L) is incremented or
decremented.

It is also possible to increment or decrement
a register pair as if they formed a 16 bit
integer. This is achieved by

00RR0011 INX increment
00RR1011 DCX decrement

RR indicates a register pair according to the following rules.

```
RR   Register Pair
00   B,C
01   D,E
10   H,L
11   SP (the stack pointer is a single 16
        bit register)
```

Branch Instructions

These occupy 3 bytes, use absolute address mode and take 2 forms.

First the unconditional branch instruction causes the contents of bytes 2 and 3 of the instruction to be copied into the program counter.

11000011	low order address bits	high order address bits	JMP to address specified

The second form is the conditional branch instruction. In this case the program counter is changed only if a condition specified in bits 5, 4, 3 of the opcode is true. The format is

11CCC010	low order address bits	high order address bits	JMP to address if condition is true

The conditions which can be tested are:-

CCC	Flag tested	Action
000	Z = 0	Branch if not zero
001	Z = 1	Branch if zero
010	CY = 0	Branch if carry is clear
011	CY = 1	Branch if carry is set
100	P = 0	Branch if parity is odd
101	P = 1	Branch if parity is even
110	S = 0	Branch if positive
111	S = 1	Branch if negative

Subroutines

The standard CALL instruction on the 8080 works in exactly the same way as that on the 6502. The CALL instruction is 3 bytes long.

11001101	low order address bits	high order address bits	CALL subroutine

The program counter which is currently pointing at the cell immediately following these 3 is copied to the stack and the stack pointer updated. The program counter is then overwritten with the contents of bytes 2 and 3 of the CALL instruction. To get back from the subroutine a return instruction is executed. The RETURN instruction is only one byte long:

11001001 RET   return to the address currently at the top of the stack.

The 2 bytes at the top of the stack are copied to the program counter and the stack pointer adjusted by 2.

Unlike the 6502 however both of these instructions have a conditional mode.

11CCC100 - CALL if condition CCC is true
11CCC000 - RETurn if condition CCC is true.

The conditions which can be tested are the same as those for branch instructions.

Stack Instructions

The contents of any of the 3 register pairs (B,C)(D,E)(H,L) may be copied to the stack by the PUSH instruction

11RR0101 PUSH - Place the contents of the register pair specified on top of the stack and update the stack pointer. RR has the same significance as indicated earlier.

The reverse operation of copying the top two bytes of the stack into a register pair (pulling in the jargon of the 6502, popping in the jargon of the 8080) is carried out by the one byte instruction -

11RR0001 POP - Copy from stack to register pair.

The instruction to PUSH the accumulator on to the stack will also copy the status of the flags into a conglomerate status word and place it on the stack. The format is -

11110101 PUSH - accumulator and status word onto the stack. The state of the stack after the instruction is executed will be

SP after	S	Z	O	AC	O	P	1	Cy
	A_7	A_6	A_5	A_4	A_3	A_2	A_1	A_0

where A_7-A_0 are the eight bits of the accumulator and S, Z, AC, P, CY are the five flags described earlier.

The reverse operation is -

11110001 POP - accumulator and reset flags from the top of the stack

Interrupts

On the 8080 there are eight reserved memory locations 0, 8, 16, 24, 32, 40, 48, 56 which can be used for the first instruction to be obeyed after an interrupt. Basically, the interrupting device effectively freezes the program counter and causes one special instruction to be executed. Unlike other instructions this RST instruction does not reside in the memory of the computer but is supplied by the interrupting device to the processor. Its form is

11NNN111 RST - restart at location 8*NNN

Thus if NNN is 111, ie, 7 the next instruction to be obeyed is 8X7=56 whereas if NNN is 101, ie, 5 the next instruction to be obeyed is 8X5=40. Before jumping to one of the above 8 instructions the "frozen" state of the Program Counter is pushed on to the stack. This means that when the routine to service the interrupt is complete, control can be returned to the address following the instruction during which the interrupt occurred, by a standard RET instruction.

Although there is no interrupt flag as on the 6502 there are specific instructions to enable and disable interrupts.

```
11111011  EI enable interrupts
11110011  DI disable interrupts
```

In both cases the enable or disable is delayed
for one instruction.

Input/Output

There are two mechanisms for handling input/
output. One is the memory mapped strategy
similar to the 6502 where no special I/O
instructions are required, since the standard
memory reference instructions allow transfer
between the accumulator and memory. A set
of memory addresses (usually in sequence) is
reserved and replaced by peripherals. Any
reference to one of these addresses causes
data to be sent or received from the peripheral
device depending on the instruction used.

```
Eg, 00110010 STA store accumulator - will
                    send data to the peripheral
                    (as it would to memory)

    00111010 LDA load accumulator - will
                    accept data from the peri-
                    pheral into the accumulator
```

The other mechanism involves specific input/
output instructions which are 2 bytes long.

```
11011011  IN transfers data into the
              accumulator from a device whose
              address is specified in the
              second byte of the instruction

11010011 OUT transfers data from the
              accumulator to the device whose
              address is specified in byte
              2 of the instruction
```

The advantage of the second approach is that
none of the memory address space is reserved
for peripherals and therefore it is possible
to attach the full 64K complement of memory
to the processor.

3.7. SUMMARY

The organisational and operational features of
three real minicomputers and two real microprocessors have been reviewed. Instruction
formats, memory addressing techniques and input/
output procedures have been illustrated for
computer structures using 8, 12 and 16 bit
word lengths.

In the next three chapters we will look at the
ways in which mini and microcomputers are
built using electronic technology, and how they
operate both internally and to effect communication with the world outside the computer.
Practical arrangements of computer systems
incorporating peripheral equipment for entering,
storing and retrieving programs and data,
and for making available the results of
computation, will be examined in electronic
detail.

3.8. REFERENCES

The Intel 8080 Microcomputer Systems User
Manual.

Programming the 6502 - Rodney Zaks.

How to Use the Nova Computers - Data General.

Alpha LSI Programming Reference Manual -
Computer Automation Inc.

Computer Electronics
Chapter 4

4.1. INTRODUCTION

The operation of a computer could be illustrated by physically moving objects labelled
'1' and '0' to and from containers representing memory locations and registers, and by
observing the rules of binary arithmetic.
The concepts of the stored program, information representation and the central processing unit could all be demonstrated in this
rather tedious way. The manpower required
would of course be greatly reduced by
handling the '1' and '0' objects mechanically,
or by using mechanical indicators. The very
earliest systems with computing capability
were indeed mechanical or electromechanical,
and were consequently unwieldy.

Today's computers owe their impressive power/
weight and power/size ratios to the state of
the electronic and microelectronic arts. The
first electronic computers of the 1940s and
early 1950s each occupied a fair sized room,
and with the thermionic valves used, kept it
warm. The 1960s and 1970s saw the headlong
development of computers for commercial and
scientific applications, with progress in
transistor and integrated circuit technology
being reflected almost immediately in smaller,
faster and more reliable computing hardware.

The technology used to implement the modern
small computer is microelectronic large-scale
integration - LSI - with more than 10,000
circuit elements on a silicon chip about a
half-centimetre square. These circuit elements are the logic circuits which perform
the digital functions necessary to store
programs and data, to execute instructions,
and to provide user-computer communication.
A review of basic digital logic elements is
a useful prelude to examination of the
electronic structure and operation of the
small computer. Design and fabrication
aspects of LSI circuitry are avoided, but
general considerations appropriate to an
awareness of the functional behaviour of the
circuits are included.

4.2. DIGITAL LOGIC ELEMENTS

The approach adopted here is first to
introduce the basic logic elements necessary
to perform data arithmetic operations, and
data transfer, control and temporary storage
functions. These logic elements are then
combined to construct combinational logic
units, data transfer circuits and data
registers.

Gates

A gate is a basic logic element whose output
takes on the value 1 or 0 dependent upon the
state of the logic levels at its inputs. A
voltage supply of +V and 0 (usually in the
range 5 to 15 volts) provides power to the
circuit, and power connections are omitted
from the diagrams. The logic levels at gate
inputs and outputs are: for a '1', at or
near +V; for a '0' at or near 0V ('earth'
or 'ground' reference level).

AND Gate

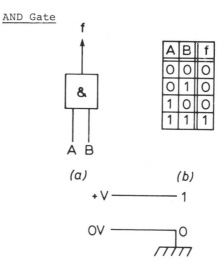

A	B	f
0	0	0
0	1	0
1	0	0
1	1	1

(a)   *(b)*

+V ——————— 1

0V ——————— 0

(c)

Figure 4.1. AND gate (a) Symbol;
                (b) Truth Table;
                (c) Logic Level Assignment.

The performance of the gate is specified by
the truth table in Fig. 4.1. Output f = 1,
when both inputs A and B are 1. This may be
extended to n inputs, in which case: Output
f = 1, when all n inputs are 1.

of a truth table as in Fig. 4.4.

OR Gate

f

|1|

A B

(a)

A	B	f
0	0	0
0	1	1
1	0	1
1	1	1

(b)

A	B	C_i	S	C_o
0	0	0	0	0
0	0	1	1	0
0	1	0	1	0
0	1	1	0	1
1	0	0	1	0
1	0	1	0	1
1	1	0	0	1
1	1	1	1	1

Figure 4.4.   Truth table of adder.

Figure 4.2.   OR gate (a) Symbol;
              (b) Truth table.

Output f = 1, when one or more inputs are 1.

Inverter

f

A

(a)

A	f
0	1
1	0

(b)

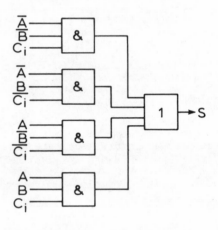

Figure 4.5.

Figure 4.3.   Inverter (a) Symbol;
              (b) Truth table.

Output f is the inversion or negation of input
A, f = NOT A, f = $\overline{A}$.

Gate Applications

Binary adder.   An application of gates,
readily assimilated at this stage, is their
role in a binary adder.   All the possible
permutations met in the addition of two
single-bit binary numbers, plus a carry-in,
are set out below.

A	0	0	0	0	1	1	1	1
B	0	0	1	1	0	0	1	1
C_{in}	0	1	0	1	0	1	0	1
S_{um}	0	1	1	0	1	0	0	1
C_{out}	0	0	0	1	0	1	1	1

The information may be arranged in the format

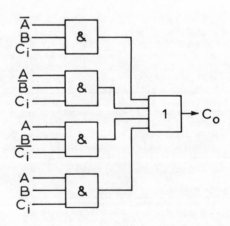

Fig. 4.6.

The logic diagrams of Figures 4.5. and 4.6.
implement the truth table of Figure 4.4.

Consider the first row of the truth table:
A = 0, B = 0, C_i = 0.   Therefore: $\overline{A}$ = 1,

$\overline{B} = 1$, $\overline{C}_i = 0$. Under these conditions the top AND gate of Figure 4.5. has all its inputs at 1 and so outputs 1 making $S = 1$.

None of the AND gates of Figure 4.6. outputs 1 so $C_o = 0$. Complete the verification of the logic circuits in this way.

Both these circuits (Figures 4.5. and 4.6.) may be incorporated in a single package as indicated by Fig. 4.7.

Note that the complemented or inverted signals, $\overline{A}$, $\overline{B}$ and $\overline{C}_i$, as required by Figures 4.5. and 4.6., are derived within the package by the use of inverters.

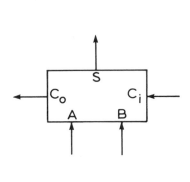

Figure 4.7. Single-bit adder.

In practice it is customary to add many bits simultaneously, ie, in parallel. A commonly used integrated circuit (I.C.) package is a 4-bit binary adder. This is simply a package containing four circuits conforming to Figure 4.7. A block schematic of a 4-bit binary adder is given by Figure 4.8.

number appears at outputs S.

Decoding

A basic computer operation coded in binary might be (in a particular 8-bit machine):

0 1 1 0 0 1 0 1 ADC (meaning ADD with carry)

In a real computer each code combination such as ADC must be decoded in the control unit to produce its own distinctive signal to select the appropriate operation.

A logic circuit to decode the above operation ADC is shown in Fig. 4.9.

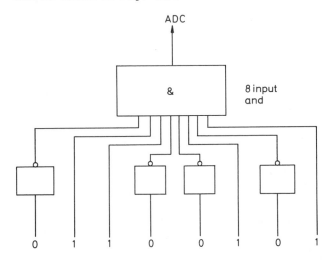

Figure 4.9. ADC decoder.

It is seen that 0 1 1 0 0 1 0 1 is the only code combination that will produce a 1 at the output of the ADC decoder.

Flipflops

J-K flipflop. Because of its versatility

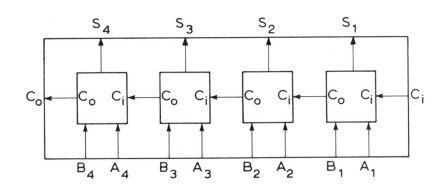

Fig. 4.8. 4-bit adder.

Incrementing

The adder is often used to increment a number by 1. This is achieved by applying the number at, say, the B inputs of the adder, putting A inputs = 0 and $C_i = 1$, when the incremented

this is by far the most widely used of the family of circuits known as 'flipflops'. Broadly speaking it can be used in different modes to embrace the characteristics of a wide variety of flipflops, including types used for counting and binary storage.

J and K refer to input terminals.

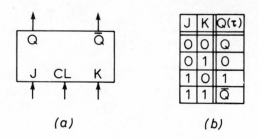

Figure 4.10.   J-K flipflop
           (a) Symbol
           (b) Truth table

The flipflop's performance is specified by the truth table. It has three inputs, J, K and CL (clock) and two outputs Q and $\bar{Q}$.

If Q = 1, ($\bar{Q}$ = 0), the flipflop is said to be in state 1. If Q = 0, ($\bar{Q}$ = 1), the flipflop is said to be in state 0. The future state, $Q(\tau)$, is the state of the flipflop after receipt of a clock pulse at CL. The future state, $Q(\tau)$, depends on the present state Q (0 or 1) and the logic levels (0 or 1) at the inputs J and K.

Take row 1 of the truth table. This may be interpreted as:

If J = 0 and K = 0 then $Q(\tau)$ = Q, ie, after receipt of a pulse at CL, the future state $Q(\tau)$ is the present state Q, ie, there has been no change in the state of the flipflop, irrespective of the present state of the flipflop.

Consider row 2.

If J = 0 and K = 1, then $Q(\tau)$ = 0, irrespective of the present state of the flipflop.

Consider row 3.

If J = 1 and K = 0, the $Q(\tau)$ = 1, irrespective of the present state of the flipflop.

Consider row 4.

If J = 1 and K = 1, then $Q(\tau)$ = $\bar{Q}$, ie, the future state $Q(\tau)$ is the complement of the present state irrespective of the present state of the flipflop.

This mode of operation (J = K = 1) is known as the complementing mode. Practical J-K flipflops usually have in addition, separate 'Preset' and 'Clear' connections. A logic '0' on Preset sets Q to '1'; a logic '0' on Clear sets Q to '0'.

Flipflop Applications

Binary counter. Figure 4.11. shows J-K flipflops connected to behave as a counter. The operation is best explained with reference to the waveform diagram of Fig. 4.12. Note that all J and K inputs are at 1.

A train of clock pulses at CL of flipflop Q_0 causes Q_0 to complement after receipt of each clock pulse, producing an output waveform at Q_0 as shown. Output Q_0 is connected to the CL input of flipflop Q_1 and this train of pulses, albeit broader, causes flipflop Q_1 to complement. Output Q_1 is connected to the CL input of flipflop Q_2, etc.

Study of the waveform of Figure 4.12. shows that after the first clock pulse the state of the counter is Q_0 = 1, Q_1 = 0, Q_2 = 0. After the second clock pulse the state of the counter is Q_0 = 0, Q_1 = 1, Q_2 = 0. The behaviour of the counter is summarised by the table of Fig. 4.13. from which the counting mechanism is evident.

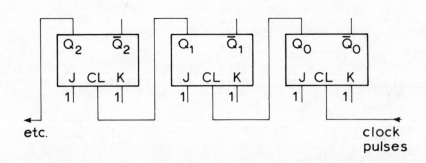

etc.   clock
                                                    pulses

Fig. 4.11. Binary counter.

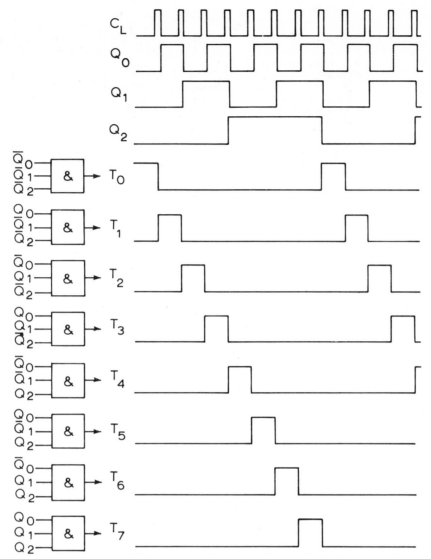

Figure 4.12. Output waveforms of binary counter and derived timing waveforms.

Note, that the last paragraph assumed the initial state of the counter to be $Q_0 = Q_1 = Q_2 = 0$. In practice this initial condition is achieved by a command signal to the CLEAR inputs of the flipflops, putting all the flipflops in state 0. The CLEAR input has been omitted from the JK symbol of Figure 4.10. and all subsequent diagrams, in the interests of clarity.

After receipt of	2^2	2^1	2^0	State of counter
CLOCK PULSE NO	Q_2	Q_1	Q_0	expressed in decimal
1	0	0	1	1
2	0	1	0	2
3	0	1	1	3
4	1	0	0	4
5	1	0	1	5
6	1	1	0	6
7	1	1	1	7
8	0	0	0	0

Figure 4.13.

Timing Waveforms

The generation of timing waveforms is an application of gates and flipflops. AND gates fed from the counter outputs as shown on the left of the waveform diagram, Figure 4.12. produced the timing waveforms, T_0 to T_7. Timing waveforms of this type are produced in this manner in the control unit of a computer to generate a sequence of signals known as micro-orders.

Registers

A register may be defined as a one-word store. The basic element of a register may be regarded as a J-K flipflop connected in the 'D' mode. It is evident that the D flipflop of Fig. 4.14. acts in accordance with the truth table of Fig. 4.15. The latter may be interpreted as stating that after receipt of a clock pulse the future state, $Q(\tau)$, corresponds to the state of the D input prior to the clock pulse, ie, the clock pulse enters the data at D into the flipflop.

Remember that the input data at the D terminals is isolated from the flipflops until the occurrence of the clock or strobe pulse on the INPUT CONTROL line. This means that the data input lines may be used to distribute data elsewhere in a system, provided they carry the relevant data for a particular register at the instant it is clocked or strobed. Thus the data input lines may be used FOR ALL inputs giving rise to the term "BUS" which is a contraction of "OMNIBUS" meaning "FOR ALL".

A similar isolation facility is required at the outputs of the register. This may be achieved by AND gates as shown in Figure 4.16.

An n-bit register may be symbolically represented as in Figure 4.17.

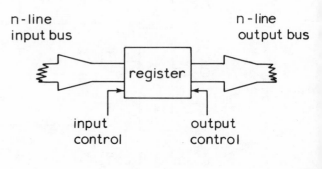

Fig. 4.17.   Symbolic representation of n-bit register.

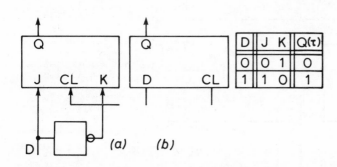

Fig. 4.14. (a) J-K flipflop in D mode (b) Symbol for D flipflop.   Fig. 4.15. Truth table of D flipflop.

Several D flipflops may be arranged as in Fig. 4.16. to comprise a register.

Data Transfer

To illustrate data transfers between registers, consider Figure 4.18. If data is to be transferred from Register 1 to Register 3 control signals are applied to $R_{1_{out}}$ putting the data of Register 1 on to the BUS, and to $R_{3_{in}}$ taking the data from the BUS into Register 3. Once again the necessity for sequenced control signals is evident.

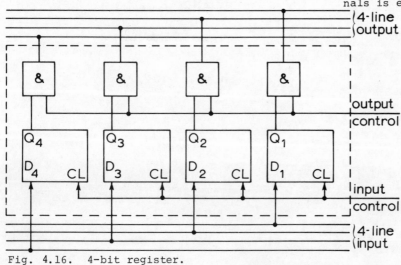

Fig. 4.16.   4-bit register.

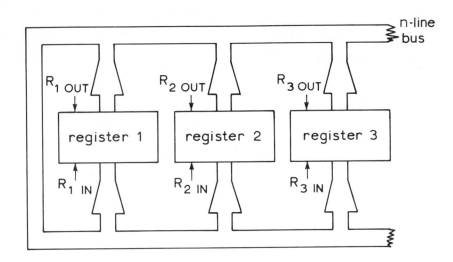

Figure 4.18. Data transfer.

4.3. LOGIC TECHNOLOGY

Background

Early electronic computers were built using thermionic valves and semiconductor diodes and transistors. A single two input gate consists of at least two transistors with possibly two or more diodes, while a J-K flipflop needs the equivalent of typically, eight such gates. The early computers using discrete devices, that is individual transistors with associated diodes, resistors and capacitors, were therefore complex, large and expensive with reliability problems directly due to the large number of separate connections.

The development of integrated circuits since 1960 has meant that computers can be implemented with fewer and fewer separate circuitry components, as the number of equivalent transistors and consequently logic functions carried on an individual silicon chip increased from about 10 in 1962 to more than 100,000 in 1980. Progress is continuing; the state of the art is already such that a complete central processing unit, with memory if needed, is available as a single integrated circuit package. This microprocessor, for such it is, contains the equivalent of rather more than 10,000 transistors, with its tiny silicon chip mounted in a dual-in-line package and with perhaps 40 connections to the outside world.

In attempting to appreciate the technology of the small computer, we have a choice of approaches. We could examine in detail the design of logic gates and flipflops at the discrete component level, and from this study progress to an analysis of individual gates on small scale integrated (SSI) chips. This way we would know a lot about logic circuitry, but it would take a long time to reach a consideration of modern large scale integrated (LSI) computer components. On the other hand, a totally 'black box' approach to LSI devices risks omitting an appreciation of basic concepts in computer organisation. The 'middle road' is to use the basic logic elements already introduced to illustrate possible implementations of computer subsystems. Such implementations are similar to the techniques used by minicomputer manufacturers in the 1960s and early 70s. The modern small computer, probably utilising a microprocessor,

also makes use of electronic logic structuring of subsystems, but these subsystems, embedded in LSI chips, are rather inaccessible. An understanding of their operation is however an aid to an appreciation of the performance characteristics of the complete microprocessor, and of the small computer. Before going on to examine electronic structures for aspects of computer operation, it is appropriate to summarise the features of modern digital integrated circuits.

Integrated Circuits

Integrated circuits are fabricated on the semiconductor silicon. A single crystal is drawn from molten silicon, and cut into circular wafers 1.5 inches to 4 inches in diameter, and $6/1000$ inches thick. Up to 40 major process steps, involving photolithography, gas diffusion and metallization are used to produce the pattern of perhaps several hundred individual circuits on the wafer. The individual integrated circuits are separated by scribing the wafer with a diamond cutter, each circuit being tested and finally mounted on a base, with very fine wire connections to the base (or package) pins.

The two most widely adopted digital technologies are bipolar transistor-transistor logic (TTL) and field effect metal-oxide-semiconductor (MOS). TTL has been very intensively used for logic design, and hundreds of device types are available in this family, ranging from a modest number of gates or flipflops on a chip (perhaps 10, designated SSI) to about 100, including for example a 4-bit full adder, designated MSI (medium scale integration). MOS technology has been adopted for LSI circuits because of its high packing density in number of functions per unit area of chip and low power dissipation, compared to TTL. It is however rather slower than TTL, in terms of switching speed which determines gate and flipflop response times. 'Slow' is a very relative term in electronics, and MOS circuits can operate at more than 10 million binary changes per second. Such speeds are adequate for small computer implementations, in both processing and memory functions and a large majority of microprocessors and microcomputers are based on MOS/LSI.

Bipolar technology, including TTL, has been used in fast modern small computers, in the form of bit-slice sets. Because of the lower circuit density, the complete central processing unit cannot be accommodated on one chip, and so the functions are allocated to a number of chips, each handling (for example) a slice of four bits. Buses interconnect the paralleled chips.

While MOS/LSI small computers are most common, TTL is very widely used in electronic equipment including peripherals for computers, particularly because of its ability to 'drive' connections and other circuits. MOS is poor in this area, and so practical computer systems commonly incorporate MOS processing and memory, with TTL 'compatible' output and input connections and TTL 'support' chips, particularly for interfacing purposes.

Type	Density (gates per mm^2)	Power required (mW per gate)	Switching Speed (ns-seconds x 10^{-4})	Logic Levels '1'	'0'
TTL	10-20	1-10	2-20	3.5V	0V
MOS	100-200	0.05-1	10-300	3V-12V	0V

This table summarises characteristics of TTL and MOS logic. Note that TTL has a fixed logic level voltage (with a supply level of 5V), while MOS circuits are more tolerant of voltage. (Many MOS systems do in fact use 5V.)

4.4.   LOGIC FOR INSTRUCTION EXECUTION

Computer Structure

The model of Figure 4.19. will be used to examine the procedures involved in the execution of an example instruction. This structure contains the major registers and components necessary to illustrate the sequence of events, but is greatly simplified relative to a real machine. The arrangement of buses is one of several possible system organisations.

The registers and buses in this example are all 16 bits wide. In this aspect the model resembles a 16 bit minicomputer. The central processing unit (CPU) could be implemented using SSI and MSI digital logic circuits, and many minicomputer models have been built in this way. We will look at electronics aspects of 8 bit computers later.

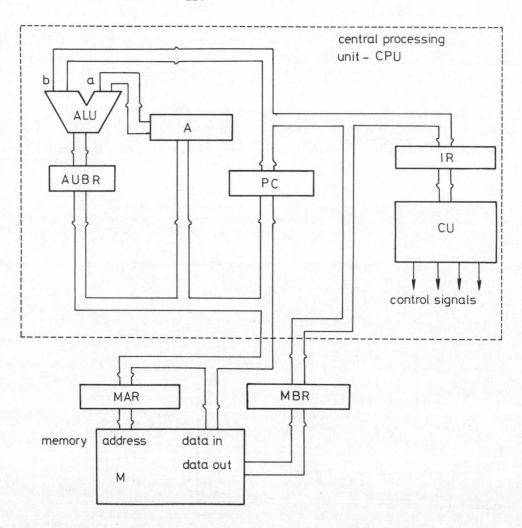

Fig. 4.19.   Small Computer Structure
A = accumulator ALU = arithmetic unit AUBR = arithmetic unit buffer register
CU = control unit IR = instruction register M = memory MAR = memory address
register MBR = memory buffer register PC = program counter.

Control signals have been omitted from the structure of Figure 4.19., but it is assumed that control signals may be applied so as to input or output data from the memory, M, or from any of the registers, and also to actuate the arithmetic unit, ALU. These control signals are designated as below:

Control Signal	Function
A_i	Input data to A
A_o	Output data from A
ALU_{add}	Add a to b, enter resultant in AUBR
ALU_{inc}	Increment b, enter resultant in AUBR
$AUBR_o$	Output data from AUBR
IR_i	Input data to IR
M_i	Input data to location in M addressed by MAR
M_o	Output data from location in M addressed by MAR and enter this data in MBR
MAR_i	Input data to MAR
MBR_o	Output data from MBR
PC_i	Input data to PC
PC_o	Output data from PC

Execution of an instruction

As an example consider the instruction:

0 1 1 0 0 1 0 1   0 0 0 1 1 1 1 1

This instruction states, "ADD contents of memory location $1F to the contents of the accumulator". The 8 bits on the left define the instruction - that is the operating code is $65. The remaining 8 bits define the memory address.

The FETCH cycle

This instruction is assumed to be stored in location $007F. Thus the first task is to address this location. It is assumed that this address may be set manually into the PC using switches, or alternatively it may have arrived there as the current address in a program sequence.

0 0 0 0 0 0 0 0   0 1 1 1 1 1 1 1
Contents of the PC.

This address requires to be transferred to the MAR, and this is only possible via the ALU. The signal PC_o presents the address data at input b of the ALU. Input a of the ALU is zero as the A has not been signalled to output. A simultaneous signal ALU_{add} adds a to b, and puts the resultant in AUBR. At this stage the unmodified address $007F is in the AUBR.

Simultaneous signals, $AUBR_o$ and MAR_i, transfer the address data to the MAR.

The timing of these control signals is summarised as:

Time Slot	Control Signals
T_0	PC_o, ALU_{add}
T_1	$AUBR_o$, MAR_i

The memory location $007F is now being addressed, and a signal M_o presents the data of this location at DATA OUT and enters it in the MBR. Simultaneous signals, MBR_o and IR_i enter this data in IR. This sequence of control signals is summarised as:

Time Slot	Control Signals
T_2	M_o
T_3	MBR_o, IR_i

At this stage it is appropriate to do some 'housekeeping', ie, to up-date the PC so that it contains the address of the next instruction.

This simply entails incrementing by one the current data of the PC and returning this incremented data to the PC. This is accomplished in time slots T_4 and T_5, thus completing the sequence of control signals known as the FETCH cycle.

Time Slot	Control Signals	
T_0	PC_o, ALU_{add}	
T_1	$AUBR_o$, MAR_i	
T_2	M_o	FETCH cycle
T_3	MBR_o, IR_i	
T_4	PC_o, ALU_{inc}	House-keeping
T_5	$AUBR_o$, PC_i	

FETCH cycle

At this stage the instruction having been FETCHED from memory location $007F resides in both IR, awaiting EXECUTION, and MBR. The program counter PC contains the address $0080 of the next instruction. This situation is represented below.

0 1 1 0 0 1 0 1 0 0 0 1 1 1 1 1

IR and MBR

0 0 0 0 0 0 0 0 1 0 0 0 0 0 0 0

PC

State of Instruction Register, Memory Buffer Register and Program Counter at end of FETCH cycle.

The EXECUTE cycle

To start the EXECUTE cycle, the instruction decoder in the control unit, decodes the op code $65 and produces an ADD 'select' signal at the output of the decoder, and this initiates a further sequence of control signals to EXECUTE the ADD operation.

At this stage familiarity with the processes involved warrants the use of simply a tabular listing of signals.

Time Slot	Control Signals	
T_6	MBR_o, ALU_{add}	
T_7	$AUBR_o$, MAR_i	
T_8	M_o	EXECUTE cycle
T_9	MBR_o, A_o, ALU_{add}	
T_{10}	$AUBR_o$, A_i	

EXECUTE cycle

Select signals from the instruction decoder, and timing waveforms from the waveform generator are inputs to the MICROPROGRAM UNIT. It is the function of the logic gates in this unit to combine these inputs to produce control signals on the appropriate control lines at the appropriate times.

Consider the control signals ALU_{add} and MAR_i. These control signals are required in time-slots T_0, T_6, T_9 and time-slots T_1, T_7 respectively. The section of the Microprogram Unit shown in Figure 4.21. implements these requirements.

Generation of Control Signals (micro-orders)

Figure 4.20. is a block schematic of the control unit, CU. Here the bits held in IR are decoded, giving a select signal on the appropriate output line from the instruction decoder.

Timing waveforms T_0-T_{31} are generated by a 5-bit counter and gates.

Note that Figure 4.21. shows the control signal ALU_{add} to be generated in time slot T_0 independently of the ADD select signal or any other select signal. This is because the control signal ALU_{add} is required as part of the FETCH cycle, and this cycle is common to all instructions. Similarly with the control signal MAR_i in time-slot T_1.

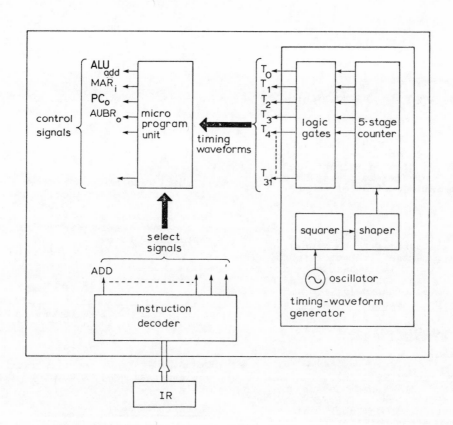

Figure 4.20. Control Unit.

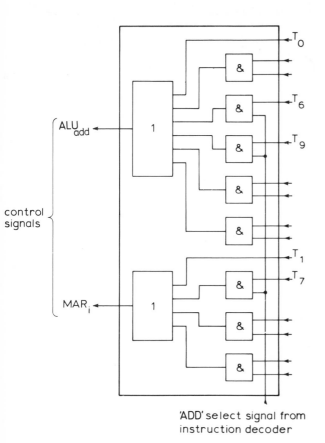

control
signals $\left\{\begin{array}{l} ALU_{add} \leftarrow \\ \\ \\ MAR_i \leftarrow \end{array}\right.$

'ADD' select signal from
instruction decoder

Figure 4.21. Partial Microprogram Unit.

For the execution of other instructions, the
control signals ALU_{add} and MAR_i are required
in other time-slots as determined by the
appropriate select signals from the instruction decoder. These requirements are met by
inputting the unassigned AND gates of Figure
4.21. with the requisite select signals and
timing waveforms.

The waveform diagram of Figure 4.22. summarises
the generation of the control signals ALU_{add}
and MAR_i. It is left to the reader to deduce
the further logic necessary to generate the
remaining control signals required to execute
the ADD instruction.

Execution of Other Instructions

The example just discussed is a direct memory
reference instruction, and was used to
indicate the sequence of electronic operations
required for its execution. Other types of
instruction are executed in a similar fashion,
but the detailed sequence is, of course,
dependent on the particular instruction. Some
of the features for execution of other memory
reference instructions are as follows.

Direct addressing has been illustrated. If
the address mode is relative, then instead of
passing $007F (the memory location) to MAR

during the EXECUTE cycle, the control signals
cause $007F to be added to the content of PC
(using the Arithmetic Unit ALU) and the result
put into MAR. This result is the effective
address to be accessed. The overall execution
time of a relative address instruction is
therefore greater than that of a direct
address instruction.

Similarly, indexed addressing involves the
addition of the current instruction offset to
the contents of the appropriate Index Register
(not shown in Figure 4.19.) before transfer of
the result to MAR.

With indirect addressing, the output data from
the location in M addressed by MAR, which is
transferred to MBR, is the actual address of
the true operand. The control signals therefore cause the contents of MBR to be transferred to MAR, for a further memory access.
This transfer takes place via ALU in the
structure of Figure 4.19. but of course other
structures exist and are possible, and in
some structures this MBR to MAR transfer can
be more direct.

Extra levels of indirection, where bit 0 of
the indirect address indicates a further level
(eg, if bit 0 is a 1, the location specified
contains an address, not an operand), are
handled by repeating the transfer of MBR
contents to MAR until an address is found with
bit 0 = 0. This is then taken as the operand.
Again there is an increase in execution time,
depending on the number of levels of indirection.

4.5. RANDOM LOGIC AND FERRITE CORE

The decoding, control circuitry with
register, ALU and buses, in the CPU of the
computer model of Figure 4.19., if implemented
be SSI, becomes quite complex, with many
connections, if the instruction set assumes
realistic proportions. Many minicomputers
were first implemented using this technique,
which is often termed 'random logic' because
of its apparently random structure - of course
the structure is in fact completely organised,
but regular patterns of connections are
uncommon. Random logic designed small computers have been built using SSI and MSI,
typically employing TTL technology, and with
word lengths of 8, 12, 16, 18, 24 and 32 bits.

Large numbers of such machines exist
particularly those with a 16 bit word length.
The memory technology most commonly used for
program and data storage in minicomputers, at
least until the mid-1970s, has been ferrite
core.

The basic device in a core memory is a small
ring (or toroid) of ferrite ceramic magnetic
material - the ferrite core. A single core
is capable of storing 1 bit of information,
represented by the direction of magnetisation
of the ferrite material, eg, clockwise = 1,
anticlockwise = 0 (Figure 4.23.).

The bit identity for a single core is
established by passing a current through a
line which threads the core. Since a practical
core memory has many thousands of cores,
techniques for selecting the cores to be magnetised (as 1s or 0s) - 'addressing' techniques - are used. In general these are based
on a matrix of X and Y selection wires, forming a core plane, eg, 64 x 64 = 4096 bits.
(For a 16-bit word computer, 16 planes are
necessary.) To 'write' a bit in a particular

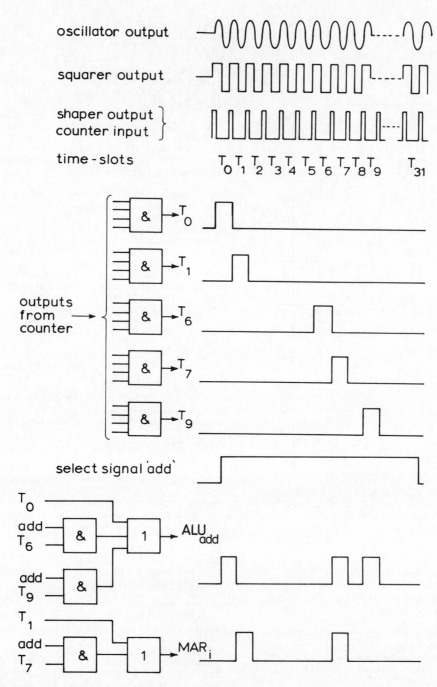

Figure 4.22.   Control Signal Waveforms.

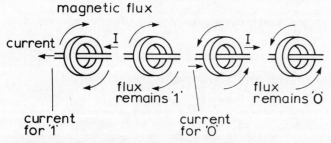

Figure 4.23.   Core magnetisation.

location requires coincidence of current in the appropriate X and Y selection wires where 1s are to be set. Setting up X and Y is the task of the memory addressing circuits.

Information is read out by reversing the current in the X wires and selecting the appropriate Y wire for each bit. Those cores where 1s are written produce a larger pulse in a sense wire (which threads all cores in a plane) than those cores with 0s (Figure 4.24.).

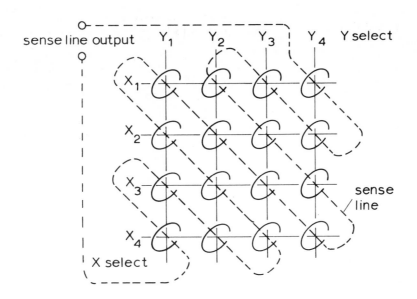

Figure 4.24. Magnetic core array principle.

In effect, when a store word is being addressed, only 1s are written or sensed, unaffected cores indicating 0.

A complete core memory module thus comprises several thousand (at least) ferrite cores, each threaded by three very fine wires (X, Y, sense). The core size governs the speed of magnetic switching, and an outside diameter of 0.5 mm corresponds to a memory cycle time (read/write) of just under 1.0 µs. Cycle times of 500 ns (0.5 µs) are available, but faster speeds are unlikely.

A useful feature of most core stores is their non-volatility; when power is switched off, the cores retain their magnetised state, so that, for example, a program held in core can be executed when power is restored. Some computers include 'Power-Fail Restart' which uses the non-volatile nature of core of eliminate the need for reloading of programs and data after a mains failure.

4.6. LSI COMPUTER COMPONENTS

Background

Just as the availability of integrated circuits in the 1960s made possible the minicomputer - in varying 'desk top' sizes - so the development of MOS/LSI technology led to the concept of a complete CPU on a single LSI chip - today's microprocessor. Early microprocessors used a 4-bit word length - the first commercial microprocessor being the Intel 4004, in November 1971. Semiconductor memory, based on flipflop circuits, provided program and data storage. Initially, microprocessors had many of the characteristics of calculator chips, but 8-bit systems soon appeared and by 1975 'second generation' LSI microprocessor systems with substantial software and processing capability were available. Most of the hardware design features of the 'traditional' minicomputer were being built into microprocessor based 'microcomputers' by this time. Microprocessors with a 16-bit word length have now been developed.

It has become possible, popular and very economic to implement complete computer systems - CPU, memory and input/output - using only LSI components (apart from perhaps a few bipolar devices). A generalised microcomputer structure is shown in Figure 4.25.

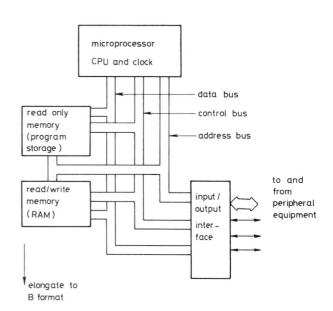

Figure 4.25. Microcomputer Structure.

The major components are:

1.   The microprocessor - that is the CPU, probably including a system clock.

2.   'Read-only' memory (ROM) for storage of programs.

3.   Read/Write memory for storage of data. This is often referred to as Random Access Memory (RAM), and is sometimes used for temporary program storage.

4.   Input/Output 'Interface' circuits to connect the system to user peripherals - in other words equipment which the human operator can use to communicate with the computer. An additional peripheral function is 'back-up' storage for relatively large volumes of programs and data.

We will review the principal LSI component types used to implement such a system, usually with an 8-bit microprocessor in mind. LSI memory technology will be considered first, as it features within the LSI microprocessor.

LSI Memory for Programs and Data

ROM (Read Only Memory).   Basically a ROM is an array of diodes or transistors. The information held by the array is established by the interconnection pattern laid down in the fabrication process, usually at the metallisation stage. In an MOS ROM rectangular matrix the presence of a transistor connection at a node gives logic '1', the absence of transistor action gives logic '0'. Since the stored bit pattern is defined by these permanent connections, the ROM is non-volatile, and retains its data when the electrical supply is switched off.

Figure 4.26. is a diagram of a simplified 4 x 4 ROM array. In this arrangement two bits of a 4 bit address are used to select 1 of 4 rows. The other two bits are used to enable 1 of 4 tri-state gates connected to the columns. Tri-state gates are widely used in small computer bus arrangements; when enabled by a logic level, a tri-state gate output carries the logic level, '1' or '0', present at the input. If it is not selected in this way, the output presents a high impedance, thus allowing the selected tri-state to establish the logic level present on the common output connection - usually one of many bus lines.

ROM chips can be based on bipolar or MOS technology. Bipolar ROMs have faster access, in terms of the delay between establishing an address at the input and having the addressed bit available at the output. Illustrative figures are access times of less than 100 nanoseconds for bipolar, up to one microsecond

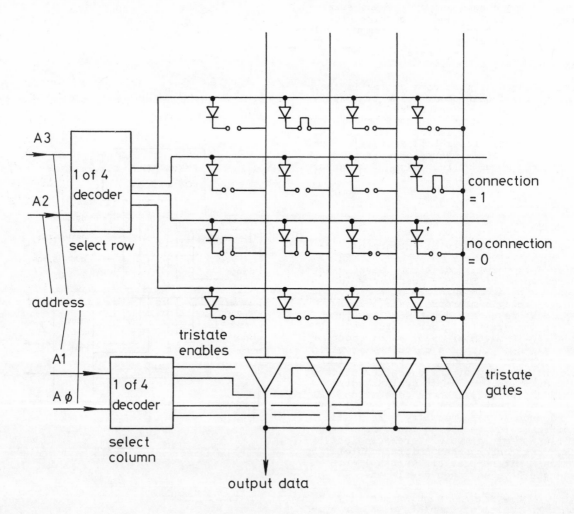

Figure 4.26.   16 x 1 ROM Array.

for MOS. Bipolar ROMs are supplied in 1K (1024) to 16K bit packages while MOS ROMs are available in 1K to 64K bit packages and are more popular. It should be noted that the ROM does in fact feature full 'random-access' addressing, in that any bit location can be accessed. Nevertheless the term random access memory (RAM) is commonly applied only to read/write memory for temporary storage.

ROMs for use with microprocessor based systems are usually arranged to provide a full 8-bit wide byte of data for a single input address. For example a 1K x 8 ROM has a 10 bit address, and holds 1,024 8-bit bytes. A production level of several thousand devices is normally necessary to justify the use of such a 'mask programmable' or 'masked' ROM. The mask referred to is the design of the metallisation interconnections. A ROM may be available as a separate device and may also sometimes form part of a multi-function chip, for example an interface device, or indeed a microprocessor with ROM on the chip, commonly used for applications requiring programs of modest size. In general, ROM is used to store fixed programs, for example those provided in a microcomputer system to permit 'debug' and 'monitor' operations on user programs. They are also used in code converters, character generators for displays, and look-up tables. Since ROM is static, no clock inputs are needed, just address bits and (probably) an enable signal.

PROM (Programmable Read-Only Memory). As the name indicates, a PROM can have information written into it by the user. For example, a program which has been developed and which is to become part of a microprocessor based product, is commonly 'burned' onto a PROM. Several types of PROM (all static) exist, but all are organised in an array structure like the ROM.

Bipolar PROMs incorporate a fusible link at each memory bit location, and programming is implemented by passing a sequence of current pulses (20-30 mA) to the addressed location until the fuse is blown. These PROMs cannot be reprogrammed. Bipolar PROMs of up to 16K, organised in 2K x 8, with access times of less than 100 nanoseconds and TTL compatible inputs and outputs, are available.

MOS PROMs differ from bipolar devices in that they are erasable, a feature of great value when programs thought to be final turn out to require change or correction. They are referred to as EPROM (Erasable Programmable Read-Only Memory), and are of two main types. First is the floating polysilicon gate type, wherein a node connection, representing a bit, is established by applying a high voltage pulse to produce a charge on an electrically isolated gate of a field-effect transistor. To erase the bit pattern, a complete EPROM is exposed to ultraviolet

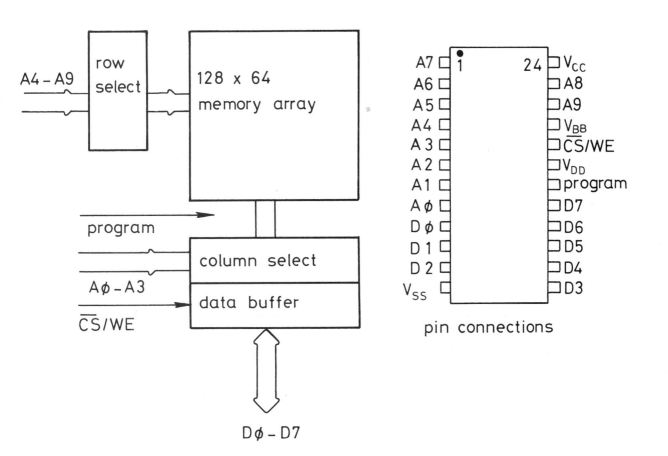

Figure 4.27. 2708 EPROM Details.

radiation, which effects a gate discharge
over a period of up to thirty minutes. Such
EPROMs have a 'window' to permit ultraviolet
erasing. Popular examples of EPROMS are the
2708 (1,024 x 8) and 2716 (2,048 x 8) types.

The 2708 EPROM is organised as 1,024 bytes of
8 bits each. When the Chip Select/Write
Enable ($\overline{\text{CS/WE}}$) input is at the high logic
level, the device is unselected and the out-
put data lines are at the high impedance
level (of the three states possible). The
device is selected when $\overline{\text{CS/WE}}$ is logic low,
and the memory location specified by the 10
address lines A0-A9 outputs its data after
the access time has elapsed (450 nanoseconds).
For programming, $\overline{\text{CS/WE}}$ is connected to +12V.
Address and Data lines are TTL compatible.
The device is fully static and no clock inputs
are required. Like many other EPROMs, the
2708 is 'pin compatible' with some masked
(non user-programmable) ROMs. This makes
possible the replacement of a masked ROM
based program by a user developed alternative
program in EPROM.

The second type of EPROM is electrically
alterable. Again a charge is introduced onto
a transistor gate by a high voltage pulse,
but the gate insulator is a very thin layer
of nitride oxide. This provides a very high
impedance to charge flow, and so the written
information is retained literally for years,
in the absence of any external power. The
trapped charges may be released, and the
information erased, by applying a further
large reverse polarity gate voltage.

EPROMs of the ultraviolet erasable type are
more widely used than electrically erasable
devices. In general, EPROM capacities range
up to 64K bits, with access time of about
500 nanoseconds.

RAM (Random Access Memory). A RAM is in fact
a read/write memory, and the electrically
erasable EPROM is essentially a read/write
device too. However the term RAM is commonly
used to describe a memory which can have
information written into it and read from it
at the same rate - in other words a temporary
data store. The LSI RAM is an array of flipflops - up to 64K or more on one chip. Again
bipolar and MOS types exist, and MOS devices
are further classified as static or dynamic.

Bipolar RAMs are static, in that information
written into them remains so long as electrical
power is applied, and continuous rewriting of
information - 'refreshing' - (as with dynamic
MOS RAMs) is unnecessary. Each bit in a
static bipolar RAM is held in a two-transistor
flipflop structure, rather like a TTL flipflop. This type of RAM exists in 64 to 4K
bit sizes, and is speed compatible with TTL.

Static MOS RAMs are also based on flipflop
circuitry, but typically each bit requires
six transistors (a function of MOS design).
This design occupies a proportionately large
chip area and this feature, together with the
associated power dissipation, limits the
number of bits stored in a typical size of
chip. While circuitry innovations have
reduced cell size, static MOS RAMs range from
1K to 4K bits capacity. They are often
organised as a 4-bit modular slice (4 x 256
bits), usable with 4, 8, and 16 bit systems.

Dynamic MOS RAMs are the most popular devices
for temporary storage of data and of programs

which are required to be resident and used
for limited time in a microprocessor system.
The simplest cell design uses a single MOS
transistor and one capacitor, and because of
the small chip area occupied, makes possible
a large number of bits stored per device.
The first 4,096 bit dynamic RAM was introduced
in 1974. The term dynamic refers to the fact
that the simple single transistor/capacitor
structure loses the stored information due to
charge leakage after a few hundred milliseconds, and the stored bit value must be
'refreshed' repeatedly. This is done by
first reading and then rewriting the
information (charge or no charge, representing '1' or '0'), at a cycle time of typically
two milliseconds for the complete RAM.
Dynamic RAM cells are organised in arrays,
with (for example) a 4K chip of 32 rows by
128 columns requiring 32 refresh cycles (one
for each row) every two milliseconds.
Typical access time for reading data is less
than 300 nanoseconds.

A popular dynamic RAM is the 16K, 4116 device.
This is available in a 16 pin dual-in-line
integrated circuit package, and has a 120
nanoseconds access time.

The 4116 RAM is organised as 16,384 x 1 bit
locations, in two 128 row by 64 column arrays.
The 14 bit address required to access one of
the locations is multiplexed onto the seven
lines A0-A6, and the RAM can decode the

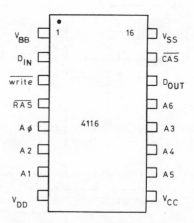

pin connections

A0 - A6	address inputs
$\overline{\text{CAS}}$	column address strobe
D_{IN}	data in
D_{OUT}	data out
$\overline{\text{RAS}}$	row address strobe
write	read/write input
V_{BB}	- 5 V
V_{CC}	+ 5 V
V_{DD}	+ 12 V
V_{SS}	ground

Figure 4.28. 4116 RAM Details.

address when it receives the two strobe signals $\overline{RAS}$ (Row Address Strobe) and $\overline{CAS}$ (Column Address Strobe). The $\overline{Write}$ signal is logic high for a Read Operation, outputting data on D_{out}. Input data on D_{in} is written into memory with $\overline{Write}$ low. Each memory cell in this dynamic RAM is effectively a capacitor, and refreshing is needed. When a 7-bit address is applied to the device in conjunction with $\overline{RAS}$, a row of 128 cells is refreshed. The 7-bit address is then incremented for the next row of cells in conjunction with the next $\overline{RAS}$ high to low transition. 128 refresh cycles are therefore needed for the complete RAM, and this takes typically two milliseconds. The device has a tri-state buffer data output, and TTL compatible inputs. Usually such RAMs are organised as banks of eight devices (or multiples of eight), each device handling one bit of an 8-bit byte. Eight chips thus provide 16K bytes of RAM memory.

64K dynamic RAMs (65,536 bits capacity) are now commercially available. To realise the memory capacity available in this semiconductor technology, consider that each letter on this page can conveniently be represented by 8 bits, and work out the amount of written material which could be coded onto a single 64K bit RAM.

The LSI Microprocessor

Many types of microprocessor now exist, and they may be categorised by such criteria as word length (4, 8 or 16 bits), speed of operation and instruction set versatility. Figure 4.29. shows a generalised 8-bit microprocessor structure.

This architecture performs functions similar to those of the CPU of Figure 4.19. and using MOS/LSI technology, is accommodated on a single silicon chip. The diagram is simplified, in that many connections are omitted. The functions of most of the registers and subsystems have already been introduced, but we will review the components of Figure 4.29. for completeness, and to conveniently comment on relevant microprocessor characteristics.

The Arithmetic unit (or arithmetic/logic unit) ALU, performs arithmetic and logical operations on data fed to it from the internal data register and (usually) the accumulator A. The result of an operation is deposited in A. In this example system the two input and one output bus of the ALU are eight bits wise. Many microprocessors have a decimal arithmetic capability, in addition to binary (2's complement) processing. This (if activated) corrects values held in A to

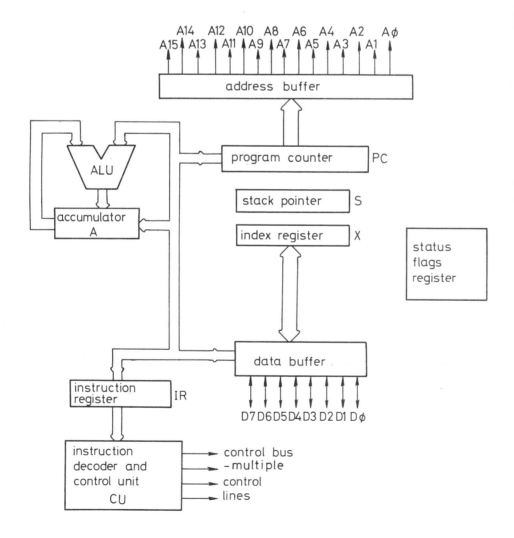

Figure 4.29. Microprocessor Structure.

binary-coded-decimal (BCD) form, two decimal
digits per each 8 bit byte.

The Program Counter PC is in this case 16 bits
wide, so that 2^{16} or 64K memory locations in
ROM or RAM can be addressed via the address
buffer. After each memory fetch operation,
to retrieve the next instruction, the contents
of PC are incremented. The execution of
branch or jump instructions is accomplished
by placing the jump address into PC.

The Index Register is 8 bits wide, and may be
used to provide a pointer to an address in
memory. Most commonly, the contents of the
index register are incremented after each
instruction, and the resulting value added
to a preset address, so that successive
locations in memory (holding for example a
table of values) are addressed in sequence.
The index register may also be used to hold
data on which the program will operate.

The Stack Pointer S is an 8 bit register which
holds a pointer (ie, address) to the top element of the stack area in memory.

The stack is a sequence of 256 locations in
RAM, and the stack pointer identifies the
most recent addition to the stack, and is
referred to when the most recent addition is
to be retrieved. The arrangement is 'Last-In,
First-Out', and is required to implement
three programming facilities: subroutines,
interrupts and temporary data storage.

The Status Flags Register is 8 bits wide,
and each bit denotes a special condition.
For example, if bit 7 (the left-most) is '1'
it indicates that the result of the most
recent ALU operation is negative. The complete meaning of the status bits is contained
in the instruction repertoire of the microprocessor.

Execution of a Microprocessor Instruction

The functions of the Data Buffer, Instruction
Register, Instruction Decoder and Control
Unit will be illustrated by considering
instruction execution in conjunction with
memory: ROM (usually) for programs and RAM
for data. Of course, programs may be held in
RAM, particularly during development of software. Further, some microprocessors have
limited ROM and RAM 'on board' the chip, and
short programs can be stored and executed,
and the results held in RAM, within this
single chip microcomputer. Such devices are
appropriate for automatic control of equipment, for example to control a washing
machine's operations, or in instrumentation.
In the context of small computers with programming facilities, for example those capable
of running BASIC, it is very much the standard
to have a microprocessor with separate RAM,
ROM and I/O (Input/Output) as in Figure 4.25.

Assuming that the Program Counter holds a
valid 16 bit address, which is the address
of the next instruction in memory, the
instruction execution process is:

1. Fetch. The contents of PC are transferred to the address bus and gated to the
memory. Simultaneously a 'Read' signal is
issued on the control bus of the system. In
response, the memory decodes the address,
accesses the specified location and a few
hundred nanoseconds later deposits the
appropriate 8 bit data word, which we will

take as an instruction in this example, on to
to the data bus and puts the contents into
the Instruction Register, IR. 'Housekeeping'
procedures include incrementing the Program
Counter after each Fetch. In a real microprocessor system, an instruction may occupy
two or even three 8 bit bytes, and corresponding two or three Fetch operations are
necessary.

2. Decoding and Execution. When the instruction (or one byte of it) is in IR, the microprocessor decodes it and generates the
appropriate sequence of internal (in the
microprocessor) and external (perhaps to RAM)
control signals. Different microprocessor
instructions can require different lengths
of time to execute, and these times are
expressed as the number of clock cycles
needed. Typically a microprocessor may use
a one-megahertz clock, giving a cycle time
of one microsecond. Instructions can require
six or more cycles, depending on their complexity and use of memory and registers. The
decoder outputs, combined with timing signals
from the system clock (which may be an
oscillator within the microprocessor chip)
form the control signal sequence to set and
clear registers, effect internal data transfers and cause the ALU to function as
required.

Internal Control Logic

The microprocessor's handling of an instruction is in principle essentially the same as
that described for the 'random logic' computer
model (Figure 4.19.) met earlier, with
specific features for 8-bit operations. An
outstanding microprocessor feature is that
the circuit complexity required for internal
control logic to decode and execute instructions has been fabricated onto part of an
LSI chip. The technology used can be an MOS/
LSI implementation of the random logic gate
and flipflop approach, and some contemporary
microprocessors have internal control logic
of this type.

An attractive alternative, now widely adopted,
is to use ROM technology within the microprocessor chip to store the control sequences,
and to call upon the required sequence by
going to the starting point in the ROM and
incrementing the address. In this approach
the operation code of the instruction being
executed provides the entry point into the
control memory, with a succession of fetch
operations. This procedure is rather like
the computer's use of external memory
for stored program accessing and as in a minicomputer, it is referred to as the execution
of a microprogram, while the stored instructions (in ROM) are microinstructions.

The instructions of the computer program held
in external memory can be termed macroinstructions to distinguish them from
microcode.

Figure 4.30. shows the interpretation procedure
that the microcode segment, in a microprocessor using ROM based control logic, carries
out. A macroinstruction is fetched from the
program memory and placed in the 8-bit instruction register. The operation code is modified
by the address translation logic to generate
an address for the microprogram ROM. The
address is then incremented to sequence
through the microcode segment, with the
microinstruction outputs from the ROM

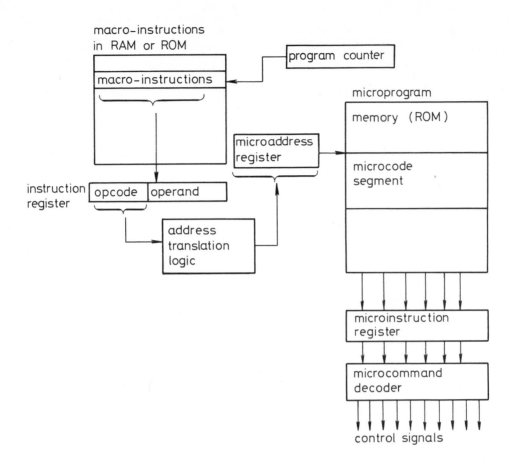

Figure 4.30. Microcode Interpretation of a Macroinstruction.

generating the particular control signals required. When the microcode segment is complete, control is returned to the fetch routine, for the next macroinstruction to be obtained for the instruction register.

Since there are many control signals needed within the microprocessor (for example,

register preset and clear and bus enable signals) a large repertoire of microinstructions is needed - perhaps more than 50. The control logic ROM can store these in coded form, (a 6-bit value giving 64 possibilities) and a separate decoder (the microcommand decoder of Figure 4.30.) used to generate the actual control signals. Of course many

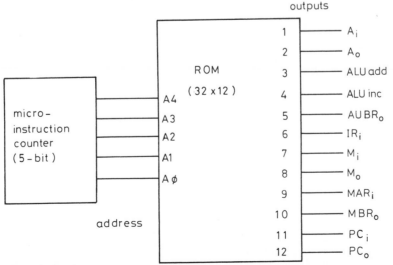

Figure 4.31. ROM control logic.

macroinstructions use common microcode segments (for example the fetch cycle), and the address translation logic permits this.

To emphasise the functional equivalence of ROM control logic and the 'traditional' random logic approach of earlier small computers, Figure 4.31. shows a ROM based circuit to implement the fetch and execute cycles for the ADD instruction (16 bit) examined in the Section 'Execution of an Instruction'.

The FETCH cycle is common to all instructions, and on receipt of any instruction the counter will start at state 0 0 0 0 0 and sequence through to 0 0 1 0 1 which will generate the required sequence and pattern of microcommand at the ROM outputs, as in the table.

Address					Outputs											
A_4	A_3	A_2	A_1	A_0	1	2	3	4	5	6	7	8	9	10	11	12
0	0	0	0	0	0	0	1	0	0	0	0	0	0	0	0	1
0	0	0	0	1	0	0	0	0	1	0	0	0	1	0	0	0
0	0	0	1	0	0	0	0	0	0	0	0	1	0	0	0	0
0	0	0	1	1	0	0	0	0	0	1	0	0	0	1	0	0
0	0	1	0	0	0	0	0	1	0	0	0	0	0	0	0	1
0	0	1	0	1	0	0	0	0	1	0	0	0	0	0	1	0
1	0	0	0	0	0	0	1	0	0	0	0	0	0	1	0	0
1	0	0	0	1	0	0	0	0	1	0	0	0	1	0	0	0
1	0	0	1	0	0	0	0	0	0	0	0	1	0	0	0	0
1	0	0	1	1	0	1	1	0	0	0	0	0	0	1	0	0
1	0	1	0	0	1	0	0	0	1	0	0	0	0	0	0	0

At the end of time slot T_5 the ADD instruction is in IR. This is decoded by the instruction decoder and initiates a jump of the counter to (say) 10000 and subsequent sequencing to 10100. From the truth table it is seen that this generates:

T_6 MBR_o, AU_{add}

T_7 $AUBR_o$, MAR_i

T_8 M_o

T_9 MBR_o, AC_o, AU_{add}

T_{10} $AUBR_o$, AC_i

as is required by the ADD instruction.

Other instructions will require some of the bit patterns generated at the output of the ROM for the ADD instruction and it is possible to use them, but this necessitates a jumping of the counter, and a corresponding complexity in the address logic. This system should be compared with the arrangements of Section 'Execution of an Instruction'.

It is usual to divide the clock pulses (say T_0-T_{31}) into groups such that the number in a group is adequate to process (say) a one cycle instruction. In our example, there could be eight such 'microcycles' for each machine cycle.

Some computers, for example those implemented on bipolar bit slices, have the internal control system as a separate logic unit. The user can generate his own special microprograms (microcode) for required instructions. Microprogramming of this kind is not possible with current microprocessors, since the user does not have access to the internal control logic section of the chip.

An alternative to the use of ROM is the programmed logic array (PLA). This is an array of combinational logic matrices, fabricated using bipolar technology. A typical PLA is functionally equivalent to a set of multiple input AND gates, with ORed outputs - for example, 14 inputs and eight outputs, to provide macroinstruction decoding. The specific logic functions required are established by fabrication of the final interconnection mask pattern. PLAs have been used in small computer CPUs.

The microprocessor is a complete CPU on a chip. It contains MOS gates, flipflops, registers, buses, arithmetic and logic circuits, with RAM and ROM to implement internal control logic. The microprocessor user is usually unaware - and probably uninterested - in the internal functioning of the chip. He does however need to know the functions of the various registers, to make programming possible. He also needs to know the external characteristics of the microprocessor, so that systems with memory and I/O can be configured. This information is provided in manufacturers' documentation for specific chips. As an example, Figure 4.32. shows the pin-out of a 6502 microprocessor chip.

Microprocessor External Characteristics

The 6502 requires a 5 volt supply, connected to V_{cc} (+5V) and V_{ss} (OV).

A0 to A15 are the address bus lines.

D0 to D7 are the Data bus lines, and are connected to both input and tri-state output buffers.

Control Connections

$R/\overline{W}$ is the Read/Write line, and controls the direction of data transfer on the data bus.

RDY is normally used to synchronize the microprocessor with slow components (usually memory). It can in fact stop the processor if required.

SYNC is a signal generated when the 6502 is fetching an operation code (or macroinstruction).

SO sets a particular flag (the 'overflow' bit) in the status register. It is rarely used.

$\overline{RES}$ is Reset, used to initialize the microprocessor.

Timing

$\emptyset_0$, $\emptyset_1$ and $\emptyset_2$ are basic clock signals (usually 1MHz nominal rate).

Interrupts

$\overline{IRQ}$ and $\overline{NMI}$ are Interrupt Request and Non-Maskable Interrupt. Each can interrupt the microprocessor which completes its current instruction and then goes into an 'Interrupt

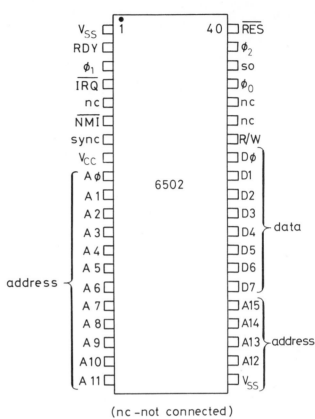

(nc -not connected)

Figure 4.32.   6502 microprocessor chip pinout.

Routine'. On completion of the interrupt
routine, the original program is resumed.
Interrupt procedures feature in I/O operations.

LSI Interface Components

The microprocessor together with memory for
programs and data, can undertake computation,
but new programs and data can be supplied to
the system and results made available to the
user only if adequate input/output (I/O) circuits are provided. It would be possible to
design random logic circuits to connect to
address and data buses in a microcomputer
system, so that user equipment could be
connected. Small computers of some years ago
did use random logic interface system, and of
course every manufacturer had a unique design.
A typical interface module implemented in TTL,
perhaps to connect a printer, occupied an A4
sized printed circuit board. Such interfaces
are still in use, but with the development of
microprocessor based small computers, a welcome standardisation of approach using LSI
components has appeared.

A key feature of modern microcomputer I/O is
that data is transferred to and from the outside world in much the same way that memory
is managed. Particular outside world devices
are assigned unique memory addresses, and the
data transfer is controlled by read/write and

timing signals. The incompatibility in
operating speed between the microprocessor
and most peripheral devices (for example an
electromechanical printer, or a keyboard
operated by a human) prevents direct connection between microprocessor address and data
buses, and peripheral devices. The solution
is the Peripheral Interface Adapter (PIA)
which provides temporary storage of data.
The PIA has many other features, notably its
programmable nature, so that control codes
from the microprocessor can adapt the I/O
characteristics of the PIA to the task in
hand. This transmission of control codes is
achieved by the execution of an initialisation
program by the microprocessor. The PIA can
generate interrupts to the microprocessor, and
some versions are equipped with timers, used
for example to generate synchronising signals.
PIAs contain MOS gating logic, registers,
buses and buffers, including tri-states.
Special types of PIA in addition contain RAM
and ROM, and with such a device a two chip
microcomputer may be implemented.

A generalised PIA is shown in Figure 4.33.

This structure connects to the microprocessor
Data Bus, D∅-D7, and other lines and from the
microprocessor are interrupt lines $\overline{IRQA}$ and
$\overline{IRQB}$, register select lines RSO and RS1,
chip select lines CS1, CS2 and CS3 and R/W

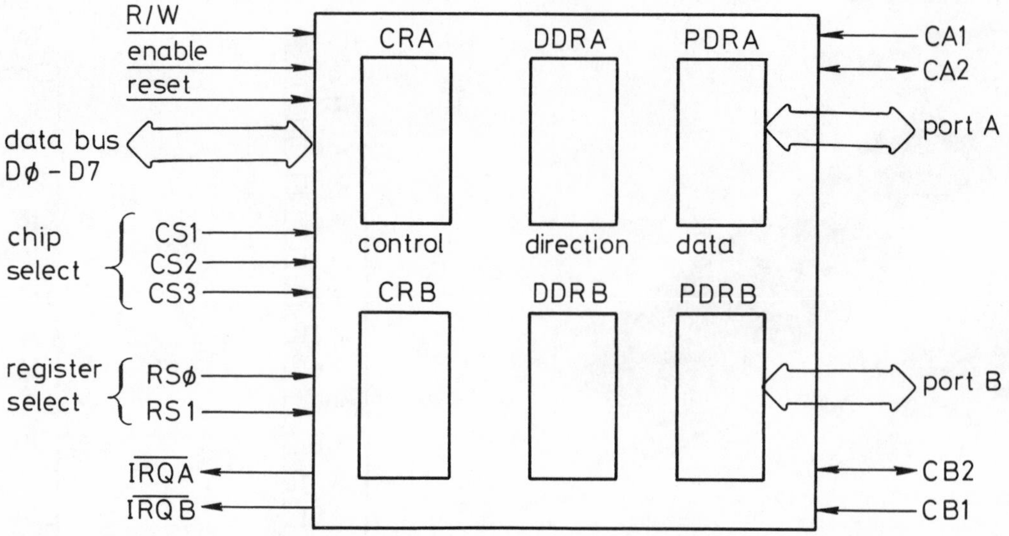

Figure 4.33. PIA structure.

(Read/Write), Enable, Reset and clock ∅2 connections. RSO and RS1 are decoded internally to identify which of four control and data direction registers (CRA, CRB, DDRA and DDRB) are being addressed, and in fact RSO and RS1 are connected to the microprocessor address bus. CS1, CS2 and CS3 are also connected to the address bus, sometimes via a decoder. For example, selection of CS1 and CS2 logic high and CS3 logic low by the microprocessor selects the PIA. The particular values of RSO and RS1 then define the internal register being accessed. The PIA thus appears to the system as four memory locations.

These address and control arrangements provide for microprocessor access to the PIA. In this way the data direction and control registers for the two parallel 8-bit 'ports' are set, prior to use of the PIA. The data direction register contents define the function of the individual port lines as input or output. The control register contents specify the function of control signals (CA1, CA2, CB1 and CB2), including such details as whether the control lines will trigger interrupts on rising or falling signal edges.

Each port has a peripheral data register for temporary storage, and the I/O lines from each port are usually TTL compatible.

A popular PIA is the 6520, and Figure 4.34. shows the pin-out.

An example of a 'multiple function' PIA is the 6530. It has 1,024 bytes of ROM and 64 bytes of RAM, together with a versatile programmable interval timer which can provide signals at intervals ranging from 1 to 262,144 clock intervals. The 6530 has been used with the 6502 to produce 'single board' microcomputers such as the KIM.

The PIA ports handle data bits in parallel, eight at a time. Some peripheral devices prefer to generate and receive data in bit-serial, on a two wire connection. Special interface components may be used with microcomputers for this purpose. They are termed UART (Universal Asynchronous Receiver/ Transmitter) or ACIA (Asynchronous Communications Interface Adapter) chips.

Many specialised LSI devices are now available, to handle a wide range of microprocessor system interfacing requirements, including control and instrumentation application areas.

Comment

The main features of LSI microprocessor, memory and interface chips have been discussed. All modern microprocessor chip families share these characteristics.

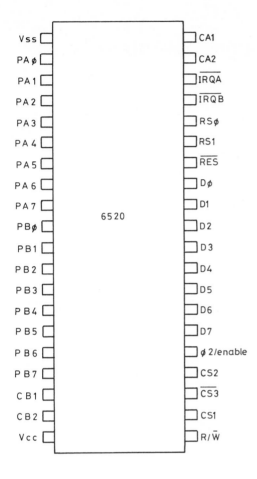

Figure 4.34.   6520 PIA chip pin-out.

4.7.   <u>REFERENCES</u>

1.   <u>Microelectronics,</u> a Scientific American
     Book, (W.H. Freeman & Company, 1977),
     also Scientific American Special issue
     September 1977.

2.   Lippiatt, A.G., <u>The Architecture of Small
     Computer Systems</u>, (Prentice-Hall
     International, 1979).

3.   Lewin, D., <u>Theory and Design of Digital
     Computer Systems</u>, second edition, (Nelson
     & Sons Ltd., 1980).

4.   Kraft, G.D., and Toy, Wing N., <u>Mini/Micro-
     computer Hardware Design</u>, (Prentice-Hall
     International, 1979).

Computer Organisation and Operation
Chapter 5

5.1.   COMPUTER CHARACTERISTICS

Architectures and electronic components for their implementation have been introduced in Chapters 3 and 4. We now wish to examine the construction of real computer systems - the configuration of components to form practical computers - and to discuss their operating characteristics. A range of implementation approaches is available, from MSI to LSI, with bipolar and MOS technology. Of these, the most popular combination is now MOS/LSI, with microprocessor based computer structures dominating the small computer market. Such computers come in many shapes and sizes, from low cost models with minimal memory and input/output all on one printed circuit board, to systems capable of supporting a complete set of peripherals for information input, display and storage. Many of the low cost systems are intended for user familiarisation with either computer technology in general or a particular microprocessor. They may feature simple hexadecimal keyboards, attached directly to the printed circuit board carrying the electronics, and seven segment displays similarly mounted. A character generator and television modulator, for output display, are often included. Such systems are configured with microprocessor, ROM, RAM and I/O chips in a manner generally similar to larger systems. They are however limited in expansion capability and are unable to carry out really useful computation - for example for scientific or business applications.

To illustrate the principal aspects of small computer organisation and operation, this chapter concentrates on microprocessor based computers capable of performing serious work, and of supporting a useful set of peripherals. This class includes the Commodore PET, the Apple II (and its near equivalent the ITT2020), the Radio Shack TRS-80 and many other machines. Such 'personal' computers may be purchased in basic configurations with minimal peripheral equipment, and may be enhanced later by the addition of memory and more powerful peripherals. To date and in general, small computers of this type have used microprocessors with an 8-bit word length - that is with an 8-bit wide data bus, handling instructions and data organised as 8-bit bytes. Microprocessors with 16-bit structures and computing power comparable with that of 16-bit minicomputer CPUs have been introduced, and computers using them are likely to replace 8-bit models in some application areas. In fact, new microprocessor chips and computers based on them appear on the market or are announced with increasing frequency. You can keep up with developments by consulting electronics and computing journals and magazines, and by obtaining manufacturers' literature.

5.2.   'STANDARD' 8-BIT COMPUTER STRUCTURE

The bus structure of a microprocessor based computer is dictated by the microprocessor itself. Popular 8-bit microprocessors such as the Intel 8080, the Motorola 6800, the MOS Technology 6502 and the Zilog Z80 each have:

An 8-bit bidirectional data bus, for data transfers
A 16-bit unidirectional address bus, for access to memory and I/O
A control bus (up to 12 lines) for coordination of data transfers in the system.

In addition, at least two lines are needed for power plus two more for connecting an external clock crystal or oscillator. The total number of connections is 40, a popular microprocessor dual-in-line integrated circuit package size.

The resulting computer structure is shown in Fig. 5.1.

The computer system components, typically the ROM, RAM and PIAs, are connected to the data, address and control buses. When the microprocessor does not have the current drive capability to allow for its direct connection to all the other chips in the system, (and this is often the case) bus buffers (bus drivers) are used. These are integrated circuits connected between the microprocessor pins and the buses. They do not change the logic levels, but provide enough drive to permit transmission of information to the buses and thence to the chips connected to the buses, and allow these chips to provide information via the buses to the microprocessor

Clock

The clock is the source of basic timing signals, and operates at a typical frequency of 1 MHz, or one million cycles per second. The clock circuit is sometimes separate from the microprocessor chip, with a quartz crystal for frequency stability. In other cases (for example the 6502 microprocessor), the oscillator and clock driver circuits are 'on-chip' and it is only necessary to add a frequency determining resistance-capacitance network and a crystal externally.

The timing of data transfers within the system is controlled by the clock, which provides two

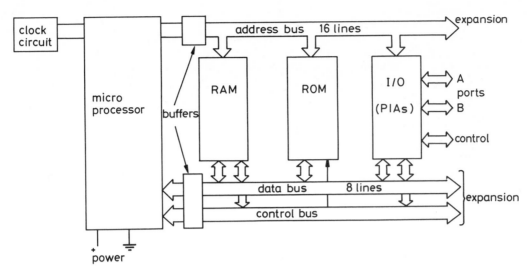

Fig. 5.1. 'Standard' 8-bit Microcomputer Structure

non-overlapping square waves - Phase One
($\emptyset_1$) and Phase Two ($\emptyset_2$) (Fig. 5.2.). In a
typical system address lines in the address
bus change logic levels during $\emptyset_1$ positive
and information is transferred via the data
bus during $\emptyset_2$ positive. This information
could be instructions fetched from memory,
input from a PIA, output to a PIA or data
taken from or written into memory. The
address bus logic levels select locations in
memory or registers in PIAs.

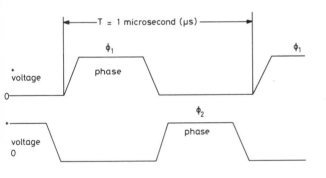

Fig. 5.2. Two Phase Clock

Control

The lines in the control bus determine the
sequence and nature of the system operation
including memory read and write and PIA
input/output. Specific details depend on
the microprocessor type, and the 6502 will
be used as an illustrative example in
further discussion of system organisation
and operation.

The 6502 is very similar in bus structure
and operation to the 6800, and is a good
example of 8-bit microprocessor 'state of
the art'.

5.3. MEMORY ORGANISATION

Each byte of ROM or RAM and the PIA registers
must have assigned to them unique (in the
system) 16-bit addresses. The range of
addresses for each type of memory is chosen
for the particular system. For example a
small program of a few hundred bytes could be
accommodated in a modest size of ROM, while
a system with a complicated large program
could need several K bytes of ROM. Data
needed for programs, for example results of
computations held temporarily for subsequent
use, is normally held in RAM, as are programs
required only intermittently and loaded into
memory as needed from an external peripheral,
for example a floppy disc.

The distinction between ROM and RAM sections
of memory is a feature of microprocessor
systems, in contrast to the use of a single
type of memory - usually ferrite core - for
program and data storage in minicomputers
and larger machines.

The total amount of ROM, RAM and PIA memory
space in a practical system will usually be
considerably less than the full 65,536
locations possible with the 16-bit address.
This means that complete decoding of all
16 address bits to uniquely identify memory
chips and memory locations within them, is
rarely necessary. Instead a limited number
of address lines are used either individually
or logically ANDed, to select large blocks
of memory.

The most basic technique is linear selection,
in which individual address lines are
connected to individual ROM or RAM chip-
select inputs. If address line A15 is chosen
for a chip-select, that chip is selected
every time A15 is at logic 1, for example.
This occurs for half of all the memory
locations. For a very small system with 256
bytes of ROM and 256 bytes of RAM, A15 = 1
could select ROM and A15 = 0 could select
RAM (if the chip select logic levels are 1
on the ROM chip and 0 on the RAM chip). To
address the 256 locations in ROM (or RAM),
lines A0 to A7 of the address bus are
connected to the 8 address lines of the chip.
A 1K memory chip (the 2708 EPROM for example)
needs 10 lines, A0 to A9 for address, plus
one line for chip select. This approach to
address allocation is illustrated in Fig. 5.3.,

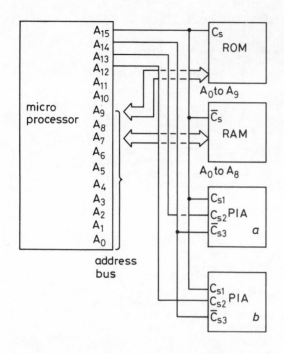

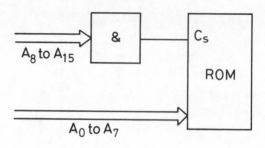

Fig. 5.4.   Decoded Selection

outputs, selected by the 3 bit address and
enabled by separate input lines. It is therefore possible to select 8 (or more) banks of
memory, with contiguous addresses (Fig. 5.5.).

A_{15}	A_{14}	A_{13}	A_{12}	
1	0	0	0	ROM
0	0	0	0	RAM
1	0	1	0	PIA a
1	0	0	1	PIA b

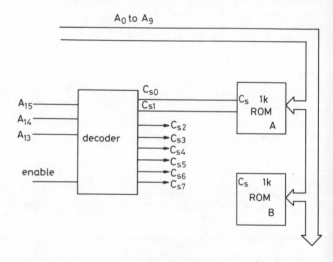

Fig. 5.5.   3 to 8 Decoder for ROM Chips

Fig. 5.3.   Address Assignment

with a 1K byte (1K x 8-bit) ROM chip
selected by A15=1 and addressed by AO to A9,
a 512 byte (512 x 8-bit) RAM selected by
A15=O and addressed by AO to A8, and 2 PIAs
each with a set of 3 chip selects, one set
provided by A15, A14 and A13 and the other
by A15, A14 and A12. In this example RAM
has been allocated low memory, ROM is in
high memory, and the PIAs are located in
between. This is a normal arrangement and
takes into account the need to allocate RAM
for stack operations, ROM for interrupt
procedures and other constraints imposed by
the 6502. Linear selection is very simple
to implement and is used in small systems
but it has limited applicability, in that
the available memory is halved every time
a separate address line is used. Decoded
addressing avoids wasting address space and
can provide access to any location. For
example if it is desired to allocate the
last 256 memory locations to ROM, we require
to access addresses 1111111100000000_2 or
hexadecimal FFOO to 1111111111111111_2 or
hexadecimal FFFF. We can select this range
by enabling the ROM chip select when the 8
high order bits A15 to A8 are 1. An 8-input
AND gate can do this (Fig. 5.4.).

General purpose decoders are often used in
systems. These chips have for example 3
address inputs and 8 mutually exclusive

We have already met decoded selection 'on-
chip' with the 3 chip selects of the PIA,
and on-chip decoding is often provided on
ROM and RAM devices. For example ROM with
3 chip selects on each chip provides for the
connection of up to 8 chips to only 3 address
lines, with no additional decoder.

Practical systems often use a mixture of linear
selection and decoding (including multiple
chip-selects), for address assignment. The
allocation of memory is normally illustrated
by a memory map, sometimes referred to as
an address map. A simple example is shown in
Fig. 5.6.

Combination chips containing PIA, ROM and RAM
(like the 6530) have separate memory areas
allocated to the separate functions.

5.4.   INSTRUCTION FETCH AND EXECUTE

Connection of specific address lines, through
decoders where necessary, to ROM, RAM and PIA

location

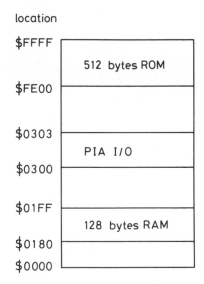

Fig. 5.6. Example Memory Map

When the system is switched on, the Reset line ($\overline{RES}$) is held at logic 0 for a short time. This resets internal registers, and when $\overline{RES}$ goes to 1, the microprocessor automatically goes to the program starting location defined by the contents of 2 reserved locations in ROM. In the 6502, these are $FFFC and $FFFD (hexadecimal). The 2 byte address defining the program starting location thus appears in the Program Counter (PC).

The microprocessor then begins the Fetch cycle, involving the placement of the PC contents (16 bits) on the address bus and the generation of control signals on the control bus for a memory read. In particular the Read/Write line R/$\overline{W}$ and the SYNC line are at 1 during this first Fetch cycle. In general the SYNC signal at 1 indicates an <u>operation code</u> (op code) Fetch, and returns to 0 at the end of the cycle. R/$\overline{W}$ stays at 1, and goes to 0 only when the microprocessor is writing data to memory or a PIA. Address bus data is valid shortly after the start of $\emptyset_1$ positive, and stays stable until the next $\emptyset_1$ positive state - that is for most of one complete cycle T.

chips implements the desired memory organisation. Assuming for the moment that a program <u>is</u> in memory (probably in ROM but possibly in RAM), instructions and data must be moved via the data bus to and from the microprocessor to execute the program. Input/output procedures for loading programs and data into the computer, and for making available the results, are discussed later.

This signal sequence is illustrated in Fig. 5.7., with the remainder of the instruction timing sequence. All instructions begin with the Fetch of the Op code (8 bits) and continue through the number of cycles required for the Execution of the instruction, to the start of the next Fetch. Cycles are commonly designated T0 (Fetch), T1, T2, etc.

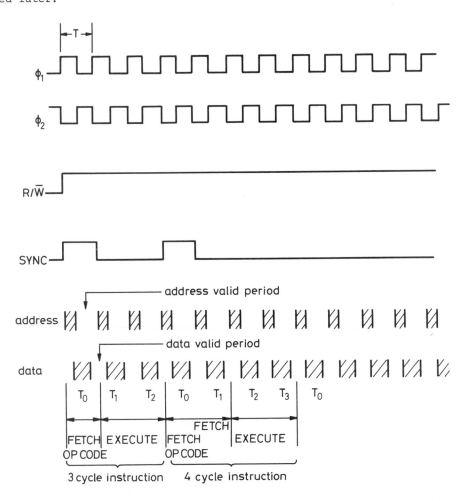

Fig. 5.7. Instruction Fetch and Execute Timing

The desired op code from memory is thus transferred via the data bus to the instruction register. The PC contents are then incremented so that the next byte of the instruction can be obtained from memory. (Most 6502 and other 8-bit microprocessor instructions occupy 2 or more bytes.) In many cases cycles subsequent to TO are Fetches of data or address from memory, followed by arithmetic operations and/or writing of data to memory or PIA (R/$\overline{W}$ = 0). The Execute phase of an instruction can occupy 6 or more cycles, depending on the function and the addressing procedures involved. The ultimate execution of the instruction, perhaps involving an arithmetic operation on data from memory, may take place during the Fetch (and decoding) of the next instruction. During memory reads and data transfers, the data bus lines are stable for the later part of $\emptyset_2$ positive and into the start of $\emptyset_1$ positive. Data transfer takes place at the positive to negative transition of $\emptyset_2$. During most of $\emptyset_1$ positive the data bus is in its high impedance (of the three possible states, 1, 0 and isolated) 'floating' condition.

The steps involved in an example instruction, 'Load Accumulator With Memory' using 'Absolute' addressing (with a direct 2 byte, 16 bit address) are as follows. The 3 byte instruction starts at location $0240 (initial value of PC).

Sync	Cycle	Address Bus	Data Bus	Comment
1	TO	$0240 (PC)	$AD (OP CODE)	Fetch OP CODE
0	T1	$0241 (PC+1)	$04 (low address byte)	Fetch low address byte
0	T2	$0242 (PC+1)	$02 (high address byte)	Fetch high address byte
0	T3	$0204	$IF (Data)	Fetch data from memory addressed
1	TO	$0243 (PC+3)	OP CODE	Next Instruction Fetch OP CODE

The data byte $IF from addressed location $0204 is written into the accumulator after T3. This instruction requires 4 cycles to Fetch and Execute. It occupies 3 bytes in memory, starting at $0240, so that PC has to be $0243 at the end for the next instruction Fetch. Incrementing PC as required is part of the microprocessor 'housekeeping'. Of course instructions such as Jump or Branch operations modify PC to allow continuation of the program at the appropriate location.

A microprocessor may have hundreds of instruction op codes (the 6502 has 151). Manufacturers' literature includes summaries of instruction Fetch and Execute sequences, so that users can examine address and data bus information at any point in the execution of an instruction, with suitable equipment. Normally of course the computer user is quite satisfied if his input data is correctly processed and results appear at the system output, and he will not wish to get involved with system operations at the byte transfer level. However, for many engineering applications and in microprocessor based product development timing is very important and the details of instruction execution times can be of considerable interest.

Control of Dynamic RAMs

ROMs and static RAMs and indeed PIAs require only chip selection, addressing and necessary control signals for their operation in a microprocessor system. Dynamic RAMs have high capacity and are popular, but of course they require refreshing to retain data. The system must include provision for this function when dynamic RAMs are used. Typical RAM chips require 32 refresh operations every 2 milliseconds, or 1 refresh every 64 microseconds approximately. The microprocessor could provide this function by generating the necessary read and address every 64 microseconds, but this can be restrictive for many systems since it 'ties up' the microprocessor. The Z80 makes special provision for dynamic RAM by 'stealing' a refresh cycle in every instruction cycle - the lower 7 address lines generate a refresh address during instruction execution, when the address bus is not being otherwise used. Other microprocessors including the 6502 require a separate 'refresh-controller' circuit which steps through the dynamic RAM rows to refresh. A counter operating directly from the 1 MHz system clock provides a divide by 64, and gives a 'refresh request' every 64 microseconds. The microprocessor may then be 'stopped' for one or two cycles, during which time the refresh operation is performed by the refresh controller. 64 microseconds later the next RAM row is refreshed. Stopping the microprocessor and taking control of the memory address lines for the RAM refresh is facilitated in the 6502 by the SYNC and RDY signals. It is necessary to take over control of the system (although for only a very short time) to ensure that there is no possibility of simultaneous attempts to write new data into RAM and refresh existing information already stored there.

The technique of stopping the microprocessor and taking direct control of memory is also the basis of a rapid method of data I/O - Direct Memory Access (DMA). We will examine DMA and other widely used I/O procedures later. At this stage it is clear that a key feature of computer operation is the use of data transfers, for example the fetching of instructions and data from memory, and the transfer of information to and from the world outside the computer.

5.5.   DATA TRANSFER PRINCIPLES

The instruction fetch operation described earlier is completely under CPU (microprocessor control, using the system clock to dictate the timing of events. This is an example of a 'single ended' or 'open loop' system, because all synchronisation comes from the CPU, and there is no feedback signal from the memory to confirm that the CPU's command has been received correctly, or later from the CPU to memory to confirm that the data read from memory has been transferred correctly. Of course if such data transfers are incorrect, the program will execute incorrectly or stop, and this will be very evident. The real value of having a response from the partner in a data transfer operation - in the instruction fetch example, from memory, - is that the initiator of the data transfer (in our case the CPU) knows as soon as possible when its command has been received and acted on. This can be very useful when a system includes a number of component subsystems (for example memory types) with differing response times. A single ended system must be designed to accommodate the performance of the slowest subsystem (perhaps the slowest memory type), whereas a system with feedback - a double ended system - is ready to go on to the next task as quickly as is possible, taking account of different response times.

A double ended data transfer, with an acknowledgement response is commonly termed a 'handshake'. Handshaking (closed loop data transfer) is used particularly for I/O data transfers, where peripheral equipment response time is dependent not only on the equipment design characteristics, but also on the activity in progress and the state of readiness. It may also be used for data transfers inside the computer to accommodate the use of different memory types but this is less common.

Fig. 5.8. illustrates the event sequence in a basic handshaking data transfer. The direction of data transfer (for example memory read or memory write) is indicated by a separate control line (not shown).

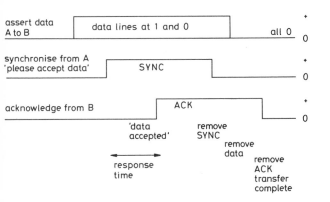

Fig. 5.8. Handshake Data Transfer

Any handshaking system must have a 'timeout' arrangement, whereby no answer from the other end (no acknowledge) does not paralyse the system, but instead after a reasonable wait (perhaps a few milliseconds) control is transferred to a continuation program, or the matter is drawn to the operator's attention.

The general handshaking principle is used within mini and microcomputers, as part of I/O procedures, and also between computer systems and remote terminals, and in networks of computers with data transmission.

5.6. INPUT/OUTPUT CONTROL

In discussing the 'standard' 8-bit microprocessor based computer, memory-mapped I/O with memory addresses allocated to PIAs, has

been assumed. Indeed this is a widely used technique and features in 6800 and 6502 systems, for example. No separate I/O instructions are used, I/O operations appearing as memory accesses. This approach was first introduced in minicomputers (notably the DEC PDP/11), and represented a design departure from the more traditional data channel I/O, where peripherals interface to the CPU through a bus structure separate from the memory bus. Data channel I/O has a set of I/O instructions separate from the memory reference class.

The limited number of pins on microprocessor packages (usually 40) made it difficult for data channel I/O, with a separate I/O bus, to be implemented on early microprocessor systems. Nevertheless the concept of data channel I/O has been adopted in modified form by some microprocessors, for example the 8080 and Z80. In such devices, I/O instructions separate from memory reference are used, with special control signals to indicate that some (usually 8) address lines are for I/O port selection, and that the data bus is acting as an I/O bus. This technique is referred to as I/O mapped, and has an advantage in that usually only 8 bits have to be decoded to identify an I/O device, instead of the full 16 address bits in memory mapped I/O.

Memory-mapped I/O on the other hand is structurally elegant and makes available to I/O operations the power of all the microprocessor instructions, including the possibility of direct arithmetic operations on data from and to external devices and peripherals. Thousands of I/O ports are possible if needed. It appears that memory mapped I/O continues to grow in popularity. Both techniques use address lines to identify I/O ports, and transfer data on the data bus, and so have a lot in common. Indeed PIAs can be used with either technique, usually with handshaking data transfers.

As well as the choice of computer I/O structure, we have a choice of I/O management procedure. Three main methods are in common use: programmed I/O, interrupt controlled I/O and Direct Memory Access (DMA, mentioned above).

Programmed I/O

In this method, all I/O transfers are performed as part of the program being executed. In its simplest form, the program could say 'OUTPUT DATA TO DEVICE 7' or 'INPUT DATA FROM DEVICE 5'. The accumulator is a convenient source and destination for I/O data. Often something more than a direct command is necessary, to ensure that the data transfer is successful. Some means of knowing that the intended destination or source is ready for the transfer is useful. This can be accomplished by polling the external device via the interface (possibly a PIA) to check on the condition of a status bit. A status bit could be 0, for example, except when a key (any key) on a keyboard has been pressed. The computer could monitor the status bit, do a data read when necessary, wait until the key is released, and go back to waiting for another key depression. This is illustrated by means of the flow chart below, which is quite self explanatory - the diamond shapes indicate decisions in the program.

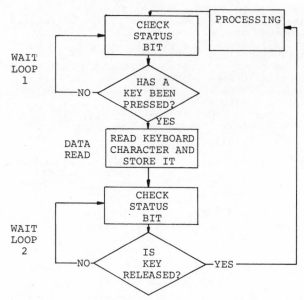

There are thus two 'wait loops' during which
no useful processing (for example computations on the input data) can take place. The
main activity of the program is waiting.
With a human operator, only a few key presses
per second are possible at best. After a key
press, the program can spend up to perhaps
one tenth of a second processing without risk
of totally missing the next key operation.
This one tenth of a second is 100,000 microseconds, equivalent to many thousands of
instruction executions, underlining the
inefficiency of waiting perhaps several
seconds in wait loop 1.

Polling can be extended to many I/O devices,
monitoring the status bits for each device
in turn, going to a short (and fast) data
input or data output program sequence when
data is ready for transfer to or from a
device, and returning to the polling loop.
Status bits can be monitored in parallel, by
forming them into a single status word
(perhaps an 8-bit byte) and reading the contents, but continuous polling is still
necessary.

This approach is very economic in hardware
(circuitry), but very wasteful of processing
time, unless a large number of devices are
active and only minimal processing is needed
anyway. Of course if the program's only
purpose is to input or output data, then a
program controlled I/O procedure may be quite
acceptable.

Interrupt Controlled I/O

Interrupt I/O takes rather more account of
the real nature of systems and devices which
are external and peripheral to the computer.
Such peripherals very often operate much
more slowly than computer components like
CPU and memory and their response times and
readiness states are less predictable. It
is therefore sensible to have the computer
proceed with the completion of its processing tasks and to interrupt the main program
being executed when a peripheral has data
ready for transfer, or when it is ready to
accept a data transfer requested by the computer some time earlier. There may be other
reasons to interrupt the computer. A real-
time-clock in the system might indicate that
it is now time to initiate some action, or a
subsystem monitoring the power supply voltages

could decide that power is failing and
initiate a 'power-fail-restart' routine to
save CPU register data in non-volatile memory
before the system becomes inoperative. This
latter procedure has been popular in minicomputers with ferrite core memory, and is
used in microprocessor systems with 'battery
back-up' hardware.

Instead of having the computer continually
checking to see if something new has happened,
interrupts tell the CPU when events of interest
have occurred. CPUs including microprocessor
types have circuitry to accept and respond
to interrupts. Usually an interrupt causes
the currently executing program to stop, the
CPU takes action to store away essential
register data (notably the program counter
contents to enable the main program to resume
execution later), the interrupt is serviced
by a predetermined sequence of instructions
which can be a substantial program in its own
right in many instances, and on completion of
the interrupt service routine, the previous
program activity is resumed from the interrupted point. The exact sequence of computer
activity is thus determined by the pattern of
interrupts, and it is very important that all
eventualities are foreseen and provided for,
including arrangements for handling multiple
interrupts from a number of sources.

Sometimes an interrupt can be processed by a
single instruction, for example an increment
register contents, to count events. It is
more usual for an interrupt to cause the
execution of a interrupt service routine program - an interrupt subroutine. When an
interrupt is 'recognised' by the CPU (probably at the end of the instruction currently
being executed), the computer executes a
single instruction held at the interrupt
location and set up there by the programmer.
In some computers, if this instruction does
not modify the program counter, the computer
continues with the original program. More
usually the PC contents are altered, to point
to the interrupt service routine starting
location in memory. It is then necessary to
'save' the previous PC contents and the contents of other important status registers.
These are usually held temporarily in the stack
(in a microprocessor system, in the designated
stack area of RAM) and retrieved on completion
of interrupt servicing, so that the original
program can be resumed.

Detailed hardware and software arrangements
for interrupt handling are dependent on the
computer being considered. By way of example,
we will consider the interrupt capabilities
of the 6502 microprocessor. The 6502 has two
interrupt request lines, $\overline{NMI}$ and $\overline{IRQ}$. Reset
($\overline{RES}$) functions rather like an interrupt
line but is primarily intended for use in
start-up or restart procedures. When $\overline{NMI}$
goes from 1 to 0, the processor is always
interrupted. The processor cannot disable
this function, hence the name nonmaskable
interrupt. The processor is sensitive to $\overline{NMI}$
change only - after it has gone to 0 it can
stay there indefinitely without causing another
interrupt. A minimum of 2 clock cycles after
the $\overline{NMI}$ transition 1 to 0, the PC and processor status register contents are put onto
the stack in RAM at 3 locations (determined
by the stack condition). The processor
status register is also referred to as the
'status flags register'. The addresses
$FFFA and $FFFB, holding the $\overline{NMI}$ vector, are
read and the contents placed in PC. The

desired $\overline{\text{NMI}}$ service routine is executed, terminated with a Return from Interrupt instruction, which reloads PC and the processor status register with the saved values from the stack. Note that special provision must be made in the interrupt service routine if other processor registers are to be saved.

$\overline{\text{IRQ}}$ is very like $\overline{\text{NMI}}$, except that it is level determined (if left at 0, the effect is of continuous interrupts), and it can be enabled and disabled, depending on whether the interrupt mask bit I (bit 2 of the processor status register) is 0 or 1. The interrupt service routine is 'vectored' from locations $FFFE and $FFFF.

In most 6502 systems, the processor receives interrupts via one or more PIAs which provide I/O functions. Even a basic system usually has two or more devices capable of generating interrupts, for example a keyboard and a display. A real time clock is frequently included in basic microprocessor systems and generates interrupts which are sometimes used to initiate display refresh/rescan procedures. It is necessary to identify the interrupting device, and software and hardware methods are available for this.

In the all-software method, the interrupt service routine initiated by $\overline{\text{IRQ}}$ or $\overline{\text{NMI}}$ includes a polling sequence which reads the control registers in the PIAs to determine the source of the interrupt. The polling sequence starts with the device which has been allocated the highest priority and services the highest priority interrupt active first. It then resumes polling until all active interrupts have been handled, in descending priority order.

The hardware vectored-interrupt method is much faster than the software polling technique. Instead of starting the interrupt service routine by polling around the possible interrupting devices before proceeding to the particular instructions to be executed for the device actually interrupting, the processor is provided with the proper starting location for the interrupting device simultaneously with the interrupt. The technique uses a special LSI component - a Priority-Interrupt-Controller (PIC) chip. This detects the fact that the processor is attempting to access locations $FFFE and $FFFF in sequence (for $\overline{\text{IRQ}}$), and alters the address

inputs to ROM so that the locations accessed are in fact determined by the highest priority interrupting device identity. The PIC has thus taken control of selection of the interrupt vector (Fig. 5.9.).

As shown in Fig. 5.9., it is usual to 'OR' multiple interrupt request lines together to provide a single input to $\overline{\text{IRQ}}$. A further PIC function (not indicated in Fig. 5.9.) is to selectively mask or disable interrupts, so that interrupt service routines can themselves be interrupted only by higher priority interrupts. This implies 'nested interrupts' and the stack may then be used to store not just the original register contents, but also register values for interrupted interrupt service routines.

The necessary flexibility and speed for multiple interrupts can thus be provided by appropriate hardware/software arrangements. In many cases adequate performance is provided by 'ORed' interrupts and a polling service routine. The $\overline{\text{NMI}}$ input can be a 'last resort' means of recovering control of a system, since it cannot be masked.

Interrupt handling capability is an important aspect of mini and microcomputer performance. Some systems automatically store all processor register contents when interrupted, unlike the 6502. Many software and hardware priority arrangements are in use, and one example is shown in Fig. 5.10.

With this 'daisy-chained' arrangement, all devices share the single interrupt request line. The processor begins the interrupt service routine by using an interrupt acknowledge signal that goes first to the highest priority device (or its PIA). If this device caused the interrupt it puts its identity code onto the data bus and stops the acknowledge signal from going further down the chain until its service routine is complete. Priority is thus determined by location in the chain. The daisy-chain procedure uses the handshake principle.

Actual interrupt priorities in a system are allocated on the basis of the performance characteristics as well as the importance of the external device or peripheral. Since it is desirable that control of the computer can be taken by the operator under any circumstances, the operator keyboard is usually

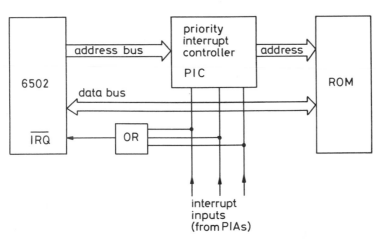

Fig 5.9.   Interrupt Vector Selection

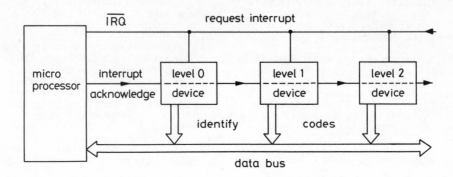

Fig. 5.10. Daisy Chained Interrupt System

assigned the highest priority - normally
designated level 0. Disc peripherals are
assigned high priority because they handle
large volumes of data at a high data transfer rate. In a computer system used in an
industrial process, immediate response to
particular events may be very critical, and
these together with the real time clock may
be allocated high priority. (Peripherals
are described in the next chapter.)

Direct Memory Access (DMA)

Program and interrupt I/O both use the CPU,
and data to and from memory passes through
CPU registers. The accumulator is normally
used. This can be useful if arithmetic
operations are to be carried out on the data.
For unmodified data transfers, movement
through the CPU is not usually a problem,
since the delay introduced is a few microseconds, negligible in comparison to the
response times of most devices and peripherals
external to the computer. There are however
some situations where the data transfer rate
achievable by program or interrupt I/O is
not acceptable. These include instrumentation
applications where activities being
monitored produce data at a very high speed,
and the use of some peripherals, notably
high speed, high volume magnetic disc storage
units. The solution is to bypass the CPU
altogether, and transfer data directly to
and from memory - direct memory access.

This involves taking control of the computer
system buses temporarily to implement the
memory read or write. Obviously this has to
be done in an orderly fashion, to avoid
creating havoc with programs executing. Most
mini and microcomputers have DMA provisions
in their control units that allow such control
takeovers. Special electronic circuitry in
the form of a DMA controller is needed to
manage the data transfer. Speed of transfer
is limited only by the memory characteristics
and can reach several million bytes per second
for solid state memory devices.

A generalised DMA structure is shown in
Fig. 5.11.

Direct connections are made between memory
data and address lines, and the interface.
The interface operates by supplying the

desired address in memory, and receiving or
sending data over the data lines. The
important point is that during a data transfer from or to memory, the program being
executed by the CPU is frozen for the time
of one memory cycle for each data transfer.
The DMA memory cycle in effect takes the
place of the program cycle, and the technique
is often referred to as 'cycle stealing'.
Data is sent or received, from or by memory,
without any indication to the running program.
The general sequence of events is:

(i)   The DMA interface generates a 'cycle
      steal request'.

(ii) At the end of the current memory
      cycle (remember that an instruction
      may require several cycles), the CPU
      acknowledges on the 'cycle steal
      available' line.

(iii) The DMA interface responds by placing
      the appropriate memory address on the
      memory address lines.
      For input (to memory), the data is
      placed on the data lines, with a
      write signal on the read/write line.
      For output (from memory), the inter-
      face indicates a read level on the
      read/write line, and accepts the
      memory data.
      (Interface timing signals, to clock
      data through the DMA interface, are
      synchronized with the CPU operation.)

Typically, a DMA data transfer will consist
of a block of say 256 8-bit bytes. The
byte counter is loaded initially with the
number of data bytes to be transferred, and
is then decremented for each cycle steal
(ie, every byte transfer). The address
counter is loaded initially (usually by a
programmed I/O instruction) with the starting
address of the data block. When the byte
counter reaches zero, an interrupt from the
DMA interface to the CPU terminates the
operation, and the computer reverts to the
main program.

Byte-count and address-count information is
held in assigned memory locations in some
minicomputers using 'increment memory'
instructions. Such DMA procedures are slower
than those with hardware interface counters,

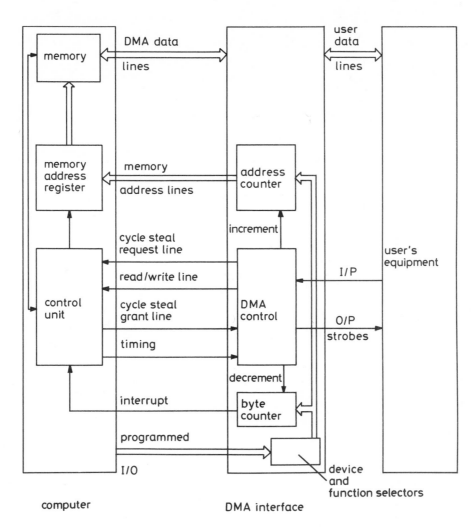

Fig. 5.11.   DMA Structure

and are sometimes referred to as Direct Memory Channel (DMC) transfers.

In microcomputers it is usual to 'float' the microprocessor address, data and control lines by putting them into the high impedance condition of the tristate bus buffers. The microprocessor is halted by a signal on a special line - in the 6502 this is the RDY line. 'Cycle steal available' is indicated, on some microprocessors by a 'Bus available' output, which signals that the processor has stopped. For the 6502 a Bus available signal can be generated from the RDY, R/$\overline{\text{W}}$ (Read/Write) and $\emptyset_2$ signals since the processor stops in the first non-write cycle after RDY goes to 0 on a DMA request. Some microprocessors permit 'interleaved' DMA, whereby direct memory access is carried out on cycles in which the processor is not using the address or data buses. DMA controllers (interfaces) are available in LSI chip form. They are as complex as some microprocessors and indeed a microprocessor with some memory may be used as a DMA controller for another system.

5.7.   PRACTICAL COMPUTERS

The final design of a real computer depends on parameters such as the technology adopted, the application area, the target selling price and the whim of the designer. Major

manufacturers often try to maintain some standardisation of design, with new models conforming to defined I/O arrangements (for example).

Microprocessor based computers use RAM and ROM in quantities dictated by the design objectives. PIAs are often used for I/O but alternatively special circuitry may be incorporated.

As just one example of a real machine, Fig. 5.12. shows schematically the structure of the Commodore PET computer. We will briefly review the principal features.

This popular 6502 based personal computer has a keyboard, tape cassette drive and video display integrated into the mechanical enclosure, so that for many purposes it is self contained. The tape cassette drive makes possible economic storage and retrieval of programs and data.

The computer is manufactured with different quantities of user accessible memory, typically from 8 K to 32 K bytes of RAM, implemented with 4116 or 4108 type dynamic RAM chips (Fig. 5.13.). These devices are pin compatible and accommodate 16 K and 8 K bits in each chip respectively.

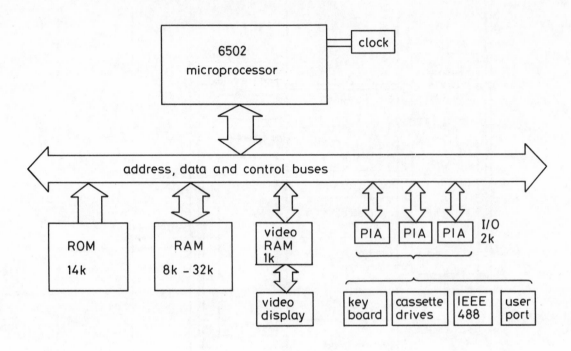

Fig. 5.12. PET Computer Structure

14K of ROM is used for the operating system (keyboard scan, display, real time clock, user command execution programs) and for storing the BASIC program interpreter. 2332 type ROM chips are organised as 4K byte blocks (4K each chip) with chip select lines. (Fig. 5.14.) Three additional ROM sockets can accommodate 2732 type EPROMS holding machine code software (the 2732 is pin compatible with the 2332).

The main I/O (not including the video) is provided by three LSI chips, two 6520 PIAs and one 6522 VIA (Versatile Interface Adapter). The VIA is indeed more versatile than the PIA and includes two timers and a shift register (8 bits). These devices handle keyboard input, tape cassette input, output and motor control (an additional external tapedrive can be used) and a general purpose I/O port which is to the IEEE488 bus

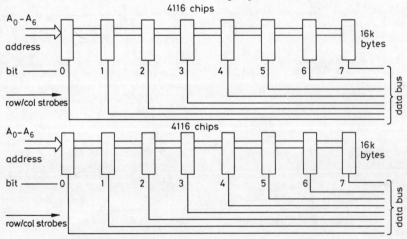

Fig. 5.13. PET 32K RAM Memory Structure

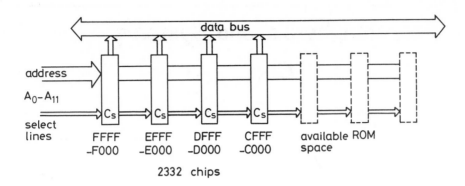

Fig. 5.14. PET ROM Memory Structure

standard. (This standard is discussed in Chapter 6.) This I/O port uses one PIA completely and part of the VIA. Address locations $E810 to $E84F are allocated to the PIAs and VIA.

The video system uses 1K of RAM ($8000 to $83E7) to store up to 1,000 coded characters (25 lines x 40 characters) for display.

An outline memory map is therefore:

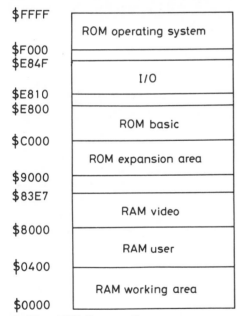

Fig. 5.15. PET Memory Map

Interrupt controlled I/O is used, with the 6502 $\overline{IRQ}$ line. Keyboard, cassette and real time clock operations use interrupts; indeed system operation is heavily interrupt dependent. The PET can also support printers, disc storage drives and other peripherals.

Information on the structure and operating characteristics of particular computers is provided by manufacturers in User Manuals and Reference Manuals. A welcome development with personal computers has been increased availability of information on machines, and comparative assessments of modern small computers appear in journals and magazines devoted to the technology.

The performance of computers based on 8-bit

microprocessors can approach that of 16 bit minicomputers designed years earlier. Microprocessors with 16 bit and indeed 32 bit handling capability, for example the 68000, Z8000 and iAPX products, are now available and computers based on them will outperform many 'minicomputers'. Indeed the terms minicomputer and microcomputer are very imprecise, and certainly do not clearly indicate computing capability. Trends in microprocessors include wider address buses (24 bits for example directly accessing up to 16 million bytes - 16 megabytes - of memory) and faster clock rates (up to 6 MHz). Many architectural features of large minicomputers (for example from the DEC PDP-11 range) and indeed of mainframes are being incorporated in the new microprocessors. In many cases I/O ports such as PIAs are usable with the new devices. Concurrent with progress towards more and more powerful processors new computers based on 'mature' 8-bit devices continue to be developed.

5.8. SUMMARY

The combination of microprocessor, ROM and RAM memory and I/O chips to form a 'standard' 8-bit microcomputer has been demonstrated. Memory organisation techniques and the operations involved in the instruction fetch and execute sequence have been reviewed. Data transfer principles and I/O methods have been outlined and features of a real personal computer have been discussed.

In the next chapter the computer is incorporated into a computer system with peripheral equipment for human interaction and information storage, and interfacing techniques and standards are examined.

5.9. REFERENCES

1. 'Microprocessor Systems Engineering', Camp, R.C., Smay, T.A., Triska, C.J., (Matrix Publishers Inc. 1979).

2. 'MCS6500 Microcomputer Family Hardware Manual' MOS Technology Inc.

3. 'An Introduction to Microcomputers', Vol. 1, Basic Concepts, Adam Osborne, (Osborne and Associates Inc. 1978).

4. 'The PET Revealed', Nick Hampshire, (Computabits Ltd. 1980).

Peripherals and Systems
Chapter 6

6.1. INTRODUCTION

A computer can perform useful tasks only if it is part of a computer system - even the simplest usable computer configuration has some means of entering data, programs and commands and of displaying or recording the results. Modern small computers often have a keyboard built into the computer unit. Sometimes an information display is included. Alternatively a television receiver or monitor is used for information display. The keyboard and the display device are not parts of the computer - they are peripheral items of equipment. A computer system includes the computer (CPU, memory and I/O), peripherals appropriate to the system function, interfacing to connect the peripherals and computer together and of course, software. Sometimes a computer system has peripheral equipment - a data terminal for example - located a considerable distance away from the computer. All peripherals have a common feature - communications capability. The communication may be with a human operator, for example by means of a keyboard and a data display, or may be inherent in the peripheral's function of storing, transmitting and receiving computer data, as in the case of a magnetic disc unit. Many peripherals provide more than one function, for example the keyboard input, data display and limited data storage features of a visual display unit. It is however convenient to classify peripheral equipment by its primary function: 'man-machine' interaction, 'back-up' data storage, or data transmission.

Equipment of the first two types is usually located geographically convenient to the computer (usually in the same room). Data transmission equipment provides for data communication over cables and telephone lines between 'data terminals' and remote computers, and between different computer installations.

6.2. PERIPHERALS FOR MAN-MACHINE INTERACTION

This class includes devices which allow the human operator to input information to the computer, and which provide visual or 'hard copy' printed output from the machine. The most familiar input mechanism is the keyboard, with alphabetic and numeric keys. Commonly used output techniques are a printing mechanism or a character generating electronic display.

The teletypewriter, or teletype, has been a popular and generally used member of this class. Visual display units (VDU) have replaced teletypes for operator input/output, for today's modern computers.

Asynchronous Data Code

In general, coded data is first generated in parallel bit form - for example the electrical code for a single VDU keyed character is initially made available on eight (simultaneously active) electrical connections. For convenience and economy, simple twisted pair or co-axial cables are preferred to multi-way cables, and so serial codes are often used for data transfer between peripherals and computers, the parallel-to-serial conversion being performed electronically.

In the transmission path between (for example) the VDU and computer each bit is represented by current and no current time intervals, if 'current loop' standard is used. (Current = 'marking' no current = 'spacing'). For the commonly used ASCII code, eleven pulses are used to represent each character or coded symbol (Figure 6.1.). The first pulse, which

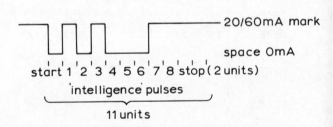

Fig. 6.1. Asynchronous character ASCII current waveform (even parity)

is always spacing, is the start pulse. The next eight pulses are the 'intelligence' pulses (and correspond to the eight hole locations in paper tape or to an 8 bit byte in memory). The tenth and eleventh pulses, always marking, are the stop pulses. When the line is 'idle', it is in the mark state. The receiving terminal (for example the computer) is alerted to the arrival of a coded character by the change to space of the start pulse. The time interval between the stop pulses and the start of the next coded character is not fixed, and depends on the operator depressing the next key or the computer generating the next output. This data format is asynchronous. With a synchronous technique, characters are transmitted at a constant rate and a clock signal is provided to mark the location of the data bit intervals. (Figure 6.2.)

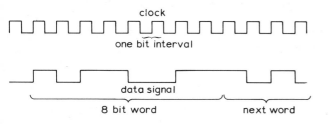

Fig. 6.2. Synchronous data waveforms

Synchronous data transmission, at 2,400 bits per second (approximately 300 characters/sec. for ASCII code) and upwards, is used for example, with fast printers and VDUs.

When a computer is receiving ASCII data it can look for single bit errors by doing a parity check on each 8-bit code. (When parity is not used, the eighth bit is always sent as a mark.)

The European CCITT (Standards organisation) recommendation V4 is that the least significant bit (b1) is transmitted first and that the parity bit b8 is chosen to give an odd number of 'ones' in the complete character.

b8	b7	b6	b5	b4	b3	b2	b1
1	1	0	1	0	0	1	1

(Parity bit)

At the receiver, the number of 'ones' in the character (or byte) is checked. This is readily achieved, for example by means of a flip-flop, which if preset to '0' will end in the '1' state after the 8 bits if the number of 'ones' used to clock the flip-flop is indeed odd, and no errors have occurred. Single errors (in the 8 bits), or an odd number of errors (1 changed to 0, or 0 changed to 1 by noise) will be detected since the parity relationship no longer holds. 2, 4, 6 or indeed 8 bit errors will be undetected, since the number of 'ones' will still be odd.

The use of a parity bit can produce a dramatic improvement in the undetected error rate. For example if the probability of a single bit being in error is 1 in 1,000 or 10^{-3}, the probability of a character being in error is improved from about 7 in 1,000 without a parity check to approximately 3 in 100,000 (from 7×10^{-3} to 3×10^{-5}) with parity. If a parity check fails, the character concerned is rejected and a retransmission of the character or of the data block containing the character in error, is requested. In some systems this process is implemented automatically. Even parity on 'ones' can be used of course. There are many additional error checking procedures possible including 'block checks' on sequences of characters.

Since 2^7 = 128, ASCII provides for 128 possible symbols. About two thirds are printing characters, while the rest are non-printing functions or are unassigned. Transmission rates are often given as Baud rates, for example 10 characters/second is equivalent to 110 bit intervals/second for asynchronous ASCII as described above, given as 110 Baud.

Current Loop Standard

The teletype data transmission standard of current levels and asynchronous format has been widely adopted, and often equipment which is to be used in a computer system (eg, a data logging unit) is specified as 'teletype compatible'. This means that it can use the teletype interface and software normally available. Current loop connections can be operated at speeds from 10 characters/second up to 1,000 characters/second, depending on the available performance of the computer interface and the peripheral equipment.

Visual Display Unit (VDU)

A Visual Display Unit comprises a keyboard and a display screen which is essentially a television tube, scanned in a similar manner. It lacks the paper tape and hard copy

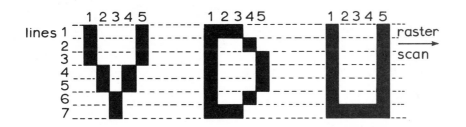

Fig. 6.3. DOT matrix display - VDU character generation

facilities of a teletype (although some VDUs
may be attached to printer units which produce an electrostatic copy of the display),
but can operate much faster.

The unit's operation is completely electronic
(apart from the keyboard), and data rates of
110 - 9,600 Baud (ie, bit intervals/second
or 10 - 1,000 characters/second) are usually
available. However, 1,200 Baud is a comfort-
able display rate for human operators. Displayed characters are made up on a 7 x 5 dot
matrix (usually) each of the seven horizontal
rows being a single scan of the display tube
(Fig. 6.3.). When a character is received
from the computer, or a key is depressed,
the digital code is stored in the VDU's memory.
For display, this code is recalled and used,
together with addressing and timing waveforms,
as inputs to character generating circuits
which produce the appropriate control signals
to the scanning display brightness.

Typically, up to 2,400 characters (a complete
display) can be held in the VDU memory, and
continuously displayed. The display can be
in either 'roll' or 'page' mode. In 'roll'
lines are added always at the bottom so that
the display 'rolls' up when the screen is full;
in 'page' the new lines are added to the bottom
of what has gone before, which remains fixed
in position until the complete screen (or page)
is filled - a new 'page' then starts at the
top.

'Line' and 'Local' operation is switch select-
able. Control characters are assigned to
provide sophistications such as 'protected'
areas (which cannot be overwritten by the
operator) and 'flashing fields' - which help
when VDUs are used as data terminals, particularly in 'form filling' applications.

Data transmission for VDUs can be synchronous
or asynchronous. For synchronous data, blocks
of characters are transmitted to and from the
VDU's store (eg, 256 characters in a block).
For asynchronous data, it is obvious that the
line is not very busy when a human operator
is using the keyboard - at 1200 Baud, each
transmitted character occupies approximately
10 milliseconds, while the operator is not
likely to key faster than a few characters
per second.

Since no electromechanical switching is used,
current loop standards are not really appropriate, although many VDUs have a current loop
interface built in to ensure 'teletype compatibility'. A voltage signalling standard
is commonly used - the European CCITT V.24
standard for data interfaces (equivalent to
the US EIA RS232C specification). This
standard uses a positive voltage (eg, +10V)
for a binary '0', and a negative voltage (eg,
-10V) for '1'. The voltages are with respect
to a zero reference connection.

Some VDUs have a 'graphics' capability, with
facilities for addressing any point in a 1,000
by 1,000 (typically) matrix display and thus
producing graphs and line diagrams. Some such
units (more expensive than conventional
character-type VDUs) utilise storage display
tubes rather than television type raster
displays.

A partial specification for a VDU is:

Number of lines displayed:	30
Number of characters per line:	80
Viewing area (screen):	9 in x 6.75 in

Character display format:	5 x 7 dot matrix
Character height:	0.125 inch
Interfaces:	Serial 20 mA/60 mA current loop CCITT V.24 asyn-chronous (RS232C) selectable speeds from 75 to 9600 Baud
Keyboard:	Standard - upper case ASCII
Video output for TV Monitor:	625 line
Display memory:	Dynamic MOS - stores full screen of data
Refresh rate:	50 frames (screen)/ second
Power:	240V, 50Hz, 100 watts

Some small computers use a completely integrated VDU - for example the Commodore Pet.
Others incorporate a keyboard in the computer
unit, and provide a VDU display signal output, which can produce a display on a TV
monitor. The most economic arrangement is
to incorporate a UHF (or VHF) broadcast
television frequency modulator, so that a
conventional TV receiver becomes an 'information' display. The display may be in
colour and have graphics capability, for
example the Apple/ITT 2020 system. For other
computers, a completely separate VDU may be
required.

Printer

VDUs are most suitable for immediate operator
interaction. There are many situations where
it is desirable to have the program listing,
or the results of computations available for
study in another location or at another time.
A good example is in the provision of a
computer service, where the customers require
their results in hard copy form.

The limited printing rate of a teletype pre-
cludes its use in this role, and a wide
range of higher speed printers, which can
operate at character rates up to 2,000/
second, is available. Each printed line can
contain up to 160 characters.

Generally speaking there are two main types:
'matrix-dot' and 'barrel'. Matrix-dot
printers use a writing head which strikes the
paper with a set of print needles to produce
a 7 x 5, 7 x 7, 9 x 7 or other dot grid for
character formation. These printers are
slower (typically up to 150 characters/
second) and cheaper than barrel printers, in
which each character position on the line has
an individual small print 'hammer'. The
printer contains a buffer which temporarily
holds the set of characters (data) which is
to be printed. The printer barrel has arranged
along it 160 (for example) sets of the complete character family, each set arranged
around the circumference of the barrel at a
print character position. The barrel rotates
at a constant speed, and the character buffer
is electrically linked to the print hammers
which are energised at the appropriate instant
to print the required line of characters.
(One line per revolution of the barrel.)
These very fast printers can be expensive
and are not commonly used in small computer
systems.

Other printing technologies are available,
including thermal printers which use heat
sensitive paper.

Printers normally used with small computers,
and operating at rates of 30 - 150 characters/
second are often provided with serial (V24
or current loop) interfaces. At higher speeds
the inefficiency of serial asynchronous data
transmission (due to the parallel/serial and
serial/parallel conversions, and the fact that
only 7 of the 11 transmitted bit signals
actually convey information) becomes very significant. High speed printers usually operate
with parallel data transfers, with multiway
(eg, 8 data bit) connections between computer
and printer, and I/O subroutines tailored for
the particular unit, including direct memory
access operation.

Some printers (particularly those at around
100 characters/second) intended for use with
small computers, have a keyboard for operator
data input.

Plotters

For graphical presentation of data, plotters
are available. Through suitable interfacing
(usually parallel I/O) a plotter pen is controlled by the computer to produce line draw-
ings on paper. The basic component of each
drawing is a line segment of about 1/100 in,
and up to 15,000 such segments can be drawn
in a minute. Such plotters are valuable in
computer aided design work.

Key-to-storage Systems

As modern alternatives to paper tape or
punched cards (popularly used with earlier,
larger computers) magnetic tapes or discs
may be used as storage media for data preparation purposes.

Discs and cassette and cartridge tapes are
discussed later in this chapter as 'back-up'
storage devices. In data preparation applications a keyboard is interfaced to a buffer
store which transfers blocks of data onto
the magnetic medium. Such systems have
facilities for editing and correcting the
keyed data, and are usually equipped with a
'built-in' VDU.

If a small computer is added, the unit becomes
an 'intelligent data terminal', with the processor controlling the operation of the unit,
particularly for data transmission. Such a
unit could be regarded as a small computer
system in its own right.

6.3. PERIPHERALS PROVIDING 'BACKING STORAGE'

Magnetic Media

'Backing stores' are used to supplement the
data storage capacity of main computer memory
(which is usually semiconductor RAM or ROM).
Normally the backing store holds considerably
more data than computer memory but there is
some delay in accessing it for use. The
specification of peripherals in this class
covers data storage capacity, rate of data
transfer between processor and peripheral,
and 'access time' - the time required to find
a particular block of data.

Magnetic storage is by far the most important
technique used - the peripherals may be
classified by the <u>form</u> of the magnetic medium
- for example tape or disc. Further, several
standard forms of tape (cassette, cartridge,
reel-to-reel) and disc (fixed, exchangeable,
flexible) are in current use.

Magnetic Tape Peripherals

All magnetic tape peripherals use magnetisable
metal-oxide coated plastic tape, which may be
magnetised by a 'write' head to store digital
information, using the same basic principle
as an audio or video tape recorder. The
digital magnetic pattern may then be sensed
and converted to an electrical digital waveform by the 'read' head, as the tape is moved
past. Tape peripherals differ in the type of
tape and the electro-mechanical arrangement
used to wind tape and move it past the read
and write heads. (Fig. 6.4.)

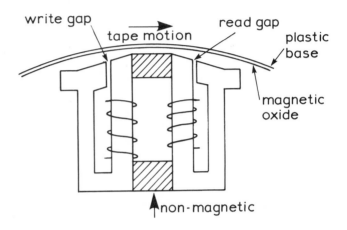

Fig. 6.4. Read/Write Head (allows read after
write)

Reel-to-Reel Units

These units conform to an 'industry-standard'
set of specifications, and have been widely
used for large computer systems. They are
less common in small computer systems, because
of their cost.

The tape is held on removable reels, which
have capacities of 600, 1,200 or 2,400 feet
(for example). As in an audio recorder a
take-up reel provides for forward and reverse
tape movements. The digital information is
stored as a row of bits across the tape width
(½ inch) - either 7 bit or 9 bit words (or
bytes) may be used. The recording density is
usually pre-selectable, and typical values
are 200, 556, 800 or 1,600 rows/inch - usually
specified as 200 bits/inch etc.

Although in general principle data recording
on magnetic tape is similar to the recording
of audio or video signals, magnetic tape
equipment for professional computer use has
some special features. The magnetic tape must
have a very uniform coating, since a very
small break (unnoticed in an audio recording)
could cause the loss of several bits, terminat-
ing the loading of a complete program or data
segment. The magnetic pattern established for
computer data is usually 'saturated', that is
the two levels used are maxima for the writing
heads, and 'in-between' levels (which would be
needed for a continuous or analogue audio
signal) are absent.

The mechanical constraints of magnetic tape
drives mean that it is impossible to start
and stop the tape fast enough to write (or
read) one or just a few 'records' or 'blocks',

each perhaps 256 or 512 bytes in length.
'Interrecord gaps' are established to allow
the tape to come up to speed before writing
(or reading) a record, and to decelerate
afterwards. Long records are sometimes used,
particularly with low cost tape systems based
on audio equipment, but professional systems
generally break programs and data up into a
'file' of equal size short records, with
'start of file' and 'end of file' markers.
Tape movements, including fast forward and
rewind, are under computer control. It is
important that the format (file, record and
interrecord arrangements) of a tape recorded
on another system be known precisely by the
intending user so that it can be correctly
read.

For 7 or 9 bit characters, up to about 45
million characters could in theory be stored
on a single tape. In practice the need for
interrecord gaps reduces this value, but
several tens of millions of characters is a
common capacity. Reading and writing speeds
are in the range 20,000 characters/sec. to
160,000 characters/sec. Access time is
governed by the location of the data on the
tape, so that reel-to-reel units are best
suited to very large volumes of sequential
data.

If a record of data is to be modified, it is
read to computer memory, amended and rewritten
- often to another tape. Error checks on
the recorded data are carried out during the
writing operation.

Cassette Systems

The familiar Philips type audio cassette was
pressed into service as a digital storage
medium, using audio quality tape drives, in
the late 1960's. Reliability was not good
but since then digital drive units, and
cassette tape made to a high standard of
consistency and suitable for saturated
recording have become available. These
systems, usually in pairs to allow for data
manipulation and tape copying, are popular
for their economy and convenience, and have
often been used as alternatives to paper
tape equipment, and in key-to-tape data preparation systems.

The digital cassette package contains two
reels, each driven by a toothed hub, and can
hold 200 to 300 feet of 0.15" tape. The data
bits are recorded in series along the tape,
in a format similar to the asynchronous ASCII
data signal. Like an audio cassette, the
digital cassette tape has two tracks. Recording densities used are in the range 400 -
1600 bits/inch and read/write speeds of 2 -
40 inches/sec. are common. At 800 bits/inch,
a single track capacity is approximately
240,000 characters - the exact figure depends
on the tape format, including block lengths
and gaps. Data is transferred at typically
1,000 characters/second (10 inches/second
tape speed).

Domestic Tape Recorders as Data Storage Units

In recent years, domestic cassette tape
recorders, particularly portable types, have
been extensively used as inexpensive data
storage peripherals for microcomputers. Their
use is confined (usually) to program storage
and retrieval, and access time is quite slow,
often tens of seconds. A modified version of
a domestic cassette recorder is used in the

Commodore Pet. A widely adopted 'standard'
for data storage on cassette is the use of
two audio frequencies (in the range 1 - 2kHz)
to represent the binary values. This non-
saturated technique is effectively converting
digital data into audio signals. Data transfer rate is usually 300 Baud. (30 characters
per second.)

Tape Cartridges

Cartridges use ¼" wide tape, but differ from
their audio tape counterparts. Two arrangements are in use, one using a two track
endless loop on one reel, the other using a
four track 300 foot length on two reels in
the same plane (the 3M type). The 3M cartridge has the better performance, with
storage of 2 million characters/tape, and a
transfer rate of up to 5,000 characters/
second (at 25 inches/second tape speed).

Like the reel-to-reel and cassette systems,
cartridge access times depend on the location
of the required data on the tape. However,
average access times for cartridge and cassette
are similarly in the range 10 to 20 seconds.

Cartridge units have found use as paper tape
equipment replacements, and compete directly
with cassette systems. Unlike cassettes,
digital cartridges were originally developed
specifically for computer applications.

One major disadvantage of all magnetic tape
systems is the restriction on data access,
which is manifested by the need to initiate
considerable 'fast forward' and 'rewind'
operations to access inconveniently located
information.

Magnetic Tape Use

Generally, magnetic tape for small computer
systems is used for high volume, long term,
economic data storage.

Magnetic Disc Peripherals

Just as a long playing record allows the
immediate selection of an individual track,
whereas getting to a particular point on an
audio tape requires winding forward or back,
so a digital magnetic disc provides much more
rapid data access than a tape peripheral.
The magnetic disc has a magnetisable surface
and data is recorded along concentric tracks,
at a density of 2,000 bits per inch or more.
The disc is rotated at a high speed which is
accurately controlled. Access to each track
of the disc is obtained either by an array of
fixed read/write heads, or by the movement of
a single head radially across the surface
(Fig. 6.5.)

All disc units include provision for error
checking.

Fixed-Head Discs

The disc is mounted on a drive shaft, and is
rotated at a high speed (usually about 3000
revolutions/minute) which is accurately controlled. 128 or more circular data tracks
(using both surfaces) have a fixed read-write
head each, which 'flies' a fraction of a
thousandth of an inch from the disc surface.
(Actuators ensure that the heads do not
touch the surface when the disc is stationary,
starting or slowing down). Data is recorded
on each track in bit serial form.

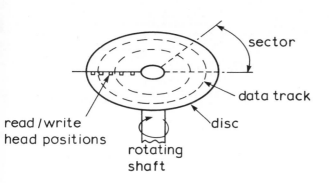

Fig. 6.5. Magnetic disc

This arrangement gives very rapid data transfer, typically about 10 microseconds per
character for continuous transfers. The data
words are recorded in records, each record
occupying a sector of a track. Up to several
thousand data words (or bytes) are contained
on each track. A single disc can contain one
million or more bytes, depending on the size
of the disc and the bit recording density.

To access data, the computer must select the
track and sector, and provide for the transfer of the stored data, in bit parallel (eg,
8 bits at a time) to memory. Direct memory
access (that is, not via the CPU) is normally
used, to avail of the rapid data transfers
possible. Access time depends on the location
of the required data on the disc, but a
typical average delay or 'latency' is about
10 milliseconds. Access time can in fact
range from ¼ millisecond to more than 30
milliseconds.

More than one disc may be mounted on a single
drive. The fixed head disc provides very
rapid data access (compared to tape systems),
and is very reliable. It is an expensive
system, and has been used only rarely with
small computers.

Moving-Head Discs

In this system, each disc has a single read-
write head, which has to be accurately positioned to read or write the required data.
Because the head can completely retract, the
disc itself is sometimes removable, and a
popular type of unit is the exchangeable disc
cartridge system. The disc is contained in a
holder, and the head accesses through an
aperture in the cover. Individual disc
cartridges can be allocated to individual users
or purposes (eg, program libraries, data files).

In general these units are of larger capacity
per disc, and slower access, than fixed head
discs.

Data is arranged in bit serial form on tracks,
which are divided into sectors. A single disc
can accommodate several million bytes (eg, 10
million characters). Data transfer rate can be
as fast as 10 microseconds per byte but access
time can range from 15 milliseconds (track to
track) to over 100 milliseconds. 'Average'
access time is about 50 milliseconds. Sometimes two drives are mounted in the same unit,
with one removable cartridge and one fixed
disc (although with movable heads on both).

In a computer system, the disc subsystem consists of a disc interface or 'controller',
and one or more disc drives. The program
interacts with the controller, which governs
all the discs, but communicates with only one
at a time. Direct memory access is normally
used.

Advances continue to be made in disc technology,
for example bit densities of over 6,000 per
inch are now in use. Many exchangeable disc
peripheral systems have been produced for use
with small computer systems. In general they
provide the largest available amount of backing
store with 'fast' random access, and are
categorised as medium term mass storage systems.

Flexible Disc Cartridge ('Floppy Disc') Units

The requirement for substantial, reasonably
fast access, medium term backing store at an
economic cost - a common small computer system
requirement - has been satisfied to a considerable degree by the advent of the 'floppy disc'.

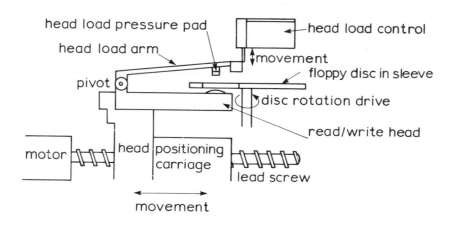

Fig. 6.6. Floppy disc drive principles

This form of magnetic disc was developed and made available by IBM in the early 1970s. Since then many manufacturers have produced drive units, and the floppy disc has been established as a very cost effective backing store peripheral for small computers.

The floppy disc itself is a flexible Mylar (like magnetic tape material) disc, coated with magnetic oxide, and 7¾ inches in diameter. The disc is enclosed in an 8 inch square plastic sleeve and is kept in the sleeve at all times; the (movable) read/write head accesses the disc through a radial slot. A central hole is for the drive spindle. The floppy disc is rotated by the drive at 360 rev/min., while the plastic sleeve remains stationary. The read/write head is actually in contact with the disc, but developments of disc materials and head technology have made possible drive service lives of more than five years. This arrangement is something of a mechanical marvel, but the technology is now well proven.

Figure 6.6. (previous page) is a schematic of a floppy disc drive.

Most floppy disc units conform to the same general specification, with some variation possible in the format of data used. An example specification is:-

Disc Capacity (recorded one side only):	242,944 8 bit bytes, nominally 250K bytes
Data Transfer Rate:	30K bytes per second
Data Tracks:	77 (73 used) (48 tracks per inch)
Sectors per Track:	26
Bytes per Sector:	128 (3,268 bits per inch)
Average Rotational Latency (between Sector accesses):	83 milliseconds
Maximum Latency:	approx. 0.5 seconds
Head movement time per track:	6 milliseconds
Start/Stop Time (Disc load/unload):	2 seconds
Disc life:	typically 2.5 million data accesses (head loaded passes)
Read Error Rate:	Better than 1 in 10^9 bits.

Dual drive units are often used, and complete drive, controller and interface systems can be specified for most small computers. In general terms, floppy disc system costs are comparable with digital cassette and cartridge units, with much faster access (eg, floppy disc total access time of approximately ½ second; cassette total access time of 30 secs.)

Floppy discs may be 'hard' or 'soft' sectored. Hard sectored discs have coding holes (detected photoelectrically) at the beginning of every sector. The more popular soft sectored discs have only one coding hole to mark the first sector; the data read from the disc identifies the sector, and such discs require sector identification codes to be written before use.

The Mini-Floppy Disc

The mini-floppy has been developed specifically for microcomputer systems. Its principles of operation are identical to those of the 'full size' floppy, but the mini floppy disc is approximately 5¼ inches in diameter and stores about 110,000 bytes (single side). Transfer rate is about 15K bytes/second and access time is comparable with the full size version. 35 tracks are used, and 'double density' types have a 220K Byte capacity. The mini-floppy has made it possible for microcomputer systems to provide computing performance comparable with earlier minicomputer systems at a fraction of the cost. It is usually desirable to have a double disc drive unit, so that discs can be copied.

The 'Winchester' Hard Disc

This 'hard disc' drive system is more expensive (by a factor of about 10) than the mini-floppy drive, but provides about 100 times the storage volume and 10 times faster access. The technology is based on solid, fixed magnetic discs, with two double sided discs each about the size of a full size floppy disc (approximately 8 inches). One side of one disc is used for head positioning (by 'reading' its location) and the other three together hold almost 10 Megabytes (10 million characters). This is equivalent to about 50,000 customer names and addresses (for example in a business system), or 1/6 of the Encylopaedia Britannica! The disc system is in a sealed enclosure (to exclude dust) and discs are therefore not interchangeable. A mini (5¼ inch) version of the Winchester drive can store $6^1/_3$ megabytes.

Bubble Memory

This technology has been developed to compete with both semiconductor and magnetic memory. It provides high capacity non-volatile storage, with information held as magnetically oriented domains - magnetic bubbles - in a sheet of material. A rotating magnetic field sets up a large shift register type memory. Commercially available systems are based on gadelinium-gallium-garnet material, with 92K bits capacity in a 14 pin dual-in-line integrated circuit size. Data transfer rate is up to 100K bits/second, and access is sequential (not random access), so that the worst access delay is about one second. An advantage of the bubble memory is that the packages can be mounted like RAM or ROM chips on the microcomputer board.

6.4. SPECIAL-PURPOSE PERIPHERALS

A human can use a keyboard to key in or prepare tapes or discs for data input to a computer and can read, interpret and where necessary act on a print out or display. The human is thus acting as in intermediary between the data source and the computer, and between the computer and any ultimate data destination. If the data rates and volumes can be handled conveniently by a human (eg, the processing of financial data generated in an office), this technique is quite acceptable, and may be the only practical method. If, however, the data rate is high, or the volume of data is large, a human may not cope - indeed where the data is produced in a hostile environment the data acquisition and the necessary action specified by the computation may be impractical or dangerous for a human.

Many examples of this situation occur in industrial or laboratory environments, where the information to be processed is produced by measuring equipment or transducers, and where the result of computation may be a requirement to set levers, turn valves or move heavy objects. Especially where the input information or data is already in electrical form, it is certainly unnecessary and potentially wasteful and error-prone to involve a human in the data inputting process.

In some circumstances input data is available in a digitised form, for example as a decimal counter value. In others a transducer electrical voltage must be converted into a form suitable for the computer. This task is performed by an analogue-to-digital converter. The complementary action is the conversion of computer output to analog values for control or recording purposes - that is digital-to-analogue conversion. A domestic application involving such conversions is for human operated controls used in electronic (television and computer) games.

Analogue-to-Digital Conversion (A-D)

The principal parameters of interest are conversion rate (number of translations of analogue quantity into digital bytes per second), and precision, which is directly related to the number of bits used to specify a value. Precision must take into account the available word length in the computer - if the value is to be held as one word in a 12 bit/word minicomputer, there is little merit in initially producing a 15 bit conversion. For example, a 10 bit conversion gives a digitised value accurate to 1 in 10^3, or 0.1%.

In general, the higher the precision (more bits per conversion), the slower the conversion rate. The simplest analogue-to-digital converters are the digital panel meter (DPM) or digital voltmeter (DVM), often used to display the current value of a parameter. These are slowest, with typical conversion rates of 50 per second, and are often used to monitor transducer outputs (eg, a thermocouple for temperature, or a pressure sensitive device). Precisions of up to 16 bits are available.

Many types and forms of A-D converter exist, ranging from small encapsulated modules, intended for building into electronic data acquisition systems, to free-standing units with extensive multiplexing capability. Multiplexing makes possible the conversion of many analogue signals, by switching each in turn to the converter input. 'Standard' input voltage ranges for A-D converters are ±1 V and ±10 V.

Expensive A-D converters can give 16-bit accuracy at several hundred thousand conversions per second, but for most industrial and laboratory applications using small computers, 8 to 10 bit accuracy, at conversion rates of 400 to 20,000 per second, is adequate. A practical limit on usable conversion rate is that imposed by the input data transfer rate to the computer. For a 16-bit minicomputer this could be about 200,000 conversions/second.

In specifying a computer system to be used with analogue sources, provision must be made

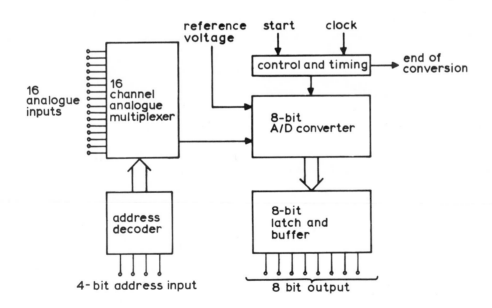

Fig. 6.7. One-chip data acquisition system

for A-D conversion. Some computer suppliers can provide multiplexing A-D converters, and interface modules, together with suitable software. This approach ensures compatibility between the component units, but of course can be more expensive than interfacing standard A-D equipment.

MOS based 'one-chip' data acquisition modules are very suitable for use with microcomputers.

Fig. 6.7. (previous page) is a schematic of a 16 channel module, which has an A-D conversion time of 100 microseconds for each channel. Channel selection is accomplished by providing the appropriate 4-bit address input to the multiplexer. The 8-bit output is compatible with PIA inputs.

Generally it is preferable if A-D conversion can take place at the signal source, as digital data transmission is less error-prone (due to noise and interference) than analogue transmission. For economy, and where high accuracy is not essential, A-D conversion can take place at the computer location, perhaps for several signals. An example of this is the arrangement for a joystick - a control stick with X and Y axes of control, using two potentiometers connected to a gimbal, and widely used for computer 'combat' games.

Digital-to-Analogue conversion (D-A)

Data words transferred from memory or accumulator via I/O may be converted to analogue quantities by a digital-to-analogue converter. Its function is to generate voltages corresponding to each bit (ie, proportional to 2^0, 2^1, 2^2, etc., for binary 'ones') and summing them. The number of data bits used as input determines the number of levels in the D-A output voltage - eg, 10 bits give 1024 levels. In addition to number of bits, 'settling time' is an important parameter - the time for the analogue output to settle to a value within the least significant bit range of the true value.

D-A converters are simpler, cheaper and usually faster than A-D equipment - they are often contained in a single integrated circuit package.

Direct Digital Inputs and Outputs

The individual bit lines of an I/O - a PIA, for example - can of course be used to transfer binary levels. In an 8-bit system up to 8 individual two-level states, for example the condition of on-off switches, can be simultaneously sensed. Likewise, the 8 output bit lines can activate (via relays for example) up to 8 individual valves, controls and lamps.

Special relay interfaces are often available, to provide for computer control of (for example) small motors or other external circuits and systems.

6.5.   LSI SPECIAL INTERFACE COMPONENTS

We have already encountered the PIA - the microcomputer 'general purpose' I/O device. With the growth of peripherals designed for use with small computer systems, many special purpose LSI interface chips have been developed, to make the connection of peripherals to small computers as easy as possible. Two important examples are the

Serial Interface Chip for V24/RS232C connections, and floppy disc controller (FDC). There are many others, and of course modern peripherals commonly utilise specialised LSI components internally, for example cathode ray tube (CRT) controllers used in VDUs. However the computer user is most likely to encounter a VDU as an ASCII serial I/O peripheral and we will briefly review the characteristics of serial interface chips which could be used as interface devices. A summary of FDC features is included in this section because of the importance of floppy disc drives.

Serial Interface Chips

Many peripherals require serial data I/O and to expedite interfacing to a microcomputer, serial interface chips are available. These include the UART (Universal Asynchronous Receiver/Transmitter) which predates the microprocessor in fact, having been widely used in earlier computer interfaces.

The MOS/LSI UART is in a 40-pin Dual-in-Line package. It has separate transmit and receive sections, each providing shift registers for storage of the byte currently being transmitted (or received) bit by bit, and for holding the next byte in line. The key feature of the UART is the use of shift registers which can accept data in bit parallel and output it in bit serial, and vice versa. The user must make external logic level connections to the UART to select the number of start and stop bits and the parity conditions to be used. For connection to a microcomputer, a separate address decoding circuit is needed so that the microprocessor can treat the UART as a memory location, and the microprocessor control signals must be interpreted properly, and some circuitry is needed for this.

In contrast to the UART's general computer and data transmission usage, the ACIA (Asynchronous Communication Interface Adapter) is very much a microcomputer I/O chip, and is one of a microprocessor chip family. For example the 6850 is a popular ACIA and is one of the 6800 microprocessor chip set. Fig. 6.8. shows the features of the device.

The ACIA behaves rather like a PIA in that it appears to the microcomputer and to the programmer as registers (4) located at two addresses in memory. The data registers for transmit and receive are at one address (for write and read operations), while the control and status registers share the other address. The device must be initialised by a program when the microcomputer is turned on. This involves a reset word for the control register (bits D0 and D1 at logic 1), followed by a program word which determines the ASCII character format (number of start and stop bits, parity arrangement and transmit/receive clock rate). These parameters are determined by the peripheral connected to the V24/RS232C serial transmit and receive lines.

To transmit data, the status register is first read to establish if the holding register for transmit data (transmit data register) is empty. If it is (as indicated by the status bit), the data write to the register can take place, and the microcomputer can continue with its program while the ACIA outputs the character bits (plus start, parity and stop) in serial form. If the status bit is not set

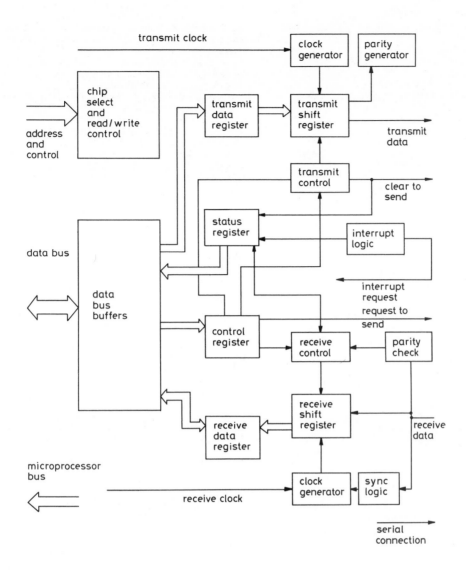

Fig. 6.8.   The 6850 ACIA

(indicating transmit data register not empty) the microcomputer must delay its write operation, preferably doing something useful in the meantime (until the ACIA is ready).

To receive data, the status bit of interest is 'receive data register full'. The ACIA can generate an interrupt request to the microprocessor, and error conditions, for example parity check failure can be monitored by the program if required. Other control/ status bits relate to V24/RS232C line conditions, particularly those for data transmission over long connections including modulated procedures for telephone lines.

Other ACIA chips are available for other microprocessor families, including 16 bit word length versions. Examples are the 8251 for the Intel 8080 series and the TMS9902 for Texas Instruments' 9900 series.

Synchronous interface chips are known as USRTs (Universal Synchronous Receiver/ Transmitter) and an example is the 6852.

If serial data transmission over telephone lines to V24/RS232C protocol is to be adopted, the 6850 described above can connect directly to a modem (modulator/ demodulator) which converts binary serial

data to audio frequency shift keyed (FSK) signals. And as we might expect, such modems are available as LSI chips. Since the outputs are analogue and must connect to public telephone lines, separate filter and voltage protection components must be added to complete the connection.

One-chip Controllers

Many peripherals require control inputs as well as data connections, and LSI interface components have been developed as controllers for floppy disc and tape cassette drives, cathode ray tube displays and external systems transferring information via direct memory access (DMA). Of this class of interface component, the floppy disc controller (FDC) is most likely to be encountered by the small computer user. FDCs specifically designed for each major microprocessor family are available, and DMA or program controlled transfers (using PIAs) may be used. 'Stand alone' FDCs can be interfaced to practically any microprocessor, with PIA chips.

The following FDC functions are normally standard:

1.   Track-to-track stepping of the floppy disc read/write head, and verification of

track identity.

2. Soft-sector timing generation, automatic sector searching and sector identity verification.

3. Read and write control for single and multiple records, up to complete track read or write.

4. Programmable control of track to track stepping time, head settling time, head engage time, DMA or program transfers.

5. Error checking, by monitoring of the cyclic redundancy check (CRC) bits appended to each record.

Examples of FDCs are the 6843 for use with the 6800 microprocessor and the UPD372 for the 8080. Normally the appropriate FDC will be built into a microcomputer system with floppy disc peripherals, or will be available for 'plugging in' when floppy discs are added. Typical FDCs have 15 to 20 connections to the microprocessor data and control buses, and a similar number of connections to the floppy disc drive. FDCs can interface to 'full size' and mini-floppies, and some can control up to four disc drives simultaneously, usually with read/write on one drive while track seeking on the others.

In addition to the functional circuits, the FDC contains several registers - typically up to 16. Some registers are used for parallel to serial and serial to parallel conversions, while others - perhaps 12 - are programmer accessible. These latter include data in (read) and data out (write), current track and sector address, and disc drive status. Complete monitoring of the disc drive is thus possible. The set-up register is user programmable and is initialised at the same time as PIAs (and ACIAs) during power up of the system. It holds data particular to the disc drive in use, for example the head settling time. The command register holds the instruction (usually 8 bits) being executed. The available set of commands includes track seeks, single and multiple sector read/write and status read (including error check). The FDC has therefore the characteristic of a microprocessor in that instructions loaded into the command register (analogous to the microprocessor instruction register) are interpreted and executed, performing quite complex disc operations that would otherwise require extensive software or hardware.

As more powerful and sophisticated peripheral equipment becomes available, suitable LSI controller chips will be developed for them. Specialised LSI components are also used to link microcomputers to industry-standard and international standard interface buses.

6.6. STANDARD INTERFACING BUSES

The problem of incompatibility between peripheral equipment from one manufacturer and computer equipment from another had reached serious proportions even before microcomputers arrived. It was not unusual for the cost of interfacing (including software) to exceed the cost of the minicomputer in for example a specialist instrumentation or industrial application. Further the owner of two or more different computers had many difficulties in ensuring that his peripherals could be used with any of these machines. In extreme cases, each computer-peripheral combination required a unique interface with appropriate software, so that A computers and B peripherals necessitated AxB interfaces for complete interchangeability. For three computers and six peripherals this would mean 18 separate interfaces! One way of trying to avoid this situation was to acquire all computers and peripherals from a single manufacturer, who had his own interfacing standard Such an approach could be restrictive and expensive, and so attempts were made to establish a general interface bus standard. This meant that each computer and each piece of peripheral equipment could have an interface to the standard bus. Then A computers and B peripherals would need A+B interfaces to ensure complete interchangeability, our example of three computers and six peripherals thus requiring only 9 separate interfaces.

The V24/RS232C serial interface standard, although widely used, is not a serious contender for such a general role. In particular the standard is defined as having a maximum transfer rate of 20,000 bits per second (normally 19,600 Baud in practice), and parallel data transfers are preferred for the higher rates needed by for example floppy disc and tape drives. The internationally accepted CAMAC interfacing standard had its origins in European nuclear instrumentation systems using minicomputers, and has all the required features. The CAMAC standard is very well defined (the American equivalent definition is IEEE-583), encompassing the specification of physical mounting arrangements and power supplies as well as parallel and serial input/output. CAMAC major features are:

1. 24 read and 24 write parallel lines - the 'dataway'.

2. 3 control lines - initialise, inhibit and clear, for control of devices connected to the bus.

3. 5 command lines, defining possible functions including read, write and status transfers.

4. 2 Timing (handshake) lines.

5. Data transfer rate up to 1 million 24 bit words (eg, 3 million 8 bit bytes) per second.

6. Separate 'request service' lines, one for each device in the system. There may be up to 24 devices for each 'controller' which is usually a minicomputer.

The devices in a CAMAC system may be peripherals, items of instrumentation such as counters and A/D converters, or microprocessor systems. Hundreds of CAMAC interface types, many microprocessor based, are now manufactured, and the standard is deservedly popular worldwide in industrial and laboratory environments. It has a major disadvantage for today's small computer user, however - its cost. While CAMAC has been and is cost justified in many professional application areas, the fact remains that the cost of a CAMAC interfacing system is very high relative to microcomputers and small computer peripherals.

The CAMAC philosophy is very sound, and the basic principles have been adopted, in a form appropriate to today's microprocessor based systems, in the IEEE-488 bus standard. This standard was pioneered by Hewlett-Packard as the HPIB (Interface Bus) and is now also known as the GPIB (General Purpose Interface Bus). It is probably the most generally useful inter-facing standard for small computers, and has the advantages of a formal definition and 'official approval'. It is therefore a 'proclaimed' standard, in contrast to de facto standards that are widely used. Examples of de facto standards are the S-100 bus (originally for 8080 systems) and the SS50 bus (designed for the 6800). Of course any popular microcomputer I/O structure is a potential de facto standard. The Apple, Radio Shack TRS-80 and DEC LSI-11 I/O buses are examples. The Commodore Pet microcomputer uses IEEE-488.

In the remainder of this section we will review the characteristics of IEEE-488, and discuss S-100 and SS50 features. The V24/RS232C serial standard can be very useful for many interfacing applications not requiring high data transfer rate and so further details of this standard are provided.

IEEE-488 Bus (GPlB)

This increasingly popular standard is indeed general purpose, in that it is independent of computer type. In fact it is not limited to computer systems, and instruments (digital voltmeters and signal generators for example) can use it to link to each other or to dis-plays and recorders. Its structure is very suitable for microcomputer interfacing, with eight bidirectional data lines to carry data plus device address and device command infor-mation, three byte transfer control lines, and five general control lines (Fig. 6.9.).

The bus can operate at up to one million byte transfers per second, with up to 15 data sources or destinations (devices) in a basic configuration. Expansion units which occupy only one device location, but which can interface a number of instruments or peri-pherals to the bus, are available.

As indicated in Fig. 6.9., devices attached to the bus can perform one or more of the following functions: control, 'talk' (that is, output data), and 'listen' (accept data).

A microcomputer is commonly the controller, capable of talking and listening as well. A digital voltmeter may be a talker and a listener, accepting range or conversion rate information and sending back results. A signal or function generator may be a listener only, and another example of a listener is a data display system. A keyboard, a paper tape reader and a digital counter are all examples of talkers.

Management of the system is provided by the general control lines:

ATTENTION from the controller indicates that the data lines carry data or a seven bit device command or device address. (In the latter case, of the data lines DIO1-8, DIO8 is not used, and DIO6 and DIO7 indicate the intended function of DIO1 to 5.)

INTERFACE CLEAR is a general reset.

SERVICE REQUEST indicates that a device needs attention.

REMOTE ENABLE sets a device to remote control.

END-OR-IDENTIFY usually indicates the com-pletion of a data transfer, but is also used in device polling.

Validation of data transfers uses the three byte transfer control lines:

DATA VALID signals that a talker has placed data on DIO1 to 8.

NOT READY FOR DATA. When all listener devices release this line, DATA VALID can be signalled by the active talker.

NOT DATA ACCEPTED is signalled while listeners are accepting data. When released by all listeners, the active talker can put new data on the lines.

These three lines implement the data transfer handshaking protocol (patented by Hewlett-Packard).

To connect a microcomputer as a controller, perhaps to implement an instrumentation or automatic test system with measurement devices as peripherals, quite an amount of buffering, decoding and temporary data storage is

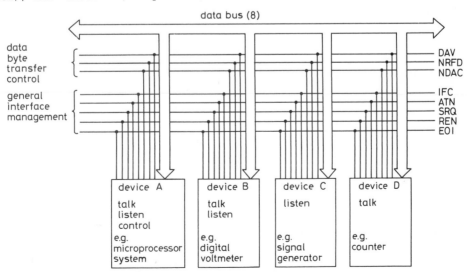

Fig. 6.9. IEEE-488 Bus (GPlB)

necessary. This is provided by current LSI chips, notably the 68488 for the 6800 family, the 8921 for 8080 and related systems, and the Texas Instruments TMS9914. New chips, including microprocessor-independent types, continue to appear.

The byte transfer rate limit of one Megabyte per second is possible only if all the devices in a system, including the controller and its interface chip, can operate at that speed.

The Commodore PET microcomputer has a built-in IEEE-488 interface and is widely used as a controller. The programming convenience and computation power of the BASIC language is a valuable feature of this approach. Over 1,000 products, world wide, are now IEEE-488 compatible.

The standard is not intended for long inter-connections, and peripheral devices in a system using the bus will be kept quite close together with maximum cable lengths of a few metres.

S-100 Bus

Unlike the IEEE-488, the S-100 bus has had no 'official' standing, but emerged as a very popular de facto standard with the rapid growth of personal computers. It is in many ways an 8080 system bus extension, but has been used with adapting circuitry in 6800, 6502, Z80 and other microprocessor systems. In the early days, S-100 definition was poor, but the specification has become much more precise and the bus may acquire the status of an official standard (that is, approved by the professional bodies).

The original purpose of S-100 was the con-figuring of microcomputer systems - micropro-cessor and memory boards, I/O boards, floppy disc and cathode ray tube controllers. There are now available many hundreds of S-100 compatible boards, for many applications and peripherals, even including speech synthesis and recognition for direct computer voice input/output. The standard board has defined dimensions and occupies a 100 pin edge connector (50 pins each side). The bus supplies unregulated voltages (+8V, +16V, -16V and ground) to the boards. Onboard regulators reduce these levels to +5V, +12V and -12V as required. The large number of connections betrays the early 8080 origins of the bus, with no fewer than 39 control lines - many more than are now needed. The bus provides:

8 data in, 8 data out lines (sometimes connected together for a bi-directional data bus)

16 address lines (normal buffered micro-processor address bus)

3 power supply lines (+8V, +16V, -16V unregulated)

2 signal and power ground lines

8 vectored interrupt lines

39 control lines (only a few are needed to implement a data transfer)

Other available lines are unused and not specified.

The S-100 bus is here to stay. Care is needed in its use, particularly when non-8080 based systems are involved. Typically all the boards in an S-100 System are mounted close together in edge connectors attached to a motherboard, within a shielded enclosure.

SS-50 Bus

This bus was developed for 6800 systems, and readily supports 6502 processors as well. The name refers to the 50 line connection arrangement for processor and memory boards. Included are the 6800 (and 6502) 8 bit data bus, the 16 bit address bus, 3 unregulated voltage supplies (for on board +5V, +12V and -12V), 3 signal and power ground lines, 9 timing and control lines, 2 interrupt lines and 5 Baud rate clock frequencies. These last are very useful for serial device inter-facing, for example to visual display units and printers. In practice, interfacing to SS-50 is nearly identical to interfacing to a 6800 system bus.

A feature of SS-50 is that a subset of lines, designated SS-30, is used for peripheral interface cards. Each SS-30 board is without the 16 address lines, and instead has a single I/O control line, decoded on the bus motherboard.

Microcomputer Manufacturers' Buses

The IEEE-488, S-100 and SS-50 buses can be used by many different processors and com-puters. A microcomputer system manufacturer can of course define his own I/O bus, and many have done so. Examples are the Apple II, TRS-80 and LSI-11 bus structures. It is often cost effective to purchase peripherals with interfaces specially designed for the computer in question, rather than to attempt to adopt 'standard bus' interfacing. In general, if more than one or two computer types are to be used and interchangeability of peripherals is required, adoption of a standard bus is to be recommended. Users with single computers, or who plan to keep their different computer systems quite separate (and not to change their minds later) can often obtain directly compatible peri-pherals with interfaces for the popular small computers.

The LSI-11 bus is derived from the DEC PDP-11 Unibus, but with fewer lines. It uses asynchronous 16 bit data transfers. The Apple II has a 50 pin I/O for expansion which closely resembles the 6502 bus driving it. The TRS-80 has a 40 pin I/O and features refresh, row and column select lines for external dynamic RAM memory.

Communication Standards

All of the parallel bus structures for micro-computers described above are severely limited in the length of connection which can be driven. This is not a problem where a system is to be operated on a desk or bench top, but it can present difficulties when a signal source is in another room or building, or when output, for example a 'slave' visual display unit, is required at another location.

If the data transfer rate has to be higher than that available from serial techniques, bit parallel methods must be used. No standards exist, and so special hardware may

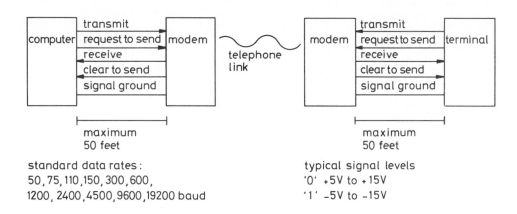

Fig. 6.10 Data Communication link

be needed. General guidelines are to use
separate input and output data buses, and to
keep the timing and control procedures for
handshaking as straightforward as possible.
If possible, non standard approaches to data
I/O should be avoided. Often the most
practical approach, although speed limited,
is asynchronous serial, V24/RS232C I/O.
UARTs or ACIAs may be used to implement the
parallel-to-serial and serial-to-parallel
data conversions.

V24/RS232C Features

This official standard defines the interface
between data terminal equipment and data
communications equipment, using serial binary
data transfer. The data terminal may be for
example a computer or a visual display unit,
teletype or printer/keyboard. The data
communications equipment is normally a modem
(modulator/demodulator) for transforming
binary voltage waveforms to frequency
modulated or phase modulated audio frequency
signals which can be carried efficiently by
public or private service telephone lines.
Since the telephone network, with landline,
cable and satellite links, is worldwide,
data communication can be local, national or
international. Fig. 6.10. shows the arrangement for a data link.

The complete standard defines mechanical as
well as electrical features of the interface,
and a 25 pin connector is specified. Many of
the lines relate to signalling and control
procedures for telephone connections, including automatic answering, so in practice
usually only 5 lines are necessary to implement a connection, as shown in Fig. 6.10.
The 'Request to Send' from the transmitter
and the 'Clear to Send' response from the
receiver can form a handshake protocol,
followed by data transmission. Other control
signals, notably Data Terminal Ready and Data
Set Ready may be used in practical arrangements, depending on the modems. Modems for
telephone connection are usually supplied on
a rental basis by the telephone authority,
and the user must conform to the protocol
defined.

A feature of V24/RS232C is that the distance
between modem and data terminal may be up to

50 feet. This distance can be extended very
considerably by means of suitable line
drivers and receivers - available as integrated
circuits. So if the 'dial-up' capability of
a telephone connection is not needed and if
the user can provide the electrical connection
from computer to remote peripheral, V24/RS232C
standard provides a convenient technique for
long data connections. It is only necessary
to ensure that the standard interface control
lines at each location 'see' the proper conditions for data transfer. This can be accomplished by setting up the necessary logic
levels at for example the 'Clear to Send' pin
at each end of the link. Both computer and
peripheral will then 'think' that its 'Request
to Send' is being continuously acknowledged,
and data can flow in each direction over the
Transmit Data and Receive Data lines which
are crossed over in the link (Fig. 6.11.).

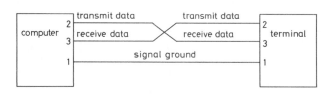

Fig. 6.11. Direct V24/RS232C connection.

This arrangement thus requires only three
lines between computer and peripheral. It
is sometimes referred to as auto-loop back.
In most practical situations, simply
connecting Signal Ground, Transmit Data and
Receive Data lines and leaving all the other
connections 'floating' and not connected to

any other lines or voltage levels, allows data transmission to take place.

So although V24/RS232C may appear intimidating at first sight, its practical application is very straightforward. Some caution is needed to ensure accurate data transfer, by checking that Baud rate, choice of parity and number of stop bits (assuming ASCII code) are selected identically at each end of the link. Note that the standard specification does not define what character code is to be used. The particular voltage levels used in the link must be identical at each end. (The standard allows for the range +3V to +25V for logic O and for the range -3V to -25V for logic 1; voltages of +10V and -10V are typical.) A useful practical feature is that connections are able to withstand open or short circuits between any pins.

Other serial standards are RS422 and RS423, which use differential (balanced) lines for transmit and receive data connections. These standards have a maximum line length of 5,000 feet. V24/RS232C is nevertheless by far the most widely used standard.

Current Loop

Although modern peripherals such as visual display units, printers, magnetic tape and floppy discs have supplanted the once ubiquitous teletype, the current loop de facto standard is still sometimes used. Some peripheral manufacturers provide a current loop I/O as well as V24/RS232C. In general it is preferable to convert current loop to

the voltage standard, usually by means of a switching transistor on the transmit end (to generate the current flow) and an opto-isolator at the receive end to produce V24/RS232C voltage levels in response to current changes in a load resistor. Fig. 6.12. shows the standard four-wire current loop arrangement. The defined current level is normally 20 mA, but 60 mA is sometimes used.

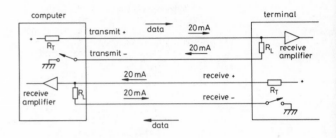

Fig. 6.12.   Current loop connection.

It should be noted that logical 1s and Os are generated by opening and closing the

Fig. 6.13.   ITT 2020 Personal Computer System.

transmit current loop, while 1s and 0s are
sensed by the change in voltage across a
resistor in the current loop, at the receive
end. Earlier equipment including teletypes
used rotating switches and current activated
solenoids for logic level generation and
detection. Nowadays switching transistors
are used.

6.7. COMMENT

The principal aspects of peripheral equipment
and of the hardware and standards adopted for
interfacing to computer systems have been
described. A complete microcomputer system
may comprise the computer itself, with
adequate RAM, ROM and I/O chips, together
with peripherals appropriate for the applications to be handled. A microcomputer configuration with integral keyboard and video
monitor providing visual display unit functions,
floppy disc drive for large volume back-up
program and data storage, and a dot matrix
printer, is shown in Fig. 6.13. Such a system,
typical of personal computer technology,
could be used for business applications or
scientific data processing, for example.
It now remains to be seen how software is
added to small computer systems to really put
them to work.

6.8. REFERENCES

'Microcomputer Interfacing' Bruce A. Artwick,
(Prentice-Hall International 1980).

'Microprocessor Interfacing Techniques'
Austin Lesea, Rodney Zaks, (Sybex Inc. 1977).

'The S-100 and other Microbuses' Elmer C.
Poe and James C. Goodwin, (Howard W. Sams &
Co. Inc. 1979).

Software:
Assemblers, Compilers & Interpreters
Chapter 7

7.1.   INTRODUCTION TO ASSEMBLER

In Chapter I we introduced the concept of a program of instructions - the 'software' - occupying a sequence of stores in the memory of the computer. Each store contained a coded pattern of bits specifying some actions to be carried out by the processor of the computer. The problem we have not yet tackled is how one gets such a large pattern of bits into the memory. We examined in detail a mechanism using switches for getting one or two instructions set up in memory, but it is clearly very difficult to use this method for programs consisting of hundreds and even thousands of instructions.

Each manufacturer of a computer recognized this problem, so very soon a technique emerged to alleviate the programming task. When a new computer was designed the manufacturer would also invent a 'language' in which he felt that the users of the system could describe their problem. He then produced a special program which would translate this language into the binary codes which represented data and instructions on his machine. These languages became known as assembly languages and the translater programs became known as assemblers.

So, armed with an assembler the programmer could write the series of statements in the assembler language, load the assembler into the processor and use it to translate his assembly statements into a machine code program. The assembler would then be deleted from memory and the newly created program loaded. An analogy to this in a non-electronic environment would be to use a metal shaping bit (the assembler) in a power drill (the processor + memory) to form a wood-shaping bit (the program). The metal shaping bit (assembler) is then removed from the drill and the wood shaping bit loaded into the drill. The wood shaping bit can now be used for shaping wood - the original problem.

Later sections of this chapter will deal with other translater programs but for the moment let us concentrate on assembly languages. Although each manufacturer designs his own assembly language, many features are common to all.

7.2.   STATEMENTS

A statement in the assembly language will normally correspond to one instruction in the eventual machine code program (often referred to as the object program) and is therefore constructed of similar fields. We have already seen that an instruction in the computer is located at a certain address and normally has three fields - the function to be performed and the two operands on which to perform this function. A typical assembler statement might look like

           52   ADD   1   93

meaning 'at address 52 of my program I want an instruction which will ADD the number in store 93 to accumulator 1'. Similarly

           53   SUB   1   92

could be interpreted as 'in store 53 of my program I want an instruction which will subtract the number in store 92 from the number in accumulator 1'.

Obviously it is a major advantage to be able to write in a language like this. It is fairly easy to understand because it allows us to refer to stores in the computer by their decimal address, and to functions by an easily remembered (or mnemonic) code, rather than have to construct the individual sections of an instruction as a set of binary digits.

Consider a section of a program which calculates in store 500 an employee's take-home pay. The number of hours he worked is in store 100, his rate per hour is in store 200, his social security payments in store 300 and his income tax in store 400.

51 LOAD 1 100 (Copy No. of hours into Acc. 1)

52 MPY   1 200 (Multiply by rate giving total pay)

53 SUB   1 300 (Subtract social security due)

54 SUB   1 400 (Subtract income tax)

55 STO   1 500 (Store result from Acc. 1 into 500)

Apart from needing to know that LOADING a register means copying from store into a register, and STORING a register means copying the contents of the register into a specified store, it is very easy to follow through the sequence in the above section of program. The comments on each statement to the right of the (bracket help to explain the function of the instruction and most assemblers allow the programmer to make notes like this on his statement.

It is obviously rather a bore to have to write the address of each instruction since these are normally in sequence, so most assemblers allow statements of the form 'SET ADDRESS = 51' to indicate that the instructions which result from the statements which follow are to be loaded into address 51, 52, ... etc. The above section of program would then be written as

```
SET ADDRESS = 51

    LOAD    1    100

    MPY     1    200

    SUB     1    300

    SUB     1    400

    STO     1    500
```

7.3. DIRECTIVES

Note that the statement SET ADDRESS = 51 will not of itself generate any instructions in the final program - it is merely an aid to the programmer to avoid having to write out the address of each of his statements. Such statements are referred to as directives or as non-executable statements. Other examples are:

PROGRAM   this is a directive to the assembler saying that the statements which follow (up to the next directive) are instruction statements.

DATA   specifies that the next set of statements are to be regarded as data and will be in a format slightly different from instruction statements.

ENTRY   indicates that the next statement is to be the first one executed when the program of instructions eventually gets loaded into the store of the computer.

7.4. LABELS

All assemblers allow labels to be used instead of store addresses. This applies whether these labels are attached to stores containing data or instructions. The section of program in 7.2. could therefore be written

```
CALCPAY    LOAD    1    HOURS      (....

           MPY     1    RATE       (....

           SUB     1    SOCSEC

           SUB     1    TAX

           STO     1    TAKEHOME
```

This eases the task of the programmer further, in that he now need not worry about the address of the store which ccntains each of his items of data. Instead, the assembler program ensures that every time he uses the label HOURS the instruction formed will always refer to the same location in store.

The assembler builds up a table of the names that the programmer uses and the addresses which it has assigned to these names. This symbol table can be printed out at the end of the assembly, to assist in finding errors in the program.

7.5. SYNTAX

Although almost any set of alphabetic and numeric characters can be used for labels, there is usually some set of restrictions. As we will see later, some special symbols have to be reserved for introducing the various addressing modes. Similarly, while it might be reasonable to label a store TAX1 or TAX15 or T1 or T15 we cannot use 15 as a label since it would be impossible to distinguish between this and the decimal number 15 which may occur elsewhere in the program. The set of rules which govern how a statement may be written is termed the syntax of the language.

A typical set of syntax rules for statements might read:

1. If an instruction statement is to be labelled, that label must be the first set of characters on the line. The label must start with a letter of the alphabet, must contain only letters and digits and is terminated by a space.

2. The function follows the label (if one is present); it must be one of the function codes known to the assembler (or a macro-name, see section 7.8.), and must not contain spaces.

3. The next field is the accumulator or register field and must be an integer in the range O to 2 (assuming the machine had 3 accumulators).

4. The next field must be either an integer or an expression resulting in an integer or a label. Labels must conform to Rule 1. Indirect and indexed addresses are introduced by * and @ respectively.

5. The comments field (if present) is the last field in any statement. It is introduced by (and this bracket and all characters which follow are completely ignored by the assembler.

7.6. ADDRESSING CONVENTIONS

As we have seen already in chapter 2, computers have different modes of addressing memory. Obviously these modes must be catered for by the assembly language. This is normally done by preceding the operand label by a special symbol which is recognized by the assembler program. For example:

direct

ADD 1 31 (Add the contents of store 31)

indirect

ADD 1 *31 (Add the contents of (the contents of 31)

indexed

ADD 1 @31 (Add the contents of (the contents of the index register + 31) (assuming there is only one index register)

immediate

ADDI 1 31 (Add 31

relative

ADD 1 $ + 31 (Add the contents of (the program counter + 31)

Some modes are catered for by special symbols (indirect, indexed) whereas others (immediate) may be catered for by a separate function code, eg, ADDI.

To avoid having to assign a label to every data store an operand label may be followed by + (or -) followed by an integer expression. Thus if we have 100 employees and the number of hours each worked is stored in 100 consecutive locations we can refer to the first of these as HOURS, the second as HOURS + 1, the third as HOURS + 2, etc.

7.7.   INPUT/OUTPUT

Just as the address section (or address field) of an instruction in the computer is used for device and function codes in I/O instructions so the operand field in an assembler statement is used for a similar purpose.

Typical statements might read

```
DOUT    2    TT1    (print on teletype 1)
DIN     1    TTO    (read from teletype0)
```

The first statement begins the transfer of the eight bit byte in the lower half of accumulator 2 out to teletype number 1 where by electromechanical means it will eventually produce a character printed on the paper. The second statement will prepare teletype 0 to transfer the next character typed on the keyboard (after conversion) into accumulator 1.

(In either case the computer is ready to proceed with the next instruction within a few microseconds, but it will take approximately 100,000 microseconds (0.1 secs) for the data to be transferred if the peripheral is operating at 10 characters per second.)

To determine when the data transfer is complete requires a special statement of the form SPBN - skip the next instruction if the associated peripheral is not busy. So it may require three statements to cater for this type of simple I/O.

```
DOUT    2    TT1    (Begin transferring to TT1)

SPBN         TT1    (Skip next instruction when
                      transfer complete)

JMP          $-1    (Go back to previous instruction
                      (ie, SPBN))
```

Note that the TT1 specified is not a labelled store as in normal instructions, but a symbol which is known to the assembler. From this symbol the assembler will generate the bits defining the appropriate device in the instruction, in the same way as it constructs the bit pattern to represent the address of a memory location in a memory reference instruction.

The following statements use most of the facilities we have discussed so far. The objective is to read a sequence of characters from a teletype into memory at locations LINE, LINE + 1, etc. A maximum of 80 characters will be allowed. A shorter line will be terminated by a CR character. The CR character in ASCII is represented by the same bit pattern as the number 13.

1	DATA		(directive to assemble saying that data statements follow.
2	COUNT	0	(reserve one store; named COUNT; content = 0
3	CR	13	(reserve one store; named CR; content = 13
4	LINE RES	80	(reserve 80 stores; first named LINE; content unknown
5	PROGRAM		(directive to assemble saying that instruction statements follow
6	SETADDRESS = 1000		(in the final program the next instruction will be at address 1000
7	LDIND	-80	(Put -80 in index register
8	NEXT DIN	2 TTO	(start input of character
9	SPBN	TTO	(skip when in
10	JMP	$-1	(go back to previous instruction
11	STO	2 @LINE+80	
12	INC	NEXT	
13	....		

Notes: The instruction resulting from (line 12) is a conditional jump. It means 'add one to the index register; if the contents of the register are not zero go to the instruction labelled NEXT; if the contents are zero, go to the instruction immediately following, ie, (line 13). The statement at (line 7) 'load the index register' sets the index register to -80. So on the first occasion that we reach (line 12) the register will be incremented to -79; this is not zero so we go back to NEXT. This leads us down to (line 12) again when the register will be incremented to -78 and we go back to NEXT again. Eventually after executing the instructions from NEXT to (line 12) 80 times we proceed to (line 13).

Because the instruction at (line 11) uses index addressing, the effect of the instruction is slightly different on each of the 80 occasions it is executed. Let us assume that LINE will eventually be allocated address 920. Then @LINE means 920 + (contents of index register). So the _effect_ of the STO instruction changes with the index register.

```
ie, STO  2  920(-80) + 80  →  STO  2  920

    STO  2  920(-79) + 80  →  STO  2  921

    STO  2  920(-78) + 80  →  STO  2  922

    STO  2  920(-1)  + 80  →  STO  2  999
```

Most assembly languages have increment or decrement statements to allow for processing of tables. (N.B. In the previous discussion it is important to distinguish the assembly phase from the execution phase. The statements from NEXT to line 12 are read once by the assembler. The assembler produces one set of 5 instructions corresponding to these 5 statements. When the assembler has completed translation of the program and is deleted from memory, the object program will be loaded into memory. During execution of the program these five instructions (1001, 1002, 1003, 1004, 1005) will be processed 80 times.)

7.8. MACRO INSTRUCTIONS

The set of three instructions for handling the input from a teletype will occur in the same sequence, wherever input is required in the program. To avoid having to write the same set of statements at different points, some assemblers allow the programmer to assign a name to a group of statements. At any time when it is necessary to use those statements, the programmer need only use the group name which he has assigned. Such a group of statements is referred to as a macro-statement and the name of the group as the macro-name. Some special directive is used to introduce the macro 'prototype', eg,

```
        MACRO   INPUT                   (1)

                DIN   2   TTO           (2)

                SPBN      TTO           (3)

                JMP       $-1           (4)

        ENDMACRO                        (5)
```

This gives the name INPUT to the three statements (2), (3) and (4).

Every time the programmer uses the statement INPUT thereafter, the assembler recognizes that this is the shorthand for the above three statements and will generate them. So the section of program in Section 7.7. could be written as

```
        PROGRAM

        SETADDRESS = 1000

                LDIND - 80

        NEXT INPUT *

                STO   2   @LINE + 80

                INC       NEXT
```

*(This would be expanded to the 3 statements above.)

A further necessary feature of a good macro-assembler is to allow the programmer to specify that a series of statements (with slight modification) is to be produced when he uses a macro-statement. In the macro-statement INPUT which we have defined, the data always comes from TTO and is always loaded into accumulator 2. It may be that at another point in the program we require to take data from teletype 1 or 2 and that we want to transfer it to an alternative accumulator. This can be done by providing parameters to the macro-statement definition.

```
        MACRO       IN, %1, %2
                DIN      %1   %2
                SPBN          %2
                JMP           $-1
        ENDMACRO
```

defines a template with two missing items and these are supplied by the programmer when he uses the macro-statement. Thus

```
        IN,   1,   TT2
```

would generate a set of instructions using the template defined above but replacing %1 by 1 and %2 by TT2, giving

```
        DIN    1    TT2

        SPBN        TT2

        JMP         $-1
```

Similarly, IN, 2, CRO would generate the three statements

```
        DIN    2    CRO

        SPBN        CRO

        JMP         $-1
```

7.9. SUBROUTINES

The function of a subroutine is very similar to that of a macro-statement in that it avoids the programmer having to reproduce similar sets of instructions for similar tasks. It has the added advantage that the pattern of instructions is only produced once in the object program rather than at each point where they are required. A simple analogy is the way that the words of popular songs are written.

1. In a cavern, in a canyon, excavating for a mine

2. Dwelt a miner forty-niner and his daughter Clementine.

3. Oh, my darling, Oh, my darling, Oh, my darling Clementine }Chorus

4. Thou art lost and gone forever dreadful sorry Clementine

5. Drove she ducklings to the water every morning just at nine

6. Hit her foot against a splinter, fell into the foaming brine

   Chorus

7. Light she was and like a feather and her shoes were number nine

8. Salmon boxes without topses . . .

   Chorus

The chorus or subroutine is written down once only at lines 3 and 4. The singer 'processes' the song by singing lines in the order 123456347834 etc. Note that this requires him to remember before going to line 3, the address of the line to which he must return after singing line 4.

All computers have a pair of instructions to carry out this task of 'executing a subroutine and then returning to the next instruction', ie, 'jumping to the chorus and then returning to the next verse'.

Consider a subroutine for zeroizing 80 consecutive stores LINE, LINE+1, ... LINE+79. This would be written typically as

```
CLEAR   LINK

        LDACC   2   O       (Put zero into
                             accumulator 2

        LDIND       -80     (set loop count at
                             80)

        STO     2   @LINE+80 (set (LINE+index+
                             80) = O

        INC         $-1     (increase index by
                             one and go back to
                             previous instruction
                             unless index has
                             reached O

        EXIT    CLEAR        (return to the
                             statement of the
                             main program.
```

The routine would be 'called' when needed in
the program by a statement of the form

```
        CALL    CLEAR
```

Some computers record the link address, (ie,
the address of the instruction immediately
after the CALL) into a blank store reserved
for this purpose at the beginning of the subroutine. The 'exit' instruction points to
this address. Others use an accumulator
register or the stack as we have seen in
Chapter 3.

7.10.   PARAMETER PASSING

Like the macro-statement, the subroutine call
is most useful when the routine can perform
a slightly different function at each CALL.
For example, the CLEAR subroutine above will
clear the 80 stores starting at LINE. It would
be more useful if the number of stores and
the start address could be altered. This is
done by providing these variables as parameters, immediately, after the CALL, eg,

```
CALL    NEWCLEAR        or    CALL    NEWCLEAR

        80                            40

        LINE                          CARD
```

The routine NEWCLEAR will pick up its parameters from the two words immediately succeed-
ing the CALL, using indirect addressing
techniques. For example

```
NEWCLEAR    LINK

            LDACC   2   *NEWCLEAR

            STO     2   COUNT

            LDACC   2   *NEWCLEAR+1

            STO     2   ADDRESS
```

Since the CALL instruction places the link
address (ie, the address of the next memory
cell) in NEWCLEAR, the indirect LDACC loads
the accumulator with the contents of the (contents of NEWCLEAR). In the first case this
places 80 in the accumulator, whereas in the
second case we get 40. Similarly *(NEWCLEAR
+1) is the address of the first word (LINE
or CARD).

When returning from the routine it is necessary
to skip over these two parameters. This can
be achieved by

```
        JMP     *NEWCLEAR+2
```

since *NEWCLEAR gives the content of NEWCLEAR
and this was set equal to the address of
the next memory cell by the CALL instruction.

7.11   LIBRARIES

As well as reducing memory space in the final
object program the subroutine provides a
useful building block for programs. As the
programmer produces programs, certain
sequences of instructions emerge as common
to more than one program. By encapsulating
this set of instructions into a subroutine,
he can then make use of them in his various
programs simply by duplicating the set of
statements once for each program. The
logical extension of this is that he can lend
his subroutines to his colleagues or make
them available to all users of this type of
computer.

Typical examples of subroutines in the
scientific environment are those to produce
the trigonometric functions SIN, COS, TAN,
SINH, COSH, TANH, ARCSIN, etc. Most computer manufacturers provide subroutines to
carry out these and similar functions.

Such a set of subroutines is referred to as
a library of subroutines and can be added to
by the programmer at will. Obviously care
must be taken not to use the same name as
that of the standard routines. The library
of subroutines will be provided on some medium
which can be read by one of the peripherals
attached to the processor.

7.12.   THE LOADER

So far we have been discussing the assembly
program. Usually the complete process of
converting a program from a set of statements
in the assembly language into an executable
binary program in the memory of the computer
is carried out in two phases:

1.   the conversion of statements into
     'relocatable binary' form (by the
     assembler). In relocatable binary all
     addresses referenced are relative to the
     first instruction of the subroutine.

     (When eventually the loader comes to
     load the program or subroutine into
     memory, the absolute address of the
     first instruction is added to all the
     relative addresses.)

2.   the loading of those subroutines from
     the library which have been called (by
     the loader).

7.13.   PRODUCING THE COMPLETE BINARY OBJECT
PROGRAM

On a minimum configuration computer with
only a teletype or tape cassette reader this
can be a slow and involved process. The
sequence of operations is as follows (see
Fig. 7.1.).

A.   Enter the tape containing the assembler
     into the reader and read this into the
     store.

B.   Enter the tape containing the program
     statements as data for the assembler.
     The assembler will process this tape,

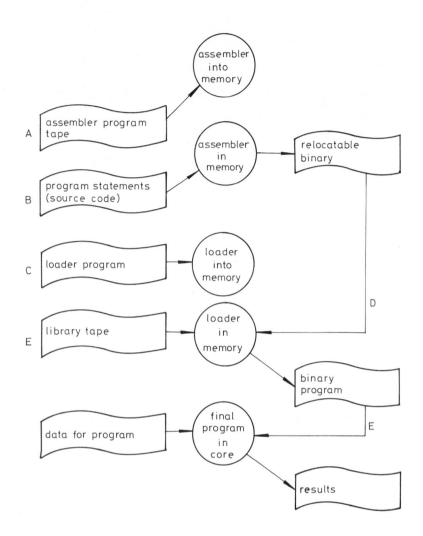

Figure 7.1.   Program Sequence

translating as many of the statements as possible into binary form,   The assembler will produce this partial coding on a tape as it proceeds.

C.   The tape containing the loader program is read into the computer.

D.   The output tape from the assembler is read in under the control of the loader program.

E.   The tape containing the library of sub-routines is read by the loader to yield any subroutines which were called by statements in the program.   The loader produces the final program on tape.

F.   The tape containing the final program is now read into store.   The computer is now under the control of the user's program, which can now 'RUN'.

For a 16 bit/word minicomputer, typical sizes (in words of store) of the assembler and loader are 4K and 0.5K respectively.

7.14.   TWO REAL ASSEMBLY LANGUAGES

We have been discussing those features which are common to most assemblers.   The style of an assembly language is often dictated by the architecture of the computer (for example, whether it has one or more accumulators, if there is a stack and what address modes are available).   We will now look at two _real_ assembly language subroutines.   The subroutines

perform the same function, ie, the conversion of a string of decimal digits into a binary number.   The two machines are a Data General Nova and a Computer Automation Alpha.   These are two of the computers which we examined in Chapter 3.

Our objective is to illustrate the structure and some of the features of real assembly languages, but not to review comprehensively either assembly language.   Each manufacturer provides comprehensive documentation of his own software, and it is usually possible to achieve competence in programming a particular computer by consulting the documentation and assembling and running programs of increasing complexity.   Most manufacturers provide self-teaching material as well as programming courses.

Assembly Language Example 1-Data General Nova

The following subroutine in Nova assembler converts a string of decimal digits into a binary number.   The decimal digits were originally coded in ASCII, using an 8-bit code.   In this example the leading bit is ignored, so that the Nova subroutine deals with 7-bit numbers in the Octal code format shown.   (Reference - 'How to use the Nova Computers'; Data General Corporation 1974, Teletype Code, p E5.)

Decimal	ASCII Hexadecimal (leading bit = 1)	8-bit pattern		7-bit pattern			Octal (NOVA)
0	B0	1011	0000	0	110	000	060
1	B1	1011	0001	0	110	001	061
2	B2	1011	0010	0	110	010	062
3	B3	1011	0011	0	110	011	063
4	B4	1011	0100	0	110	100	064
5	B5	1011	0101	0	110	101	065
6	B6	1011	0110	0	110	110	066
7	B7	1011	0111	0	110	111	067
8	B8	1011	1000	0	111	000	070
9	B9	1011	1001	0	111	001	071

Notes on Subroutine below

1. The 7-bit codes each occupy bit positions (6-0) in a store location. Since the Nova uses 16-bit words, the remaining 9 bits are all 0. Accumulator 2 (AC2) is set (before entering the routine) to contain the address of the most significant digit. Similarly accumulator 0 (AC0) initially contains the number of digits in the decimal number which is to be converted. This value must be stored away in store CDDCT as AC0 is used in the computation.

2. Since the decimal digits are represented by Octal 060, 061, etc., the binary equivalent of a single digit is obtained by subtracting 060_8 from the 7-bit code. For example decimal 7 is held in store as 067_8 and $067_8 - 060_8 = 007_8 \equiv 0000111_2$

3. The conversion is carried out by adding the 'next' digit into AC0, multiplying the accumulator by ten and then adding the next digit and so on. For example, the digits 4, 7, 8, 9 would give rise to the following states of AC0 (expressed as decimal equivalents) -

```
set accumulator to zero   0
add next digit            4
multiply by ten          40
add next digit           47
multiply by ten         470
add next digit          478
multiply by ten        4780
add next digit         4789
```

4. The multiplication by ten is carried out by a series of add and shift instructions (remember that shifting a binary number left one place is equivalent of multiplying by 2, eg, 0001 = 1, 0010 = 2; 0011 = 3, 0110 = 6). So if we have any binary number x and we

```
add it to itself         2x
shift left once          4x
add original number      5x
shift left once         10x
```

we get the desired 10x.

5. On the Nova computer the CALL instruction (see Section 7.10.) uses accumulator 3 to contain the link address. Since we want to use this accumulator during the routine it is necessary to preserve its original value. A store named CDLNK is used for this purpose.

SUBROUTINE

```
; IN NOVA ASSEMBLER
COMMENTS ARE SIGNALLED
BY ;

ZERO:     60       ; octal equivalent of zero
                   ; in 7-bit code

CDLNK:    0        ; will contain return addres

CDDCT:    0        ; will contain count of
                   ; digits still to be
                   ; processed

      STA  3,CDLNK ; copy the link address
                   ; from AC3 into CDLNK

      STA  0,CDDCT ; copy the number of digits
                   ; into CDDCT

      LDA  3,ZERO  ; copy 7-bit code from zero
                   ; into AC3

      SUB  0,0     ; set AC0=zero, ie, subtract
                   ; AC0 from AC0, answer in
                   ; AC0

      JMP  CDB2    ; go to CDB2 (to avoid
                   ; multiply by ten first
                   ; time) the next 3 state-
                   ; ments cause number in AC0
                   ; to be multiplied by 10

CDB1: MOV  0,1     ; copy 'number so far' into
                   ; AC1 (AC0=x, AC1=x)

      ADDZL 0,0    ; AC0 = (AC0+AC0) *2 ie (x
                   ; +x) *2 ie 4x

      ADDZL 1,0    ; AC0 = (AC0+AC1) *2 ie (4x
                   ; +x) *2 ie 10x
                   ; the next instruction uses
                   ; indexed addressing (AC2
                   ; is the index

CDB2: LDA  1,0,2   ; AC1 - number in store (0+
                   ; contents of AC2) ie, next
                   ; digit
```

```
      SUB  3,1      ; AC1=AC1-AC3 ie convert
                    ; digit from 7-bit code to
                    ; binary

      ADD  1,0      ; ACO=ACO+AC1 add digit to
                    ;'number so far'

      INC  2,2      ; AC2=AC2+1 set pointer to
                    ; next digit

      DSZ  CDDCT    ; subtract 1 from CDDCT,
                    ; skip next instruction if
                    ; zero results

      JMP  CDB1     ; go back to CDB1
                    ; the previous instruction
                    ; will be executed until
                    ; the count of digits to
                    ; be processed reaches
                    ; zero

      LDA  3,CDLNK  ; eventually we get here
                    ; to reset AC3 to the link

      JMP  0,3      ; this is the equivalent
                    ; of the EXIT (see Section
                    ; 7.10).  It means return
                    ; to the address specified
                    ; in accumulator 3.
```

Assembly Language Example 2-Computer Automation Alpha (LSI)
This subroutine converts a string of decimal digits into a binary number, as in the previous example. The Alpha has only one accumulator but the instruction set includes MPY, which is a multiply and add instruction, so that the subroutine becomes much simpler.

To sequence through the successive digits, the IMS instruction is used. This is 'Increment Memory and Skip on Zero'. It is used here to count from -N up to O (to loop N times) where N is the number of decimal digits. Initially N is held in the X-register, and the address of the first decimal digit is held in the A-register (the accumulator).

In this example the decimal digits are coded as 8-bit ASCII characters (BO, B1 etc in hexadecimal) so that the binary equivalents are obtained by subtracting BO.

At the end of the computation, the binary result is in the X-register (assumed less than or equal to 15 bits in length).

The set of subroutine instructions is listed below, with explanatory comments (indicated to the Alpha by * as the first character of the statement).

SUBROUTINE

```
           *A register contains first data
            location

           *X register contains number of
            decimal digits

NAM CDB    *A directive, in this case an
            External Name Definition (to allow
            for external referencing and entry
            to subroutine from another (main)
            program)

CDB ENT    *Causes the assembler to reserve a
            word to be used to hold the return
            (link) address
```

```
      NXR         *Negate count (X register
                   contents)

      STX NEGCT   *Store negative count (-N)
                   in store NEGCT

      STA NXTDD   *Set NXTDD to point to (first)
                   digit

      ZAX         *Zero A and X registers

NEXT  LDA         *NXTDD
                  *set next digit into A register
                   (indirect addressing*)

      SUB ASCII   *converts ASCII to binary

      MPY TEN     *X = X *TEN + A (effect of
                   MPY

      IMS NXTDD   *Add 1 to NXTDD, to point at
                   next digit

      IMS NEGCT   *Add 1 to NEGCT ; (skips next
                   instruction when zero)

      JMP NEXT    *Go back for next digit

      RTN CDB     *Return to main line program
                   using link address in CDB

NEGCT RES 1       *reserves 1 location for
                   NEGCT

NXTDD RES 1       *reserves 1 location for
                   NXTDD

  TEN DATA 10     *reserves 1 location and defines
                   contents

ASCII DATA :BO    *reserves 1 location and defines
                   contents

      END
```

Printed Output from the Assembler

The primary function of the assembler is the translation from source code (the programmer's list of statements) to binary object code. In addition to doing this, the assembler usually produces a 'hard copy' listing (on the teletype, for example) of the assembled program, with locations assigned to instructions and stores.

The assembly listing for the Alpha subroutine of the previous Section is:

```
PAGE 0001
0001              *
0002              *      A REGISTER CONTAINS FIRST
                         DATA LOCATION
0003              *
0004              *      X REGISTER CONTAINS NUM-
                         BER OF DATA POINTS
0005              *
0006                     NAM CDB
0007 0000 0800 CDB       ENT        *causes the
0008 0001 0508           NXR        *assembler to
0009 0002 EA0A           STX NEGCT  *reserve a
0010 0003 9A0A           STA NXTDD  *word
0011 0004 0118           ZAX        *
0012 0005 B308 NEXT      LDA *NXTDD
0013 0006 9209           SUB ASCII
0014              *
0015              *      CONVERTS ASCII TO BINARY
0016              *
0017 0007 1960           MPY TEN    X=X*TEN+A
     0008 000F
0018 0009 DA04           IMS NXTDD
```

```
0019 OOOA DAO2        IMS NEGCT
0020 OOOB F606        JMP NEXT
0021 OOOC F7OC        RTN CDB
0022 OOOD       NEGCT RES 1
0023 OOOE       NXTDD RES 1
0024 OOOF OOOA TEN    DATA 1O
0025 OO1O OOBO ASCII  DATA :BO
0026                  END
OOOO ERRORS
```

Notes

The assembly listing is formatted to identify labels and statements.

The listing is divided into pages of convenient size, and each page is numbered (only one page in this case).

Column 1 of the listing contains the source statement line number in decimal. Note that a single statement may generate more than one line of assembler listing text (eg, the MPY statement).

Column 2 contains the location counter value in hexadecimal - this is the instruction location relative to the starting address of the subroutine. There are no location values associated with comment statements, or with any statement which does not generate a word of storage at load time (eg, NAM CDB). Statements which generate more than one sequential word of storage have a location counter value for each word required.

Column 3 contains the actual program - the assembled data and instructions (in hexadecimal). In general, these data items are stored in the Alpha at load time (step D of Section 7.13.). For example, the code O118 is the assembled machine language for the ZAX instruction.

The END statement is required by the assembler to indicate the last statement of the program.

In this example the assembler found no errors, but if errors had been detected, error messages would have followed the appropriate line.

Programs and Subroutines

As has already been indicated, a subroutine is simply a program which may be used one or more times within another program, or as a programmer's 'building block'. To run a subroutine as a 'free-standing' program, it is only necessary to include appropriate directives in the source coding and remove the CALL and EXIT instructions.

To illustrate this, here is the assembly listing of a self-contained program to perform the task of the previous example subroutine.

To run this program, the starting address (:1OO) is loaded into the PC register (using the console switches) and the minicomputer set to RUN. When the program is completed it will halt (HLT instruction), having processed the data held in the store locations indicated by the initial contents of the A and X registers. So in this case it would first be desirable to make sure (by entering data into memory and the A and X registers) that the appropriate initial conditions exist before running the program.

```
PAGE OOO1
OOO1       *
OOO2       *        A REGISTER CONTAINS FIRST
                    DATA LOCATION
OOO3       *
OOO4       *        X REGISTER CONTAINS NUM-
                    BER OF DATA POINTS
OOO5       *
OOO6 O1OO           ORG  :1OO
OOO7 O1OO O5O8      NXR
OOO8 O1O1 EAOA      STX NEGCT
OOO9 O1O2 9AOA      STA NXTDD
OO1O O1O3 O118      ZAX
OO11 O1O4 B3O8 NEXT LDA  *NXTDD
OO12 O1O5 92O9      SUB  ASCII
OO13       *
OO14       *        CONVERTS ASCII TO BINARY
OO15       *
OO16 O1O6 196O      MPY  TEN  X=X*TEN+A
     O1O7 O1OE
OO17 O1O8 DAO4      IMS  NXTDD
OO18 O1O9 DAO2      IMS  NEGCT
OO19 O1OA F6O6      JMP  NEXT
OO2O O1OB O8OO      HLT
OO21 O1OC     NEGCT RES  1
OO22 O1OD     NXTDD RES  1
OO23 O1OE OOOA TEN  DATA 1O
OO24 O1OF OOBO ASCII DATA:BO
OO25               END
OOOO ERRORS
```

7.15.   COMPILERS AND INTERPRETERS

The assembler program was a significant step forward in the history of computing. It paved the way for the production of much more useful tools. The assembly languages although much easier to use than pure binary coding, suffer from the disadvantage that each manufacturer designs his own language. If however a translater program can be written to translate such a language into binary, why not design a single language which every programmer could learn - the manufacturer could then produce a translater to convert this "standard" language into the binary codes expected by his computer system.

Well the idea caught on but unfortunately various individuals had different ideas about what this standard language should look like. The scientific community were first to attempt the scheme but the Americans and Europeans could not agree so we ended up with two major scientific languages FORTRAN and ALGOL. The commercial community were more successful and only one commercial language has really captured the limelight - COBOL. By far the majority of programs existing today were written in one of these three languages.

Development has not ceased however and over the past twenty years a virtual BABEL of languages has emerged with strange names - APL, PL/1, SNOBOL, LISP, etc. Recently with the advent of small computers especially those termed "home" computers an "easy to learn language" BASIC has emerged. It is widely used - especially by the amateur programmer. Professionals tend to scorn its "get writ quick" capability, because it leads to ragged programming. Their new champion is PASCAL which is very like ALGOL in structure

These different languages have evolved over a number of years and there are now a number of international organizations which are attempting to draw up standards, viz.,

The International Standards Organisation (ISO)
The American National Standards Institute
(ANSI)
The European Computer Manufacturers Association
(ECMA)

It would be impossible to deal at any length
with these languages but to give some flavour
we will now look at examples of FORTRAN,
COBOL and PASCAL in this Chapter. BASIC is
described more fully in Chapter 9.

First however it is important to realize that
there are different types of translater programs, viz., assembler, compiler and interpreter and while these perform similar tasks
it is worth noting the essential differences.

As assembler translates a machine oriented
language, ie, a language where, in general,
one statement gives rise to one machine
instruction. The internal registers,
accumulators, etc., are accessible and the
programmer in the language is always aware
of the machine structure.

A compiler translates a problem-oriented
language (eg FORTRAN, ALGOL, COBOL) into
machine code. Each statement in the language
usually gives rise to more than one, and
sometimes many, machine instructions. The
programmer is normally not aware of the machine
code being generated.

An interpreter translates a problem-oriented
language (eg, BASIC) as well, but there is
one important difference. When we have a
correct COBOL program which we want to execute
a number of times, it is compiled once only
to generate a machine language program and
then this program is executed as often as
necessary. Each statement is translated
only once. However, a BASIC program is normally not translated to machine code, but
held as data inside the interpreter. Then
as each statement is required for execution
it is interpreted. Every time we wish to
execute the program, every statement is
'translated' every time it is required.

Thus, in general, FORTRAN programs are more
efficient than BASIC programs and ASSEMBLER
programs are more efficient than FORTRAN
programs. Some manufacturers, however,
produce BASIC compilers as well as interpreters and FORTRAN interpreters as well as
compilers.

7.16 FORTRAN

The FORTRAN language (short for FORMULA
TRANSLATOR) was invented by IBM in the late
fifties and is now mainly used in the scientific environment. A FORTRAN program can
have access to many I/O units of many different types (card reader, card punch, paper-
tape reader, paper tape punch, line printer,
magnetic tape, discs, etc.). In addition
there are powerful facilities for producing
an elegant layout of results using the FORMAT
statement. Arithmetic can be performed on
integer, real or complex values and if
necessary variables can be defined as DOUBLE
PRECISION which effectively doubles the
accuracy of calculations when required.

However, the main attractions of FORTRAN
today are

(i) the large number of subroutines which
     already exist for carrying out specific

functions (probably tens of thousands).

(ii) the fact that nearly all manufacturers
      provide a FORTRAN compiler which nor-
      mally produces fairly efficient machine
      code.

(iii) an international standard for the
       language exists, meaning that programs
       written for one type of computer can
       relatively easily be run on an entirely
       different machine.

The program in Fig. 7.2. is included to give
some idea of the language.

The program reads an integer N indicating the
number of quadratic equations to be solved
and then reads the three coefficients (A,
B, C where $Ax^2 + Bx^2 + C = 0$) for each equation. Provided that the roots are not complex
they are printed alongside the coefficients.

Notes on Program "Quadratic"

Statements are punched on 80-column cards
(assuming use of punched cards) but only
the first 72 columns are significant (columns
73-80 are card-sequence numbers).

Columns 1-5 may contain a statement number. This
allows for jump statements. If column 1
contains a C this indicates that the card contains a comment and the card is ignored by
the compiler.

20 READ (1,100) N reads an integer from a
record on unit 1 using statement 100 into
variable N. (Variable names beginning with
the letters I, J, K, L, M, N are assumed to
be integer - the rest are real.) In our case
unit 1 is the card reader. Statement 100
(card 270) gives the format of the data on the
card - I3 indicating an integer consisting
of up to 3 digits.

30 WRITE (2,200) N writes an integer on the
line printer (unit 2) using format statement
200 which says

1H1   - throw to the top of the next page
           (H stands for Hollerith character)

13H SOL..- prints the thirteen characters
           following H, ie SOLUTIONS OF

I4   - print as an integer the first
           variable mentioned in the WRITE
           statement in this case N

11H QUA - print the 11 characters after H,
           ie, QUADRATICS

//   - skip two lines

40 DO 50 I = 1, N will cause all the instructions up to 50 (card 240) to be repeated N
times.

50 READ (1,300) A, B, C will read three real
numbers from the next data card using statement 300 to define the card layout (3F10.4)
ie three (floating point) real numbers each
occupying 10 columns on the card. The decimal
point is to be considered as existing 4
columns before the end of the 10. Thus on
card 370 the characters would be interpreted
as 3 numbers.

182.4, 267.3, 177.45

QUB COMPUTER CENTRE   **FØRTRAN** CODING SHEET   Sheet 1 of 2

Programmer _R.A. McLAUGHLIN_   Job No. _ABAC 0102_   Title _QUADRATIC_   Date _17/06/76_

Identity repeat
73 _QUADR_ 77

```
      PROGRAM QUADRATIC                                    QUADR 010
      READ (1, 100) N                                            020
      WRITE (2, 200) N                                           030
      DO 50 I = 1, N                                             040
      READ (1, 300) A, B, C                                      050
    4 WRITE (2, 400) A, B, C                                     060
      IF (A .NE. 0) GOTO 10                                      070
C-----------------------------------                             080
C                   EQUATION IS LINEAR                           090
      R = -C/B                                                   100
    6 WRITE (2, 500) R                                           110
      GOTO 50                                                    120
C-----------------------------------                             130
   10 DISCRIM = B**2 - 4*A*C                                     140
      IF (DISCRIM .GE. 0) GOTO 20                                150
C-----------------------------------                             160
C                   ROOTS ARE COMPLEX                            170
      WRITE (2, 600)                                             180
C-----------------------------------                             190
      GOTO 50                                                    200
```

aa/dg/8.70   ● The Queen's University of Belfast

QUB COMPUTER CENTRE   **FØRTRAN** CODING SHEET   Sheet 2 of 2

Programmer _R.A. McLAUGHLIN_   Job No. _ABAC 0102_   Title _QUADRATIC_   Date _17/06/76_

Identity repeat
73 _QUADR_ 77

```
   20 ROOT1 = (-B + SQRT(DISCRIM)) / (2*A)                       210
      ROOT2 = (-B - SQRT(DISCRIM)) / (2*A)                       220
      WRITE (2, 700) ROOT1, ROOT2                                230
   50 CONTINUE                                                   240
      STOP                                                       250
C     END OF EXECUTABLE STATEMENTS                               260
  100 FORMAT (I3)                                                270
  200 FORMAT (1H1, 13HSOLUTIONS OF, I4, 1H QUADRATICS//)         280
  300 FORMAT (3F10.4)                                            290
  400 FORMAT (4H  A=, F10.4, 4H  B=, F10.4, 4H  C=, F10.4)       300
  500 FORMAT (1H0, 50X, 22HEQUATION LINEAR ROOT =, F10.4)        310
  600 FORMAT (1H0, 50X, 17HROOTS ARE COMPLEX)                    320
  700 FORMAT (1H0, 50X, 12HROOTS ARE :-, 2F12.6)                 330
      END                                                        340

    3                                                            350
    7.1264      4.2500    3.7500                                 360
   1.824      2.673     1.7745                                   370
    0.0       2.0       3.0                                      380
```

aa/dg/8.70   ● The Queen's University of Belfast

Fig. 7.2 Fortran program

If the decimal point exists on the card as in 360 and 380 then this overrides the FORMAT statement.

60 <u>WRITE (2,400) A, B, C</u> will print three numbers on the lineprinter using format statement 400. Since the first character sent to the printer controls line spacing (1 = new page, ∇ = next line, 0 = same line)

<u>4H∇∇B=</u>, causes ∇∇B = to appear on same line etc.

So the complete output on reading and writing the data A, B, C will be
VA = ∇∇∇7.1264∇∇B = ∇∇∇4.2500∇∇C = ∇∇∇3.7500

70 <u>IF (A.NE.0) GOTO 10</u> if value of A is not equal to 0 then go to statement 10 otherwise proceed to next statement.

80, 90 The next two cards beginning with C do not produce any code.

100 <u>R = -C/B</u> set R = -C divided by B.

110 <u>WRITE (2,500) R</u> This prints one value on the printer using format statement 500.

<u>1H0</u> means print on same line, ie overprint last line output

<u>50X</u> is a shorthand way of writing 50 spaces

<u>22H</u> causes EQUATION LINEAR, ROOT =

<u>F10.4</u> prints the number in R with 4 figures after the point in a total field of 10.

So for example having read the third data card (where A = 0) the result would be output by statements 4 and 6 as:

VA=∇∇∇0.0000∇∇B=∇∇∇2.0000∇∇C=∇∇∇3.0000

3   10   4   10   4   10

∇∇∇∇∇∇∇∇∇EQUATION∇LINEAR,ROOT∇=∇∇-1.5000

9   22   10
(The complete result would be on one line.)

You can probably work out what the rest of the statements mean and you should do this as an exercise.

7.17. COBOL

COBOL (an acronym for Common Business Oriented Language) was originally developed for general commercial use under the sponsorship of the United States Department of Defence. It is now the internationally accepted language for programming business applications such as payroll, stock control, financial reports, etc. The language is much more oriented to file handling than FORTRAN but has less powerful arithmetic statements. It was designed to be easily read and the language is more "natural" than FORTRAN. Because of this it is much less compact. The program ISSTEST demonstrates the style of the language. (A full treatment is given in McCracken, D.D., 'A Guide to COBOL programming', Wiley 1963).

Traditionally the minicomputer has evolved in the scientific and industrial environments, consequently not many early minicomputer manufacturers offered a COBOL compiler. More recently however, the minicomputer because of its low capital outlay and recurrent costs, has been making inroads into the commercial environment, and COBOL compilers have even been written for some microcomputers.

Notes on COBOL program ISSTEST

Numbers in brackets refer to the lines of source in Fig. 7.3.

(i) The program is a very simple one which reads 20 integers from a single card, and prints the maximum, minimum and mean. The example shows some specimen input and output data - the program prints the numbers read (10 on each of 2 lines) and then the results.

(ii) All COBOL programs have four DIVISIONS:-

IDENTIFICATION (10-60) - gives the program name and optional details about the author and function of the program.

ENVIRONMENT (70-150) - this contains two sections.

CONFIGURATION SECTION (80-100) - defines the source computer (on which the program will be compiled) and the object computer (on which the program will be run).

INPUT-OUTPUT SECTION (120-150) - defines the peripherals to be used and the files. Note that as far as COBOL is concerned a deck of cards is an INPUT file and printed output is an OUTPUT file.

DATA (160-690) - describes the records to be read/written on each file, and the format of the records. Also any variables or constants used in the program are defined here.

PROCEDURE (600-940) - contains the instructions of the program.

(iii) The Identification and Environment Divisions are self-explanatory.

(iv) The Data Division has three sections:

The File Section defines the records which are to be read/printed on each file and also the format of each record.

(180-190) indicate that a record called DIGITFIELD will be read from file INPUTCR.

(200-210) then define the structure of this record as an array called NUMB of four digit numbers. The array contains 20 items.

(220-230) indicate that three different records RECLPI, NUMBERS, MESSFD may be output to the file OUTPUTPR.

DATA PROCESSING

COBOL
program sheet

Programmer *R.A. McLAUGHLIN* Job No. *ABAC 0102* Title *ISSTEST* Date *14/11/76* Sheet *1* of *5*

```
 10  IDENTIFICATION DIVISION.
 20  PROGRAM-ID.  ISSTEST.
 30  REMARKS.
 40      THIS PROGRAM READS 20 FOUR DIGIT NUMBERS
 50      FROM A CARD, FINDS THE SUM, MAXIMUM, MINIMUM AND MEAN,
 60      AND PRINTS THE MAXIMUM, MINIMUM AND MEAN.
 65  AUTHOR.    R A MCLAUGHLIN.
 70  ENVIRONMENT DIVISION.
 80  CONFIGURATION SECTION.
 90  SOURCE COMPUTER.    B700.
100  OBJECT COMPUTER.    B700.
120  INPUT-OUTPUT SECTION.
130  FILE CONTROL.
140      SELECT INPUTCR ASSIGN TO CARD-READER 1.
150      SELECT OUTPUTPR ASSIGN TO PRINTER 1.
```

DATA PROCESSING

COBOL
program sheet

Programmer *R.A. McLAUGHLIN* Job No. *ABAC 0102* Title *ISSTEST* Date *14/11/76* Sheet *2* of *5*

```
160  DATA DIVISION.
170  FILE SECTION.
180  FD INPUTCR
190      DATA RECORD IS DIGITFIELD.
200  01  DIGITFIELD.
210      02 NUMB PICTURE 9999 OCCURS 20 TIMES
220  FD OUTPUTPR.
230      DATA RECORDS ARE RECLP1 NUMBERS MESSFD.
240  01  RECLP1.
250      02  MAXNM  PIC  A(10).
260      02  MAXRC  PIC  9(4).
270      02  MINNM  PIC  A(10).
280      02  MINRC  PIC  9(4).
290      02  MEANM  PIC  A(10).
300      02  MEANR  PIC  9(4).
310      02  FILLER PIC  X(90)
```

Fig.7.3(a) Cobol program

DATA PROCESSING

COBOL
program sheet

Programmer *R.A.McLAUGHLIN* Job No. *ABAC0102* Title *ISSTEST* Date *14/11/76* Sheet *3* of *5*

```
320 01  NUMBERS.
330     02 NUMFIELD OCCURS 10 TIMES.
340        03 FILLER PIC A(6).
350        03 NUMF PIC 9(4).
360     02 FILLER PIC X(20).
370 01  MESSFD.
380     02 MESS1 PIC X(20)
390     02 FILLER PIC X(100).
400 WORKING-STORAGE SECTION.
410 77  I PICTURE 99 COMPUTATIONAL SYNCHRONIZED.
420 77  J PIC 99 COMP SYNC.
430 77  K PIC 99 COMP SYNC.
440 77  MINI PIC 9(4).
450 77  MAXI PIC 9(4).
460 77  SUM PIC 9(6) COMP SYNC.
470 CONSTANT SECTION.
480 77  MESSIF PIC X(20) VALUE IS "THE NUMBERS ARE :-  ".
490 77  MAXNMF PIC A(10) VALUE IS " MAXIUM   ".
500 77  MINNMF PIC A(10) VALUE IS " MINIMUM  ".
590 77  MEANNF PIC A(10) VALUE IS " MEANUAL  ".
```

DATA PROCESSING

COBOL
program sheet

Programmer *R.A. McLAUGHLIN* Job No. *ABAC 0102* Title *ISSTEST* Date *14/11/76* Sheet *4* of *5*

```
600 PROCEDURE DIVISION.
610 START.
620     OPEN INPUT INPUTCR
630     OPEN OUTPUT OUTPUTPR
640     READ INPUTCR
650     MOVE NUMB(1) TO MAXI MINI SUM.
660 PARA1.
670     PERFORM PARA2 VARYING I FROM 2 BY 1 UNTIL I=21.
680 PARA3.
690     MOVE SPACES TO MESSFD.
700     MOVE MESSIF TO MESS1.
710     WRITE MESSFD AFTER ADVANCING TO-TOP-OF-FORM
720     PERFORM PARA4 VARYING I FROM 1 BY 1 UNTIL I=3.
730     MOVE SPACES TO RECLPI.
740     COMPUTE MEANR = SUM/20.
750     MOVE MINI TO MINRC.
760     MOVE MAXI TO MAXRC.
770     MOVE MAXNMF TO MAXNM.
780     MOVE MINNMF TO MINNM.
790     MOVE MEANNF TO MEANN.
```

Fig.7.3(b) Cobol program

IMMC – H

COBOL program sheet

Programmer R.A. McLAUGHLIN Job No. ABAC 0102 Title ISSTEST Date 14/11/76 Sheet 5 of 5

Sequence No.		
800		WRITE RECLPI AFTER ADVANCING 2 LINES.
810		CLOSE INPUTCR.
820		CLOSE OUTPUTPR.
830		STOP RUN.
840	PARA2.	
850		IF NUMB(I) < MINI THEN MOVE NUMB(I) TO MINI.
860		IF NUMB(I) > MAXI THEN MOVE NUMB(I) TO MAXI.
870		ADD NUMB(I) TO SUM.
880	PARA4.	
890		MOVE SPACES TO NUMBERS.
900		PERFORM PARA5 VARYING J FROM I BY I UNTIL J = 11.
910		WRITE NUMBERS AFTER ADVANCING 2 LINES.
920	PARA5.	
930		COMPUTE K = I*J.
940		MOVE NUMB(K) TO NUMB(J)

COBOL program sheet

Programmer _____ Job No. _____ Title SAMPLE DATA Date _/_/_ Sheet 6 of ___

IF THE INPUT DATA FOR THE PROGRAM WAS :-

123654 78 999 8745682 14569874521 45362896521 547874565698 14536521236917967410 56329874

THEN THE OUTPUT WOULD BE :-

THE NUMBERS ARE :-

1236	5478	9998	7456	3214	etcetera
5478	7456	5698	1453	6521	etcetera

MAXIMUM 9998, MINIMUM 1236, MEAN VAL. 5155.

Fig.7.4(c) Cobol program

(240-310) defines RECLPI.

(320-360) defines NUMBERS.

(370-390) defines MESSFD.

(240) 01 RECLPI indicates that this record
is at level 1. Everything up to
the next level 1 is considered as
part of the record. The record
is made up of fields at level 2.
These fields may in turn be split
up into smaller blocks at level 3
and so on.

In this case when an instruction
is given to write RECLPI the contents of the stores labelled MAXNM,
MAXRC, MINNM, MINRC, MEANN and
MEANR will be printed on the printer
as a 10-character alphabetic field,
a 4-digit integer, a 10-character
alphabetic field, etc. The layout
of each variable is defined by the
PICTURE or PIC clause. A indicates
alphabetic and 9 indicates numeric.

(320) 01 NUMBS defines the record number as
consisting of 10 subordinate
fields NUMFIELD and one FILLER
field. Each of these is further
divided into an alphabetic filler
and a numeric field of four digits.
FILLER is the COBOL term which
allows for spacing over unwanted
areas on the record.

(370) 01 MESSFD defines a heading field
consisting of 20 alphanumeric
digits (X) from the store MESSI
and 100 alphanumerics from the
FILLER field.

(v) WORKING STORAGE SECTION (400-460)
contains any variables which are going to
be used in the program and their format. If
the variables are going to be used in
arithmetic they are defined as COMPUTATIONAL
items. They must all be defined at level 77.
I, J, K are going to be used as counters,
SUM will contain the sum of all twenty numbers from the card so it has a larger field
9(6) then each of the individual numbers
NUMB defined as 9(4). MINI and MAXI will not
be used in arithmetic.

(vi) CONSTANT SECTION (470-590). Any
internally created data items which are not
going to be altered are defined in this
section eg 490 sets the characters ∇MAXIMUM∇∇
into the store MAXNMF.

(vii) The PROCEDURE DIVISION contains
the instructions of the program. These are
usually grouped into paragraphs,

eg, PARA 2 contains the instructions 850-870.
A PERFORM statement causes this set of
instructions to be executed from another part
of the program either once or a number of
times. Thus 670 will cause PARA 2 to be
executed 19 times, and each time I will be
increased by 1 starting at 2 and ending at
20.

(viii) The program execution starts at line
(610). (620) and (630) "open" the "files"
INPUTCR and OUTPUTCR. (640) reads the first
record from INPUTCR - into DIGITFIELD (see
180, 190) which causes the 20 four digit

numbers to "appear" in NUMB (1), NUMB (2),
NUMB (3), etc. (650) then moves this first
number into MAXI, MINI, and SUM. Most of
the work in the program is then done by
statement (670).

(ix) The remainder of the instructions
are concerned with printing the output, and
as an exercise you may follow through the
code to see how the program functions.
Sample input and output are provided at the
end of Figure 7.3.

7.18. PASCAL

The main advantages of the FORTRAN language
over an assembler lie in the simplification
of the instruction statements. The machine-
oriented concepts of a subroutine and a loop
controlled by a counter are augmented by
simplified arithmetic statements, conditional
statements based on IF, and a FORMAT statement for simplifying input and output. Later
dialects have added more complex statements
and concepts but in general there is very
little attempt to organize the data section
of the program.

COBOL on the other hand insists on a very
specific definition of all the data that are
going to be used in a program. This is
evident from the length of the DATA DIVISION.
Less attention however was devoted
to the design of program statements with the
result that even the most trivial arithmetic
requires extremely verbose statements.

In PASCAL an attempt has been made to force
the programmer to structure both his data
and his sequences of instructions. All
variables and subroutines (called PROCEDURES)
must be uniquely defined at the start of the
program or at least before they appear in the
list of statements. In addition to the
arrays of FORTRAN and the records of COBOL
the programmer can define new types of data
structures and supply limits for elements
of a particular type.

The language also mirrors the latest techniques of problem solving, where the task is
split up into a relatively small number of
sub tasks. The number of such sub tasks is
sufficiently small that the problem solver
has a total overview of tasks at the next
level.

Each sub task is then subjected to the same
treatment, so that in general there is only
an awareness of a small section of the overall problem. This technique is sometimes
referred to as stepwise refinement and the
block structure of PASCAL is particularly
suited to describe solutions which have
been thought out this way.

The program SORT presented at the end of this
chapter will read ten random numbers (in the
range 0-255) into random access memory on an
INTEL 8080 based microcomputer, sort them in
ascending order in the same memory cells,
and "print" them out in this sequence.

There are three major sections in the program:-

(38-42) will read the 10 numbers into cells
called NUMBER (1), NUMBER (2).... NUMBER (10)
(43-57) will sort them in ascending order
(59-63) will print out this sorted set

Let's look a little closer at the middle
section (lines (43-57) and assume that the

ten cells referred to as NUMBER (1), NUMBER (2) . . . NUMBER (10) contain →

	NUMBER	
(48-54) will compare the	1	44
number in NUMBER (I) with		
that in NUMBER (J) and if	2	27
it is greater will swap the		
two numbers. Thus putting	3	18
I=1 and J=2, then 3, then 4		
... 10 will cause NUMBER (1)	4	33
to change to 27, 18 and then		
17 ie, the smallest number	5	32
eventually gets into NUMBER(1).		
Then putting I=2 and	6	95
and J=3,4,5,...10 will		
eventually cause 18 to be	7	46
brought into NUMBER (2), ie,		
the second smallest number	8	29
gets into NUMBER (2). This		
sequence of settings for	9	131
I and J is achieved by the		
combination of lines (43,	10	17
45, 46, 55) to give		

I=1; J=2; J=3; J=4; J=5; J=6; J=7; J=8; J=9; J=10

I=2; J=3 J=4   5   6   7   8   9   10

I=3 J=4 J=5   6   7   8   9   10

I=4   5   6   7   8   9   10

     5   6   7   8   9   10

     6   7   8   9   10

     7   8   9   10

     8   9   10

I=9 J=10

(5-34) define the data and subroutines (procedures) which are to be used later in the program; (5-18) describe the data; (20-26) describe a procedure called WAITFORBIT and (28-34) a procedure called NEWLINE.

(24) uses a built in function of the compiler called GETBITS. GETBITS (PORTSTATUS, BITSSET) will read the status of the port PORTSTATUS and will produce a list (in the variable BITSSET) of those bits which are set = 1. For example if the PORTSTATUS word was 01101001 then the variable BITSSET would contain the list (6, 5, 3, 0) whereas if the PORTSTATUS word was 10000010 then the variable BITSSET would contain the set (7,1).

(23-25) will arrange that the processor repeatedly looks at the port status until bit N appears in BITSSET. The parameter N (provided when the procedure is called) is defined as type BITS. In line (11) BITS was defined as being an integer in the range 0 to 7 so on line (21) we can use this type BITS to describe the variable BITSSET. BITSSET is defined on line (21) as a SET OF BITS. A set is a built in type in the compiler.

(30) is a typical call of this procedure. In PASCAL a procedure is called simply by writing the procedure name followed by the parameters. The peripheral interface is described at (16-18) which indicate that the data for the port named IOPORT will be available at "address" 250, and that "address" 251 will indicate the status of the peripheral. If bit 0 is set then the peripheral

is ready to receive output; if bit 1 is set the peripheral is ready to transmit data to memory.

WAITFORBIT (0) will therefore cause the statement at (24) to be executed until bit 0 appears in the peripheral status word. (Peripheral is then ready to receive output)

WAITFORBIT (1) (line 40) causes the statement at (24) to be executed until bit 1 appears in the peripheral status record. Data is then available at the port for the next READ instruction (at line (41))

It should be reasonably obvious by now how the PASCAL program builds up into a neat structure. Any data which are to be used are defined at the start. Certain data types are implicitly defined by the language, eg, integer, real, array but any new types of data structure which the programmer wants to use in his program must be defined. All procedures need to be described before they can be used together with their parameters.

(5-7) Constant data items which are to be used in the program are introduced by the reserved word CONST. In this case two constants CARRIAGERETURN and LINEFEED are set to be equal to the integer equivalents of the ASCII code for CR and LF.

(8-11) Any new data types are introduced by the reserved word TYPE. Here three new data types are being described. BYTE = 0..255 means that any data which is later defined as being of type BYTE can only have integer values in the range 0 to 255. Similarly RANGE and BITS describe data types consisting of a range of integers (1..10 and 0..7)

(12-15) Names for variable data items are introduced by the reserved word VAR. The data items can be described using the types which are implicitly known by the compiler (eg, integer, real etc) or by referring to the new types which were introduced in lines (8-11)

Thus line (13) indicates that two variables called I and J will be used in the program both of type RANGE (ie integers between 1 and 10). This means that an assignment statement of the form
I:=8 is legal but
J:=11 is illegal

Line (14) specifies an array of bytes called NUMBER (1), NUMBER (2) ... NUMBER (10)

(16-18) are not standard PASCAL but are an extension of the language in this particular compiler.

Everything defined between lines (5-18) is available throughout the whole program. However within a procedure extra types, constants, variables etc may be defined but these will only be usable within that procedure.

(20-26) describe a procedure called WAITFORBIT. Inside that procedure at line (21) a variable BITSSET is defined as a set of BITS (defined at line 11). This means that the variable BITSSET can only be referenced in lines (22, 23,24) thus making error detection much simpler.

7.19. OUTPUT FROM PASCAL COMPILER

The program SORT (next page) was compiled using a specially modified PASCAL compiler. The compiler program may be executed on a machine which is different from the machine on which the object program is going to be executed. In such cases the machine used for compilation is termed the HOST machine and the machine on which the program will eventually be run is the TARGET machine. When HOST and TARGET are different in architecture the compiler is referred to as a cross-compiler. The program above was compiled on a large ICL 1906S with 1 Megabyte of memory. The target machine was an Intel 8080 based microcomputer.

This gives a clue to the meaning of lines (0-2). They are directives to the compiler indicating which memory addresses are to be used in the target machine. In this case

%PROGRAM = 32775 indicates that the instructions are to occupy cells 32775, 32776, etc.

%VARIABLES=33275 indicates that any variables used in the program should occupy cells 33275, 33276 etc.

%IO = ISOLATED is a directive to this compiler to indicate the use of ISOLATED I/O (as opposed to MEMORY MAPPED I/O). These are the two mechanisms for I/O on an Intel 8080.

The SOURCE program (ie, the list of statements which the programmer writes) is in the middle of the column. As the compiler reads each line it prints the line number at the left of the column followed by the source statement. At the far right of each line the compiler also prints the first address which will be used (on the target machine) for the machine code instructions generated by the statement on that line. By looking at the subsequent line we can see where the machine code instructions for that line start and by subtraction determine how many bytes will be required on the target machine by each statement. For example

line (51) TEMP: = NUMBER (I) requires 14 bytes between 32938 and 32951
line (52) NUMBER (I): = NUMBER (J) requires 22 bytes between 32952 and 32973
line (53) NUMBER (J): = TEMP requires 14 bytes between 32974 and 32987.

Similarly the addresses allocated to variables are indicated:-

line (13) I,J: RANGE. Since RANGE only permits integers of maximum 10 these two variables occupy only one byte each. I will occupy cell 33275 and J cell 33276.

The VAR and PRO preceding the address indicate whether the content of the memory location is an instruction (PRO) or data (VAR).

7.20 MACHINE CODE

This compiler also produces a listing of the eventual machine code of the object program and a "pseudo-assembly" listing to give some idea of the function of each of the individual machine code instructions. This output is listed following the source program.

To show the connection between the source and the object code let's examine line (45) of the source.

45   J:=I+1;   PRO 32898

The programmer provided the bit in the middle ie J: = I+1 which means that he would like to take the contents of the cell which he has called I, add 1, and store the result in the cell he has called J. The compiler indicates at the right hand side that the instructions to do this will start at 32898. Since instructions for the next statement start at 32905 we can deduce that the 7 memory cells from 32898-32904 contain the instructions to perform the task on line 45,

If we now go to the listing produced by the compiler **we** see that these cells will contain the following bit patterns when eventually this object program is loaded into memory

Address	Bits	Hexadecimal	Integer
32898	00111010	3A	58
32899	11111011	FB	251
32900	10000001	81	129
32901	00111100	3C	60
32902	00110010	32	50
32903	11111100	FC	252
32904	10000001	81	129

Referring back to the description of the Intel 8080 codes in 3.6. we will see that

(a) the OPCODE 00111010 in 32898 means "Load the accumulator with the contents of the cell whose address is given by the next two bytes". Again recalling that the low order bits of the address come first we can evaluate the address as

$$129 \times 256 + 251 = 33275$$

(b) the OPCODE 00111100 (in cell 32901) is a single byte instruction meaning "Add 1 to the contents of the accumulator". There is no address field.

(c) the OPCODE 00110010 in 32902 means "Store the contents of the accumulator in the cell whose address is given by the next two bytes. This address is 16 bits long.

32904	32903
10000001	11111100

$$= \quad 129 \times 16 + 252 \quad = \quad 33276$$

So there are three instructions between 32898 and 32904

(32898,32899,32900) means load accumulator with contents of 33275
(32901) means add 1 to the accumulator
(32902,32903,32904) means store accumulator in cell 33276

If we now refer back to line (13) of the source program we can see that cell 33275 was reserved to contain the variable I and

33276 to contain the variable J.   So the above three instructions will

Load accumulator with I
Add 1 to accumulator (giving I+1)
and Store the accumulator in J

Thus achieving the objective of the PASCAL statement on line 45

$$J: = I + 1$$

The third column gives the assembly mnemonic codes which are equivalent to the machine code in the second column.

PASCAL Program 'SORT'

```
0    %PROGRAM = 32775
1    %VARIABLES = 33275
2    %IO = ISOLATED
3
4    PROGRAM(SORT);
5    CONST
6    CARRIAGE RETURN = 13;
7    LINEFEED = 10;
8    TYPE
9    BYTE = 0..255;
10   RANGE = Ø..10;
11   BITS = 0..7;
12   VAR                              VAR 33275
13   I,J:RANGE;                       VAR 33275
14   NUMBER:ARRAY(RANGE) OF BYTE;     VAR 33277
15   TEMP : BYTE;                     VAR 33287
16   PORT
17   IØPØRT : BYTE at 250;
18   PORTSTATUS : BYTE AT 251;
20   PROCEDURE WAITFORBIT (N:BITS);   VAR 33288
21     VAR BITSSET:SET OF BITS;       VAR 33289
22     BEGIN                          PRO 32775
23       REPEAT                       PRO 32775
24         GETBITS (PORTSTATUS,
                    BITSSET)          PRO 32775
25           UNTIL N IN BITSSET       PRO 32784
26   END;                             PRO 32784
27                                    PRO 32829
28   PROCEDURE NEWLINE;               VAR 33291
29     BEGIN                          PRO 32829
30       WAITFORBIT(O);               PRO 32829
31       WRITE(IOPORT,CARRIAGE
                RETURN);              VRO 32837
32       WAITFORBIT(O);               PRO 32841
33       WRITE(IOPORT,LINEFEED);      PRO 32849
34   END;                             PRO 32853
35                                    PRO 32854
36   BEGIN                            PRO 32854
37     NEWLINE;                       PRO 32854
38     FØR I:=1 TØ 10 DØ              PRO 32857
39       BEGIN                        PRO 32862
40         WAITFORBIT(1);             PRO 32862
41         READ (IOPORT,NUMBER(I))    PRO 32870
42       END;                         PRO 32883
43     FOR I:=1 TO 9 DO               PRO 32893
44     BEGIN                          PRO 32898
45       J:=I+1;                      PRO 32898
46       WHILE J<11 DO                PRO 32905
47         BEGIN                      PRO 32913
48           IF NUMBER (I)>NUMBER(J)  PRO 32913
49           THEN                     PRO 32913
50           BEGIN                    PRO 32958
51             TEMP:=NUMBER(I);       PRO 32938
52             NUMBER(I):=NUMBER(J);  PRO 32952
53             NUMBER(J):=TEMP        PRO 32974
54           END;                     PRO 32974
55           J:=J+1                   PRO 32988
56         END                        PRO 32988
57     END;                           PRO 32995
58     NEWLINE;                       PRO 33008
59     FOR I:=1 TO 10 DO              PRO 33011
60       BEGIN                        PRO 33016
61         WAITFORBIT(O);             PRO 33016
62         WRITE(IOPORT,NUMBER(I))    PRO 33024
63       END;                         PRO 33037
64   HALT                             PRO 33047
65   END.
```

Assembly/Machine Code Listing for 'SORT'

```
32775   DB
32776   FB    IN      251
32777   21
32778   09
32779   82    LXI H,  33289
32780   36
32781   OO    MVI H,      O
32782   23    INX H
32783   77    MOV M,A
32784   21
32785   08
32786   82    LXI H,  33288
32787   66    MOV H,M
32788   CD
32789   2B
32790   80    CALL    32811
32791   4D    MOV C,L
32792   47    MOV B,A
32793   21
32794   09
32795   82    LXI H,  33289
32796   7E    MOV A,M
32797   23    IHX H
32798   5E    MOV E,M
32799   AO    ANA B
32800   57    MOV D,A
32801   7B    MOV A,E
32802   A1    ANA C
32803   91    SUB C
32804   5F    MOV E,A
32805   7A    MOV A,D
32806   98    SBB B
32807   C2
32808   O7
32809   80    JNZ     32775
32810   C9    RET
32811   2E    MVI L,      1
32812   O1
32813   3E
32814   OO    MVI A,      O
32815   25    DCR H
32816   EA
32817   3C
32818   80    JMP     32828
32819   5F    MOV E,A
32820   7D    MOV A,L
32821   17    RAL
32822   6F    MOV L,A
32823   7B    MOV A,E
32824   17    RAL
32825   C3
32826   2F
32927   80    JMP     32815
32828   C9    RET
32829   21
32830   08
32831   82    LXI H,33288
32832   36
32833   OO    MVI M,      O
32834   CD
32835   O7
32836   80    CALL    32775
32837   3E
32838   DA    MVI A,      10
32839   D3
32840   FA    OUT     250
32841   21
32842   08
32843   82    LXI H,33288
32844   36
32845   OO    MVI M,      O
32846   CD
32847   O7
```

Addr	Code	Instruction	Comment
32848	80	CALL 32775	
32849	3E		
32850	OD	MVI A, 13	
32851	D3		
32852	FA	OUT 250	
32853	C9	RET	
32854	CD		
32855	3D		
32856	80	CALL 32829	
32857	21		
32858	FB		
32859	81	LXI H, 33275	
32860	36		
32861	01	MVI M, 1	
32862	21		
32863	08		
32864	82	LXI H, 33288	
32865	36		
32866	01	MVI N, 1	
32867	CD		
32868	07		
32869	80	CALL 32775	
32870	DB		
32871	FA	IN 250	
32872	21		
32873	FB		
32874	81	LXI H, 33275	
32875	4E	MOV C,M	
32876	06		
32877	OO	MVI B, O	
32878	21		
32879	FD		
32880	81	LXI H, 33277	
32881	09	DAD B	
32882	77	MOV M,A	
32883	21		
32884	FB		
32885	81	LXI H, 33275	
32886	7E	MOV A,H	
32887	34	INR M	
32888	D6		
32889	OA	SUI 10	
32890	C2		
32891	5E		
32892	80	JNZ 32862	
32893	21		
32894	FB		
32895	81	LXI H, 33275	
32896	36		
32897	01	MVI M, 1	
32898	3A		
32899	FB		
32900	81	LDA 33275	Load I into A
32901	3C	INR A	Add 1
32902	32		
32903	FC		
32904	81	STA 33276	Store A in J
32905	3A		
32906	FC		
32907	81	LDA 33276	
32908	D6		
32909	OB	SUI 11	
32910	F2		
32911	E6		
32912	80	JP 32998	
32913	21		
32914	FC		
32915	81	LXI H, 33276	
32916	4E	MOV C,M	
32917	06		
32918	OO	MVI B, O	
32919	21		
32920	FD		
32921	81	LXI H, 33277	
32922	09	DAD B	
32923	7E	MOV A,M	
32924	21		
32925	FB		
32926	81	LXI H, 33275	
32927	4E	MOV C,M	
32928	06		
32929	OO	MVI B, O	
32930	21		
32931	FD		
32932	81	LXI H, 33277	
32933	09	DAD B	
32934	96	SUB M	
32935	F2		
32936	DC		
32937	80	JP 32988	
32938	21		
32939	EB		
32940	81	LXI H, 33275	
32941	4E	MOV C,M	
32942	06		
32943	OO	MVI B, O	
32924	21		
32945	FD		
32946	81	LXI H, 33277	
32947	09	DAD B	
32948	7E	MOV A,M	
32949	32		
32950	O7		
32951	82	STA 33287	
32952	21		
32953	FC		
32954	81	LXI H, 33276	
32955	4E	MOV C,M	
32956	06		
32957	OO	MVI B, O	
32958	21		
32959	FD		
32960	81	LXI H, 33277	
32961	09	DAD B	
32962	7E	MOV A,M	
32963	21		
32964	FB		
32965	81	LXI H, 33275	
32966	4E	MOV C,M	
32967	06		
32968	OO	MVI B, O	
32969	21		
32970	FD		
32971	81	LXI H, 33277	
32972	09	DAD B	
32973	77	MOV M,A	
32974	3A		
32975	O7		
32976	82	LDA 33287	
32977	21		
32978	FC		
32979	81	LXI H, 33276	
32980	4D	MOV C,M	
32981	06		
32982	OO	MVI B, O	
32983	21		
32984	FD		
32985	81	LXI H, 33277	
32986	09	DAD B	
32987	77	NOV M,A	
32988	3A		
32989	FC		
32990	81	LDA 33276	
32991	3C	INR A	
32992	32		
32993	FC		
32994	81	STA 33276	
32995	C3		
32996	89		
32997	80	JMP 32905	
32998	21		
32999	FB		
33000	81	LXI H, 33275	
33001	7E	MOV A,M	
33002	34	INR M	
33003	D6		
33004	OA	SUI 10	
33005	C2		
33006	82		
33007	80	JNZ 32898	
33008	CD		
33009	3D		

```
33010    80    CALL    32829
33011    21
33012    FB
33013    81    LXI  H,33275
33014    36
33015    01    MVI  M,    1
33016    21
33017    08
33018    82    LXI  H, 33288
33019    36
33020    00    MVI  M,    0
33021    CD
33022    07
33023    80    CALL    32775
33024    21
33025    FB
33026    81    LXI  H,33275
33027    4E    MOV  C,M
33028    06
33029    00    MVI  B,    0
33030    21
33031    FD
33032    81    LXI  H,33277
33033    09    DAD  B
33034    7E    MOV  A,M
33035    D3
33036    FA    OUT     250
33037    21
33038    FB
33039    81    LXI  H,33275
33040    7E    MOV  A,M
33041    34    INR  M
33042    D6
33043    0A    SUI     10
33044    C2
33045    F8
33046    80    JNZ     33016
33047    FB    EI
33048    76    HLT
```

7.21. COMMENT

This Chapter has presented Assembly languages
and has covered in some detail the translation
process from a number of "high level"
languages such as FORTRAN, COBOL and PASCAL
into the binary or machine language which
the processor can "understand". The use of
such languages simplifies considerably the
task of program construction. In the next
Chapter we will be looking at some further
special programs which are available from
most manufacturers to simplify the handling
of peripherals and assist program testing
and development.

7.22. REFERENCES

1. 'How to Use the Nova Computers', Data
    General Corporation, 1974.

2. McCracken, D.D., 'A Guide to COBOL
    programming', Wiley 1963.

More Software
Chapter 8

8.1. INTRODUCTION

In general after a computer has been purchased
the hardware remains reasonably static.
Occasionally the configuration is augmented
by the addition of further memory or new
peripherals. The real versatility of the computer arises from the programs which are
either provided with the computer in the
first place or developed by the user of the
system. The user may also purchase from an
independent source programs to perform
specific tasks. This collection of programs
is the software.

So far we have stretched the capability of
our system by compilers, interpreters, assemblers
which allow us to "speak" to the computer in
a variety of languages. (The day may come when
we will have a translator for English.) The
hardware configuration on which these programs
were executed consisted only of

memory   - to hold the data and instructions
processor - to execute the program
teletype or cassette - for loading compilers
            and libraries from tape
teletype or VDU - to allow data or programs
            to be typed in.

Many computers operate in this fashion on such
a minimum configuration. However, for the
more sophisticated user there are a number of
drawbacks,

(i) The tape reader is an extremely slow
device (10 characters/s for a teletype) and
therefore it requires a long time to read in
the program - usually a matter of minutes.
In particular, when the user is developing
his program, we have seen that he needs to
read a number of tapes before the source
program is eventually transformed into a binary
program ready for execution. If an error is
discovered during execution then the whole
tape reading sequence of assembler, link loader
and relocatable binary has to be repeated to
repair the error, no matter how trivial.

(ii) The fact that only one program occupies
the main store is a distinct disadvantage.
If, for example, the store was sufficiently
large, the assembler program and the link
loader could be left in store during the
development phase. To achieve this we need
a mechanism for keeping the instructions and
data making up each of these programs separate
in store, and an easy system of switching
from one program to another.

(iii) Unfortunately main memory is still a
relatively expensive element in a small computer

and it is not economic to hold a library of
programs in main memory.

What is really required is a cheaper form of
storage to hold the dormant programs. The
cheap store is usually not sufficiently fast
to allow the processor to directly execute
programs contained therein, so a system is
needed to transfer programs from the cheap
store to the main store for execution.

8.2. NEED FOR A SUPERVISOR PROGRAM

From the hardware point of view there is little
difficulty in adding additional peripherals,
but it is apparent that the more complex
the configuration becomes, the more control
is required to sort out interrupts from
different peripherals and to allocate priority
to different tasks. It is also natural to
investigate whether the cumbersome techniques
involving the mounting and reading of tapes, and
the loading and deleting of programs in memory
can be improved by using a program in the
machine to assist. In the next few sections
the need for such a program often referred
to as a supervisor or operating system or
system monitor will emerge. Let's first look
at the capability of the rotating disc store
which in conjunction with the supervisor
program allows us to overcome the disadvantages
outlined in 8.1.

8.3. DISC STORAGE

Discs are normally of two broad types, the
fixed-head disc and the movable-head disc.
The rate of transfer is not significantly
different on each type, but the access time
is usually much faster on a fixed-head disc.
This is because the fixed-head disc has
one head   for   every track on the disc,
already positioned over the track, whereas
the movable-head disc has only one read/
write head per surface. The time taken to
move the head to a given track may be of the
order of 60 ms. A further 10 ms is required
on average to permit the appropriate section
of the track to rotate under the reading
head.

Compare the time taken on two such discs
rated at 100,000 bytes/s to transfer 1,000
bytes (eg, 1,000 characters, using 8 bit
bytes).

Movable   (i) move head to track   60 ms
          (ii) await data (latency) 10 ms
         (iii) transfer 1000 bytes   10 ms

                              TOTAL 80 ms

Fixed head   (i) no head movement   -
             (ii) await data   10 ms
             (iii) transfer data   <u>10 ms</u>

                          TOTAL   20 ms

So there is a factor of four in transferring
randomly distributed 1K byte blocks between
disc and memory, and this factor is important
when a program which is too large to fit into
memory needs to use <u>overlaying</u>.

8.4.   OVERLAYING

Overlaying is the most commonly used technique
for running large programs on a small machine.
Basically it requires a knowledge of the
different phases of the program as it is
executing. If one considers a small loop in
a program which may be executed hundreds or
thousands of times it is obvious that only
that loop of instructions (and the data upon
which it operates) need to be in memory for
the duration of the execution of the loop.

By a detailed examination of the program it
is therefore possible to divide the program
up into sections, such that, over reasonably
long periods of time the only instructions
executed or data accessed fall into a specific
section.

The Table represents
such a situation for a
program which is 37K
words long (to sim-
plify the arithmetic
each section is assumed
to be an integral num-
ber of K words long).

			4K
4 s	S1	6K	
12 s	S2	1K	
1 s	S3	3K	
10 s	S4	5K	
2 s	S5	2K	
19 s	S6	8K	
2 s	S7	2K	
1 s	S8	5K	
9 s	S9	1K	

Again for the sake of
simplicity we will
assume that the program
executes instructions
in section 1 for 4 secs,
section 2 for 12 secs,etc,
and finishes up in
section 9 for 9 secs.

The program would
therefore occupy 37K
of memory store for 60 secs.

By overlaying the program we can arrange that
these 9 sections normally reside as disc
storage and that the main memory is occupied
only by the 'permanent' section (the first 4K)
and the particular section necessary for
execution. The 'changing' area of store must
obviously be large enough to hold the largest
section (in this case 8K).

main   }   4K permanent
memory }   8K overlay area

disc }   S1 S2 S3 S4 S5 S6 S7 S8 S9
store }

The permanent area will contain not only
data and instructions which are accessed
frequently but also the code to read each
section in,(when it is required)from disc
store. The organisation is very simple if
the overlay sections have been written using
relative addressing, since the section can
then be executed from anywhere in memory.
Otherwise it may be necessary to carry out
some address modification when the section is
loaded.

The obvious advantage gained is that our 37K

program will now run on a computer with only
12K of memory. The disadvantage is that the
program requires longer to execute, but if
the overlaying is properly organised this is
not a significant factor. If we take the
timings given earlier for a fixed-head disc,
and assume that each word is 16 bits long
(two bytes) then the total time for the
program would be 60.75 s.

Section	Size K	Transfer time S	Execute Time s	Total Seconds
S1	6	.01 + 12(0.01)	4	4.13
S2	1	.01 + 2(.01)	12	12.03
S3	3	.01 + 6(.01)	1	1.07
S4	5	.01 + 10(.01)	10	10.11
S5	2	.01 + 4(.01)	2	2.05
S6	8	.01 + 16(.01)	19	19.17
S7	2	.01 + 4(.01)	2	2.05
S8	5	.01 + 10(.01)	1	1.11
S9	1	.01 + 2(.01)	9	9.03

                          TOTAL   60.75 s

This represents a 1.25% increase in execution
time. In practice, however, the program does
not divide into sections which need to be
fetched only once from the disc. A section
may be copied in hundreds of times during
execution, so the gain is not as spectacular
as is indicated by our trivial program.

Nevertheless many computer systems make considerable use of overlaying techniques
particularly in the area of data acquisition,
where the permanent section of the program
accepts data from various sources which requir
to be serviced immediately, and the processing
of the data and its reporting can be carried
out quite satisfactorily by overlays.

Most manufacturers provide in their assemblers
and other high-level languages an easy mechani
for the program writer to overlay his program.
This is normally done by introducing the
appropriate section of code by an assembler
directive of the form

                          OVERLAY

The assembler will then set up the appropriate
links and ensure that instructions are available in the permanent area to fetch the overlay from disc when the program branches to it.
The programmer need not concern himself with
explicitly writing the disc handling routine.

8.5.   MULTIPROGRAMMING

Overlaying is a technique for optimizing the
use of the memory of a computer; multiprogramming is a means of optimizing the use
of the central processor. Let us again examin
the behaviour of a rather simple program in
the machine. Assume that we have a deck of
1,000 punched cards each of which contains the
name, hours worked, rate of pay per hour, and
tax code of an employee. We write a program
which reads each card, calculates the total
pay (hours x rate), subtracts the amount of
tax due and prints a wage slip for each
employee.

Consider the time taken for each of these functions.

(a) reading a card - a typical reader on a small computer would operate at 150 cards/min so to read each card requires 60/150 s = 400 ms.

(b) performing the calculation - allowing for the conversion from bytes to binary 5 ms should be sufficient.

(c) printing the wage slip - a typical printer might operate at 100 characters/s. Suppose 50 characters have to be printed, then the operation requires 500 ms.

During card reading and printing the processor is effectively idle so that as the program proceeds we find the following pattern of processor usage:

```
                      (5)
read card (400)    -      print (500), read
                process
                (5)
card (400)    -       print (500), read (400)
            process
  (5)
  -
process
```

This means that of the total time required to execute the program (about 15 min) the processor was being used for only 5 secs (much less than 1%).

Obviously if we had another program in store which was able to use the processor during the idle periods of the first program, this would be a distinct advantage. We come up against the standard management problem now - if two people are appointed to carry out similar tasks, they must have a supervisor to allocate tasks to them. Since computers, like well trained monkeys, emulate their masters, we end up with a third program aptly named the executive or supervisor to share out the processor between the two "useful" programs.

Having decided that it is necessary to have a supervisor program, to police the use of the processor, permanently resident in store, we may as well give it something else to do. Since many of the programs written have to perform similar tasks it is sensible to examine if any of these could be carried out by the supervisor. There are practical limits of course - the more activities we get the supervisor to perform, the more store will be permanently occupied. So only those activities which are necessary for practically every program should be considered as the job of the supervisor.

8.6. INTERRUPT HANDLING

Normally when a program begins execution, the computer hardware processes each instruction in sequence, unless specifically directed to do otherwise by a branch instruction. The processor threads its way through the various instructions, guided along by data in the memory. There are, however, events which may occur during the execution of the program of which there is no knowledge in the memory and these events require action by the computer. The program may deal with these 'external' events in one of two ways: 'polling' or 'interrupt handling', as outlined

in Chapter 5, and we can illustrate these approaches by a domestic example.

Consider the busy housewife carrying out the normal domestic morning chores - bedmaking, sweeping, dusting, etc. She desires a cup of tea and so puts on the kettle. Being very efficient she does not want to wait for the kettle to boil but returns to her duties in another room. She will have to 'poll' the kettle until it has boiled, ie, she will have to come back every so often and have a look to see if steam is billowing from the spout.

There was, however, a significant technological advance in the recent past when a whistle was added to the kettle spout. When the kettle boils the whistle sounds and 'interrupts' the housewife in the other room. So the choice exists of recognizing this event (kettle boiling) by either polling (intermittently checking to see if it is) or by interrupt (being told when event occurs). Some events must be polled and some monitored on interrupt. Running the bath has to be polled since devices are not available to tell when it is full, whereas waking at a certain time in the morning must be by interrupt (you can't waken every so often and look at the clock to see if it is time to get up).

The main sources of these 'events' for the computer are from the peripherals attached to the computer, and every computer has instructions to handle such events. For example, in Chapter 3 we saw the polling instructions of the Data General Nova which permit us to skip an instruction after examining the state of a peripheral device if the BUSY or DONE flags are set. Typically the program would issue an instruction to send a character to the teletype; it would then continue normal operations until it needed to send the next character. The program has to organise a loop of instructions which will be executed until the teletype becomes ready to accept the next character. Thus a typical flow might be

```
  (i) send character to TTY
 (ii) normal operations
(iii) skip next instruction if TTY DONE
 (iv) jump to previous instruction
  (v) send next character to TTY
```

In the worst case (if there are no instructions which can be obeyed between successive characters) instructions (iii) and (iv) will be executed alternately up to 50,000 times (to waste the necessary tenth of a second).

Rather than waste the processor in this unproductive loop checking every 2 μs it might be more appropriate to check only every 1/5th of a second or even 1/10th of a second. To do this we require some form of timer interrupt, and in fact most computers have an in-built 'clock' for just such a function. Counter may be a more appropriate word than clock because all that happens is that every fraction of a second, one is added to a special register or store. The program can however set an 'alarm' requesting that it be interrupted (no matter what it is doing) when the count reaches a certain value. Each manufacturer has a separate technique for handling interrupts. The example below shows how a routine called POLL would be called every second to carry out some specified function on an Alpha system.

Store	Content		Comment
24	IMS	79	24 is a special store on the Alpha machine whose contents are executed every 10 ms. IMS 79 adds one to store 79. When store 79 becomes zero, control is passed to instruction 26.
26	JST	80	This records the address of the last instruction to be obeyed (+1) in store 80 and jumps to location 81.
80	blank		
81	STA	ASAVE	Store the accumulator in ASAVE
82	SIA	STATUS	Store the special word in STATUS
83	STX	XSAVE	Save the X-register in XSAVE
84	LAM	100	Load accumulator with -100
85	STA	79	Set 79 = (accumulator) = -100
86	JST	POLL	Jump to the routine POLL
87	LDX	XSAVE	Reset X-register to original value
88	LDA	STATUS	Reset status
89	SOA		
90	LDA	ASAVE	Reset accumulator
91	RTN	80	Return to the instruction whose address is contained in store 80

Notes:

(i) If 79 contains -100 to start then after 10 ms it is increased by 1, -99. After another 10 ms it becomes -98 and so on. Let us assume we are executing instructions in the 2000 region as 79 approaches zero

2010

2011

.

.

2021

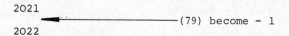 ———————— (79) become - 1
2022

2074

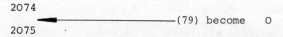 ———————— (79) become   0
2075

(ii) A timer interrupt occurred during the execution of instruction 2021. This instruction is allowed to finish. Then instruction 24 is executed (increasing (79) to 1). The processor resumes at 2022. A timer interrupt occurs during 2074. This instruction is allowed to complete. Then

instruction 24 is executed as before.

(iii) This has now caused (79) to become zero which causes instruction 26 to be executed. 26 is a store and jump which causes the PC register (program counter) currently pointing at 2075 (the next instruction) to be stored in 80 and proceeds to 81. Because the program may have been using the A or X registers at 2074 we would like to have them unchanged when we get to 2075. So we must save the current contents (81, 82, 83) and restore them again (87, 88, 89, 90) before returning to 2075. (84, 85) reset the count back to -100 in 79 ready to be counted up again. (86) calls the POLL routine which when completed returns to 87. (87 - 90) reset any special registers which were altered and (91) returns to the instruction whose address is in 80 (ie, to 2075).

(iv) During the execution of the interrupt routine, ie, from 81 to 91, interrupts are inhibited otherwise we could get into a recursive loop.

(v) Some computers automatically save all necessary registers on an interrupt and allow these to be reset by a single instruction.

Interrupts from peripherals are handled in much the same way as the timer interrupt, ie, the "mainline" program is stopped at an instruction whose address is noted, a special subroutine is entered to carry out the required function, this routine saves and restores any registers it intends to use, and control is eventually returned to the mainline program. In the case of an 80-column card for example, the program would issue an instruction to start the card moving and then continue to do some arithmetic processing. Every 2½ ms (for a 300 card/min reader) an interrupt would occur, indicating that a column of the card was available to be read. A routine would then be entered to transfer the contents of that column to store and probably update a count to indicate the number of columns read. As well as the data on the card the status of the peripherals may be examined at this time, eg, to check parity error, or if it's the last card in the hopper, etc.

For systems with a large number of different types of peripherals attached, a number of different priorities of interrupts must be handled. The card reader may take precedence over the disc which may take precedence over the printer. The priority is usually inversely proportional to the amount of time that the data is available at the peripheral. The highest priority is given to the POWER FAIL interrupt. This forces the processor to a given location when the mains voltage drops below a certain value. The program then has about 100 μs to save any 'volatile' registers in non-volatile store before the processor ceases to function. A similar facility exists when the computer is switched on again, ie, an interrupt routine is called into play immediately.

8.7. TYPICAL SUPERVISOR FUNCTIONS

Sharing Processor and Store

We have already referred to multiprogramming. The supervisor is responsible for allocating the store and processor to each program as required. In the case of store this means that there must be a method whereby each program, when it is running, is prevented from accessing that part of store outside its own limits. Establishing these limits is a function of the supervisor - typically by setting a base register and limit register. The hardware then checks before accessing an operand, that its address is less than the limit (these are both relative) and then by adding the contents of the base register, the absolute memory location can be identified. The instructions to set these registers are usually privileged instructions which can be executed only when the supervisor is running.

Sharing of the processor demands that the program 'informs' the supervisor when it has temporarily ceased to use the processor. This is carried out by special supervisor call instructions. On receipt of such an instruction the supervisor will swap the base (and limit) register to hold the absolute address of the start of another program (and its size) and then release the processor so that the new program may start.

Basic Peripheral Handling

In section 8.6. we discussed the way in which a program handles interrupts from a peripheral, but let us consider briefly the remaining operation necessary to transfer the contents of a punched card into memory.

We need to check that the reader is physically connected to the computer, to switch on the motor, suspend the program, cause the next card to start moving under the read heads, transfer the first column when the column is correctly positioned, check for non-valid characters and reject if necessary, accept data similarly from other columns, recognise end of card, and start the program running again.

Any program using a card reader will be carrying out similar functions, so it makes sense to have only one copy of these instructions in memory (inside the supervisor) and allow the program using the reader to CALL upon this set of instructions in the supervisor when it requires a card to be read.

Peripheral Protection

When more than one program is in memory there may be a conflict for access to a basic peripheral. Obviously if one program is using the card reader to read a deck of 1000 data cards, we cannot have a second program stealing the odd card. The supervisor ensures that only one program uses such a peripheral (eg, teletype, tape reader/punch, card reader/punch, line printer, magnetic tape).

File Store

There are some peripherals which by their nature can be accessed by more than one program pseudo-simultaneously. They are the random access devices already described (such as discs). It is quite normal for two programs to be running in memory, each alternately requiring a record from its own area of a single physical disc. This is possible because of the high speed at which the disc head can move from one set of records to another (on a card reader it would require a superhuman operator to be able to select the next card from two separate decks). Apart from handling the interface protocol as for basic peripherals, another problem emerges - that of sharing the surface of the disc among those programs which

require to use it. So we require a system similar to that for main memory, in that each program will have a base address on disc indicating the start of its area, and a limit indicating the extent of the area.

Unlike main memory however, when the program ceases to run, the data which was written during that run is usually required at some time in the future, either by the same program or by an entirely separate program. To provide these facilities the disc is divided up into a number of areas called files. Each of these files is given a name, and this name and other information (start address, length, owner) about the file is recorded in a directory.

The directory itself is a file on the disc (at an address known to the supervisor). A program during running can then request the use of a certain area of disc simply by quoting the name of the file. Records may be read from or written to the file by specifying a record number. The supervisor is then responsible for translating the file name and record number into an absolute track and sector address on the disc.

Library

As well as storing data on disc it is also possible to store programs. So the concept we developed earlier of having a library of programs and subroutines on tape can easily be achieved on disc as well. Each program or subroutine can be regarded as a file and used when necessary.

In the case of subroutines, the compiler reads the supplied source statements from tape or cards or a keyboard of a VDU and is then told by a directive to include from the appropriate files on disc, those subroutines which have been used in the program but not explicitly supplied as source statements. In this instance the compiler interacts with the supervisor just as any other program would in accessing disc files.

Programs, however, are usually loaded into memory by the supervisor in response to a request from a keyboard. The supervisor contains a primitive loader program and when a user wants to bring in a specific program he simply types a LOAD command on the keyboard. A typical sequence might look like

LOAD ASSEMBLER (DISC 4)	Search the directory for a file called ASSEMBLER on disc number 4, and load the program from that file into store.
RUN ASSEMBLER (CARD)	Begin executing the assembler program, reading the source from cards. When cards are exhausted return to the keyboard for further commands.
STOREPROGRAM FRED	The resultant program will be stored in a file called FRED.
LOAD FRED	Search the directory for the file FRED and load the program into memory.

RUN FRED

Begin executing the program.

Thus we have reduced the rather complicated tape sequencing procedure in Chapter 7 to a few straightforward commands to the supervisor on a keyboard. The list of possible commands that may be used is often referred to as the command language.

File Editing

It is obvious that a mechanism is necessary for changing the information recorded in a file on disc. For example, if we were holding the source statements of a program in a file and after assembly we found an error in the source, then we may need to change one or more statements on the file. The changes may also require the addition of more statements or deletion of some already there. These operations are carried out using a special program called an EDITOR. This program is also used for getting the statements on to the disc file in the first place.

The simplest type of editor is a line-editor, where complete lines (or statements) are inserted or deleted. The editor is driven by a series of editor commands, usually typed in on a keyboard. The following examples shows a rather poor initial attempt at getting the well known nursery rhyme onto a disc file using a visual display unit as input.

CREATE MARYONE   (This establishes an 'empty' file on disc called MARYONE

INPUT KEYBOARD   (Characters will be typed in on the keyboard

OUTPUT MARYONE   (Characters will be copied to the file MARYONE

MARY HAD A LITTLE
LAMB   (First line

ITS FLEECE WAS
WHITE AS COAL   (Second line

THE LAMB WAS SURE
TO GO   (Third line

ENDFILE   (Indicates there are no more lines.

We now want to correct the rhyme. The operation is a little like editing a tape on a tape recorder. We first have to get another tape, and then by copying, skipping and inserting sections we can produce the correct version.

CREATE MARYTWO   (A different file

INPUT MARYONE   (Input will come from file MARYONE

OUTPUT MARYTWO   (Output will go to file MARYTWO

COPY 1   (Copy the previous file up to the end of line 1

REPLACE 2   (Replace line 2 by the following line

ITS FLEECE WAS WHITE
AS SNOW

INSERT   (Insert the following line

AND EVERYWHERE THAT
MARY WENT

COPY 3   (Copy across the third line of the input file. Note this becomes the fourth line of the output file.

PRINT MARYTWO   (This displays the contents for checking purposes on the screen.

FILE MARYTWO (4 RECORDS)

001 MARY HAD A LITTLE LAMB

002 ITS FLEECE WAS WHITE AS SNOW

003 AND EVERYWHERE THAT MARY WENT

004 THE LAMB WAS SURE TO GO

     END OF FILE MARYTWO

Note that the line numbers are printed out with the records; this makes editing simpler. We can now remove all trace of the original file by typing the command.

DELETE MARYONE

and this file name will be removed from the file directory and the space which the file occupied made available for further use.

Debug Routine

When programming in assembler language, it is often very frustrating during the test running of a program to find some small error in logic or coding which could be corrected by altering one or two words in the program while it is in memory. Techniques we have examined so far would necessitate editing the source of the program on disc and then re-assembling, a process which will require 5-10 minutes probably. Manufacturers often provide a facility whereby a program in binary can be altered from a keyboard.

On a single program machine where there is no supervisor, this is usually achieved by loading a small program (normally called DEBUG in an area of memory at the high address end. When the main program requires to be changed, the absolute address of the initial instruction of DEBUG is loaded into the program counter by switch settings. DEBUG then begins to run and 'converses' with the VDU. Typicall only three primitive commands are needed P, M, J.

P 46 - 62   Display the contents of stores 46 - 62 on the screen. Each word is printed out in a standard format (eg, a decimal integer, octal integer or alphabetic character).

M 57, 124   Modify memory location 57. Overwrite what is there with 124. Any number of modify memory command may be given. Eventually when we wish to return to our original program at word 72 say, we leave the debug program by issuing a jump command.

J 72   This causes 72 to be copied into program counter and the processor resumes execution at that address.

It is possible to construct a program in memory using only the M command of the DEBUG program and to begin executing the program so constructed by use of the J command.

On a multiprogramming machine, however, the user is normally not aware of the absolute memory locations which his program occupies, so the DEBUG function is usually carried out by the supervisor. The same set of primitive commands are sufficient except that addresses are usually relative addresses within the program, and the supervisor has to be informed, either by program name or number, to which of the programs in memory the modify operations refer. This facility is also available on some microcomputers where the supervisor (including a debug facility) is located in ROM).

Program Swapping

Earlier we discussed the concept of processor sharing, and outlined how the supervisor was responsible for establishing the contents of certain special registers to switch the processor's 'attention' from one program to another. We can now extend the concept of overlaying from that of swapping in sections of the same program, to swapping entire programs. Using the timings we assumed for disc, it is possible to load a 24K byte program in 0.25 s.

Consider a program running in interactive mode, ie, one which receives a line of input from a person sitting at a keyboard, does some processing of that information and displays a response. To make the arithmetic simple we will assume that the user types in 20 characters at 5 per second. This takes 4 secs. Then we will assume the program, in processing this input, executes about 40,000 instructions of average length 6 μs (ie, about 0.25 s). The result (say 40 characters) is printed out at 10 per second (taking 4 secs). The user may then sit examining the output for say 10 secs before being ready to type his next input. So we get the following pattern for a typical transaction:

	process				process	
type in		print out	think	type in		print
4 s	0.25 s	4 s	10 s	4 s	0.25 s	4 s

During the 18.25 sec cycle the processor was really in use for only about 0.25 sec yet the program was occupying 24K bytes of memory during the whole of the 18.25 secs. If we could isolate the typing and printing from the program, it would be feasible to load the program from disc (taking 0.25 sec) immediately before the processing phase and thus release the memory for the other 18 sec.

Here again the supervisor is used; when the user is typing in his request, the supervisor stores each character he types in a buffer inside the supervisor; it then loads the appropriate program, passes the input message to that program (in a few microseconds), and starts the program executing. When the program is ready to display the response, the supervisor intervenes and collects the output (again in a matter of microseconds). It can now safely copy the user program out to disc and at leisure (10 characters per second) transfer the response out to the terminal. This roll in/roll out of the program has obviously extended the transaction time by 0.5 sec but the fact that 24K bytes of memory

are now available for some other tasks is a distinct advantage. Note also that although the transaction time is increased by 0.5 sec the response time (ie the time between the user pressing the last input key and the first character of the output appearing) is only increased by 0.25 secs, because the output to the screen and the rolling out of program to disc can proceed in parallel.

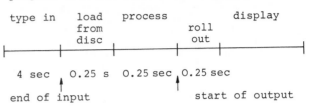

```
type in   load      process        display
          from              roll
          disc              out
  ├──────────┼─────────┼──────────┼────────┤
  4 sec   0.25 s   0.25 sec  0.25 sec
         ↑                   ↑
end of input          start of output
```

In theory, therefore, we could run simultaneously 36 such programs each of which is 24K bytes long in only 24K bytes of real memory. In practice the program profile is not as simple as our example but factors of 10 - 15 are not uncommon.

Foreground/Background

The response time is often the key to the mode necessary for executing a particular program. In section 8.5. we looked at a program for reading employee details from cards and printing wage slips. This program when loaded into memory and initialized will proceed as fast as the supervisor and peripherals will permit, without any human intervention until it is completed. All of the input data is available before the program commences execution, and during execution the response time (ie the time between reading a card containing the employee's hours, etc., and printing the slip) is not terribly significant. In one case it may be fractions of a second and in another case tens of seconds, depending on the other activities being undertaken by the processor. This type of program is normally run in background mode and is usually not swapped out to disc but left in core to mop up any spare processor time.

However, the program we discussed earlier in this section (Program Swapping) was different. After the program issued the equivalent of the read card instruction to invite input from the keyboard, it had to wait (usually for a matter of seconds) until the human interacting with the program responded by typing in the appropriate character string. The computer system is quite patient and will wait indefinitely while the user scratches his head, works out what to type and then slowly types his request, but unfortunately we human beings are not quite so tolerant. Experience has shown that if we have to wait more than 5 - 10 secs for a response, we become progressively fidgety, annoyed, rude and downright violent with the unsuspecting terminal and resort to hammering on the keys, typing the same message in two or three times (to confuse the beast), shaking the terminal violently and eventually turning off its life blood (the power). Therefore an interactive program is usually run in the foreground system - it may be rolled in and rolled out but it is the function of the scheduler in the supervisor to ensure that the response time is tolerable, and to that end programs in the foreground normally get a much higher priority of access to the central processor than those in the background.

There is a third mode of operating known as
real-time. Like interactive programs, real-
time applications require a fast response
time. Unlike interactive systems, however,
failure to provide immediate response in
some instances may be quite catastrophic.
Consider a computer controlling some chemical
process. The input may be a reading of
pressure, temperature, etc., and the output
a signal to turn off a valve, release pressure
or sound an alarm. Such real-time applications need even higher priority than interactive programs and for this reason may be
'locked' down in memory to avoid the possible
overhead of having to be swapped in when
required.

Distinction between the three types of
application is not always as clearcut as the
discussion indicates. For example, airline
seat reservation systems are regarded as
real-time systems rather than interactive
systems. The important factor, however, is
the response time and it is this which will
determine whether the program is to be run
background, foreground or real-time.

8.8.   SUMMARY

It should now be clear that writing a program
to carry out a reasonably complex task is
not as daunting a prospect as it appeared in
earlier chapters. A large portion of the
eventual program may already exist as a
series of subroutines in the appropriate
library on disc or as a function provided
by the operating system or supervisor. In
fact a suitable application program may have
been supplied by the manufacturer which only
requires that the appropriate data be supplied
in some standard format. The library of
subroutines and programs, the various language
compilers and the supervisor all simplify
considerably the task of the programmer.

Programming in Basic
Chapter 9

9.1. INTRODUCTION

The language described in this chapter is a high-level interpreted language called BASIC. By high-level we usually mean a language which does not depend on the special features of any particular machine. On small computers and particularly microcomputers BASIC is the most common high-level language. Every brand of small computer will have a BASIC interpreter. The "interpreter" is the equivalent of a human interpreter. Consider the case of a Chinese visitor who speaks no English addressing a conference in England. He will have an interpreter with him. Every statement which the Chinese dignitary issues will then be translated into English by the interpreter. Note that every time the speech is given the interpreter must be there to translate.

The BASIC interpreter is somewhat similar. It is a program which is usually always resident in the Read Only Memory of the computer; it was provided by the manufacturer of the machine so that we humans could write our programs in a language which is easier for us to understand than the machine's own binary based language.

A major feature of the language is that once a program is written then in theory it can be typed into any machine (which has an interpreter) and executed. Unfortunately this ideal has not yet been achieved because each manufacturer tends to place certain limitations on some sections of the language, while providing additional features elsewhere.

This chapter introduces the BASIC language available on an Apple Microcomputer, and shows how programs in BASIC may be written. BASIC on any other computer is very similar, but care should be taken in case of differences of detail.

What is a Program?

A set of instructions telling the computer what to do. A program is written in a language (in our case) BASIC, which the computer can understand. Like English the language has certain grammatical rules which must be obeyed and a program which is written in a language and is grammatically correct is referred to as syntactically correct. That is not to say that a program which meets this requirement is capable of performing a useful function, only that the set of instructions presented to the computer can be understood and executed. Even then the computer may at

run time detect a hidden flaw, a typical example being that we ask the computer to divide a value by zero. This will result in an error message from the computer and the program execution will be terminated. Another example of a similar type of error is an attempt by the program to find the square root of a negative number.

Constants

Numbers may be represented in one of two ways, Decimal Notation, eg, 1234.5, and Exponent Notation, eg, 1.2345E + 03. That is 1.2345 times 10 to the power of 3 = 1234.5. A numeric constant is a number within the specified range for the computer on which the program will be run. In our case -1E+38 to 1E+38. A number with an absolute value less than about 3E-39 will be converted to zero. These are real values. True integer (whole number) values must lie in the range -32768 to 32767 and may not include a decimal fraction part. We may also have string constants. A sequence of characters is referred to as a 'Literal'. A 'String' is a literal enclosed in quotation marks. These are string constants; "FRED" "THIS IS A STRING CONSTANT" "AND ANOTHER". The characters enclosed in quotes may include numbers and other symbols, eg, "1234" "ABC123DEF456" "£$%&()*:". String constants may consist of from 0 to 255 characters. A string of zero characters is referred to as a null string, ie, "".

Variables

A named location where we may store a value is referred to as a variable, ie, its contents may vary. Names may be any letter A-Z or any combination of two letters or a letter followed by a digit (0-9). The following are all legal variables; A, B1, BA, Z9, CC. The following are not legal variables; 1A, D£, 89. In fact even though only the first two characters of a variable name are significant we may use more than two characters, eg, DATA, PAY, COUNT, COUNTER. Note however that because only the first two characters are significant count and counter are recognised by the computer as CO and represent the same location. This may lead to confusion in a program so always ensure that the first two characters of all variables are unique.

A variable name may be up to 238 characters long but beware there are certain reserved words which have a special meaning in BASIC. A variable name may not include any reserved word thus while EN is a legal variable name END is not as END is a reserved word. More about reserved words later.

A variable, or to give it its full title a
real variable, can hold a real value, ie,
within the limits set for real constants.
Two additional types of variable exist. The
integer variable which is denoted by append-
ing the % character to the variable name. An
integer variable can hold an integer value
within the limits of size imposed on integer
constants. The third type of variable is the
string variable which is denoted by the
addition to its name of the suffix $. A
string variable may hold a string value as
defined for string constants. So AB may contain the real number 1.23, AB% may contain
the integer 17, while AB$ may contain the
letters FRED.

Arithmetic Operators

These are symbols which tell the computer what
arithmetic operations to perform. They are:-
ADD +, SUBTRACT -, MULTIPLY *, DIVIDE /,
RAISE TO THE POWER OF ^. They are used with
constants and variables to form arithmetic
expressions.

Arithmetic Expressions

These take the form of constants and/or variables linked by arithmetic operators, eg, 5+3
7-4 2*3 4/2 3^2. The results of these are 8
3 6 2 9.

Expression Evaluation

Expressions have certain rules about the
manner in which constants and variables are
linked by operators. Operators may never
appear adjacent to one another. The one case
when you might wish to do this is in the case
of the unary minus sign, eg, 2*-3. This form
is not allowed, however it may be rewritten
as -3*2 which has the value -6.

The arithmetic operators have different levels
of precedence. The order being:- ^ then
(* and /) then (+ and -). Thus in an
expression all ^ are done first, then all *
or / operations followed by + and - last.
Applying the above rules 1+3*2^2 has the value
13.

It is not always convenient to write expressions in this way and the rules of operator
precedence may be over-ruled by the use of
brackets. The rule for brackets is that they
must always appear in pairs one (matched by
one). Where brackets are needed the expression enclosed within the innermost pair is
evaluated first. Evaluation within brackets
obeys the rules of precedence. Thus
(1+(3*2))^2 is evaluated as
(1+ 6)^2
   7   ^2
      49
We may overcome the problem above with the
unary minus by the use of brackets thus
2*(-3).

9.2. PROGRAMMING TECHNIQUES

It is often convenient for us to draw out the
logic of a program in the form of a flow
chart. The flow chart is not a suitable form
to give to the computer but is often a useful
aid to show what we are going to do. It is
not always necessary to draw a flow chart
before writing a BASIC program but if you are
in any doubt about the need for one, draw it,
it is never wasted. We shall use only four
symbols.

To indicate start and end

To indicate an operation

To indicate a decision

and where long joining lines
are inconvenient or impossible

It is assumed that the lines joining these
symbols run from top to bottom of the page and
from left to right unless indicated to the
contrary by the use of an arrow.

Consider a program to sum a set of numbers and
print the result. The number of numbers in
the set is not known and is indicated by a
negative number as a terminator. We have
assumed that only positive numbers or zero are
valid.

The program is required to read each number
on the set into the store N and to check if it
is negative. If not then the contents of
store N will be added to the contents of store
S and we repeat the process to read in the
next number. When we come across a negative
number, however, we print the contents of
store S which by now contains the sum of all
the numbers read so far. Just to be on the
safe side we set the contents of store S equal
to zero at the start of the program.

The flowchart looks like this:-

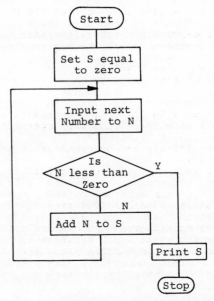

The above analysis allows the human to break
the problem down into a set of simple instructions which the computer is capable of executing. It is now necessary to translate these
instructions into a language which the computer can understand, eg, BASIC.

A BASIC program to do this is as follows:

```
10 LET S=0
20 INPUT N
30 IF N<0 THEN 60
40 LET S=S+N
50 GOTO 20
60 PRINT S
70 STOP
80 END
```

This illustrates a number of programming concepts and structures.

Conditional Decisions

The flow of a program may be altered by testing a condition and going to the next operation in one case or elsewhere in another. In the example above we tested to see if the value of the number stored in the variable N was negative by comparing it with zero and if it was less than zero doing one thing while, if it was greater than or equal to zero doing another. In carrying out these tests we use relational operators. Unless instructed otherwise the computer will normally proceed to the next instruction.

Relational Operators

These operators are:-

Equality	=
Inequality	<>
Greater than	>
Less than	<
Greater than or equal to	>=
Less than or equal to	<=

Rational Expressions

A simple relational expression comprises of two variables or constants separated by a relational operator, eg,

A = B	A equal to B
A < B	A less than B
A > B	A greater than B
A <> B	A not equal to B
A <= B	A less than or equal to B

These expressions normally appear in decision making statements in the program, eg,

If A = B Then S = S+4
If A < B Than S = T-V

More complex relational expressions may be built up with arithmetic expressions on either side of a relational operator, eg,

A+B <> B*B ie, A+B not equal to B times B.

A+Y^2 <= 10 ie, A+Y squared less than or equal to 10.

It is also possible to form a relational expression with string variables and constants on either side of the relational operator. Relational expressions have the value 1 if true and the value 0 if false.

Jumps

Normally the computer will execute instructions in the sequence in which they are written. A jump in a program is a break in the normal logical flow of the program and is the result usually of a conditional decision. In the above example after adding to the sum of numbers we jump back to get the next value. When however the number is negative we jump to print the sum of values. Statement 30 is a conditional jump. Statement 50 is an unconditional jump.

Vectors

A vector is a set of consecutive locations each of which may be uniquely addressed by an index number referred to as a subscript. The vector or one dimensional array is referred

to by a variable name and each element by a subscript. Then if the vector is called H and if it is made up of 5 elements these are referred to as:

H(0), H(1), H(2), H(3), H(4)

Note that the first element of the vector is element zero.

Tables

We may also have a table of variables composed of rows and columns. Each variable in the table is referred to by a name followed by two subscripts enclosed in brackets and separated by a comma. For two rows (horizontal) and three columns (vertical) then the elements are:-

M(0,0) M(0,1) M(0,2)
M(1,0) M(1,1) M(1,2)
where M is the value of the table and the total number of elements is 2 by 3, ie, 6 elements.

Arrays

Vectors and tables are referred to collectively as arrays. A vector is a one dimensional array (eg, a street of houses). A table is a two dimensional array (eg, a calendar). If the subscripts which we use to refer to the various elements of the array were only permitted to be constants then the value of an array would be very limited. We may however use expressions as subscripts. If we consider the two dimensional array M again and if the two simple variables I and J hold the values 1 and 2 respectively then M(I,J) is the same as M(1,2) and the location M(I,J) will itself hold a value which may be any allowable number within the range of the computer for a real variable. Also these array elements may be used in arithmetic or logical expressions as one would use a simple variable, eg,

M(I,J)+A/2
T(R+F,G+F) = Q(W(I*D),S-15)
M(1,2)<=24.7.

We may in addition to having arrays of real variables have arrays of integer variables and arrays of string variables. Nor are we limited to two dimensions in our arrays we may have multiple dimensions up to a maximum of 88.

9.3. BASIC STATEMENTS 1

Let us refer back to our earlier simple example, the flow chart and associated BASIC program. Note that each statement of the basic program is numbered and the numbers increase with each statement from beginning to end. This number serves to uniquely identify each statement.

LET

The LET statement is an assignment statement used to assign a value to a simple variable or an array element. It takes the form LET 'variable' = 'expression'. The simplest form of an expression is a constant as in LET S=0, and in this context the = is not as in the balancing of an algebraic equation but is read as becomes.

So LET S=0 means set the contents of store S equal to zero. This overwrites whatever was in store S before this statement was executed.

At the statement number 40 we see a more complicated expression, ie, LET S=S+N. This at first may look strange as S appears on both sides of the = assignment. Consider however what it means. LET the value of S become S plus N. Thus if before executing this instruction S had the value 20 and N had the value 3 then we would read this as: LET the value of S become 20+3. Now in order to avoid any subsequent confusion we will consider a more difficult example.

LET C=C+15-C^2. If C has the value 3 then if we substitute 3 for C on the right hand side of the assignment we have LET C=3+15-3^2 and evaluating according to the rules of precedence we have:

LET C=3+14-9
LET C=18-9
LET C=9.

Thus after this assignment C has become equal to the value 9. Note that all substitutions for C in the expression were made with C having the value 3 and only when the expression was fully evaluated was C set equal to 9. When both real and integer types are present in an assignment statement all arithmetic is carried out in real form then the result is converted to the type of the variable on the left of the assignment '=' symbol. We may also use the assignment statement to assign a value to a string variable as well as numeric variables thus LET A$="pork pies" assigns to the string variable the value "pork pies". 'LET' is a reserved word in BASIC. All key words in the language which perform a special function are reserved words. A list of reserved words for the computer being used is usually to be found in the BASIC manual associated with that computer system. The vocabulary of reserved words may vary sli htly from one implementation to another. In many implementations of BASIC one may drop the 'LET' from an assignment and more conveniently write A=B+C-27*X rather than LET A=B+C-27*X.

INPUT

It is usually necessary to enter values to the computer program and to enter data from the keyboard we use the INPUT statement. The INPUT statement allows us to enter values to one or more variables and the computer program when it reaches an INPUT statement will display a question mark '?' and await input from the keyboard. Statement 20 requests a value from the keyboard for store N INPUT N.

Other examples of INPUT statements which include both simple variables and array elements are: INPUT A,H(I),M(1,2). We may also have string variables, eg, INPUT A$, which when executed will take the sequence of letters, digits and symbols which the operator depresses on the keyboard and plant them in the variable A$.

PRINT

As well as getting data into the computer program we must get answers out. This is achieved by the PRINT statement which causes values to be displayed on the computer screen or printed on the printer as in statement 60. PRINT S, which outputs the value of S. We may print more than one item in a PRINT statement by separating the print items by a comma or a semicolon. When separated by commas the

items are spaced out acress the print line while with semicolons the items are packed together as closely as possible.

PRINT statements may include a mix of ',' and ';' separators and a mixture of numeric and string values, eg, PRINT A,B;C,R$;H(1),T. The output from each print statement starts on a new line unless the previous print statement executed by the computer ended with a ',' or a ';' thus PRINT F,G;H,I; PRINT J,K;L is the same as F,G;H,I;J,K;L. The print items need not be variables; they may be any expression including in particular we may wish to use string constants to make our results more easily understood as in PRINT "length =",A*B +C;"CMS" which if A=2, B=3 and C=4 would cause length=10 cms to be printed on the next line.

IF

The IF statement corresponds to the decision symbol of the flow chart. It takes the form: IF 'relational expression' THEN 'statement' or IF 'relational expression' THEN 'statement number'. The relational expression is evaluated and if the result is 'true' (value 1) the program executes the statement immediately following the THEN or in the second form jumps to the statement number immediately following the THEN. If the expression evaluates as 'false' (value 0) program execution continues at the beginning of the next numbered statement line. In our simple example, statement 30 corresponds to the decision symbol in the flow chart.

IF N<0 THEN 60. This tells the computer that if N has a negative value the logical expression is 'true' (value 1) and a jump is to be made to statement number 60. If however N has a positive value or is zero the computer will GOTO to the statement at the beginning of the next numbered line, ie, 40. We may place more than one executable statement on a single numbered line. 100 A=B+C:D=F*G. The statements are separated by a colon and it is impossible to execute subsequent statements on a line without the logical flow of the program having passed through earlier ones. By the use of the multiple statement facility we may as a result of an IF statement carry out more than one operation, eg, 100 IF A>10 THEN B=C*27:D=F-G^3:T=R+5-15 110 M=B+D-T. In this example if the relational expression A>10 evaluates as 'true' all the statements following the THEN will be executed in turn before proceeding to line number 110. If however it evaluates as 'false' then none will be executed and control passes immediately to line 110.

GOTO

While the IF statement may be thought of in one of its forms as a conditional jump, ie, go somewhere if a certain condition is true, a GOTO is an unconditional jump and means go to this statement number always.

Statement number 50 of our example shows this, it is used always to jump back to get the next input value after adding the last value entered N to the sum S. A GOTO statement has the form GOTO 'statement number'.

9.4.   PROGRAMMING EXERCISE 1

In this example we shall consider a problem similar to the previous example but this time we shall find the mean of a series of positive values, terminated by a negative number.

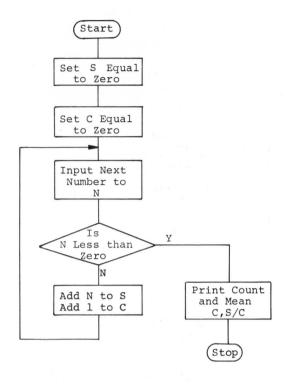

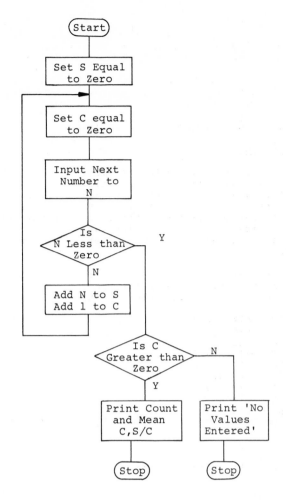

A BASIC program to do this is -

```
10  S=O
20  C=O
30  INPUT N
40  IF N<O THEN 80
50  S=S+N
60  C=C+1
70  GOTO 30
80  PRINT "COUNT =";C,"MEAN =";S/C
90  STOP
100 END
```

This program of instructions is syntactically correct; it can be executed by the computer and most of the time it will produce the correct answer. However, the program has an error in it.

Consider the case where the first and only value entered from the keyboard is a negative number. Then C and S will be zero and an attempt to divide by zero will be made causing an error. It may seem pedantic to worry about such a possibility. Who would seek to find the mean of no values? We shall see later however that where the code used to find the mean forms part of a larger program this can occur. In any case we should always try to make our programs idiot proof, or indeed 'clever dick' proof as there is always someone who will say 'I wonder what if ...'. A simple addition to the program will resolve this problem. If before trying to print the results we test for the value of C greater than zero and if it is not jump to another part of the program to report that no values have been entered.

In this example we shall consider a revised solution to the previous problem, catering for the possible zero condition.

Revised BASIC program -

```
10  S=O
20  C=O
30  INPUT N
40  IF N<O THEN 80
50  S=S+N
60  C=C+1
70  GOTO 30
80  IF C>O THEN 110
90  PRINT "NO VALUES ENTERED"
100 STOP
110 PRINT "COUNT =";C,"MEAN =";S/C
120 STOP
130 END
```

9.5.   BASIC STATEMENTS 2

When we design a program we sometimes want to build into the program certain data values which are fixed or will seldom be changed.

DATA

We may use for this the DATA statement to hold a series of values. This statement has the form DATA followed by one or more numeric or string constants separated by commas. It is used in conjunction with a READ statement.

READ

This statement is similar to the input statement but, instead of taking the values for the variables listed from the keyboard it takes the next value from the DATA statement, eg, READ A,B,H(2),M(I,J)A$. The computer keeps a data pointer which points to the next value to be used from a DATA statement. When

a program starts executing this pointer points
to the first value in the first DATA statement and as each value is used, it moves to
the next. When the last value in a DATA
statement is used the pointer moves to the
first one of the next DATA statement and so
on until all values in all DATA statements
have been used. If a further attempt is made
to read data after the last data item has
been used an error will result.

RESTORE

The numbers in a data statement may be used
more than once. This is achieved by moving
the data pointer back. The RESTORE statement does this. It restores the computer's
pointer to the same state as when a program
is first run, ie, it points at the first
value in the first DATA statement in the
program.

Consider the following trivial programming
example which illustrates the operation of
the data READ and RESTORE statements.

```
10   DATA 1,2,3,4
20   READ A
30   READ B,C
40   DATA 5,6,7
50   READ D,E,F,G
60   READ H,I
70   DATA 8,9
80   RESTORE
90   READ J,K
100  PRINT A","B","C","D","E","F","G","H","J",
     "K
110  END
```

The output from this program would be

1, 2, 3, 4, 5, 6, 7, 8, 9, 1, 2

From this we see that DATA statements may
appear anywhere in a program and we may use
the RESTORE statement to re-use values.

9.6.   PROGRAMMING EXERCISE 2

Continuing to develop the example we have used
we will modify the problem to calculate the
mean of a series of values within given
truncation limits and to accept batches of
values, each batch terminated by a negative
number. The end of data indicated by a null
batch comprised of only a negative number.

We will print the result for each batch as
follows:

Batch Number
Total Count
Over Limit
Under Limit
Within Limits
Mean Value

In the program we will use the variables U,
O, W to count the number of values UNDER,
OVER and WITHIN the limits respectively.
Obviously only those within will contribute
to the mean.

The flow chart shows a possible solution to
the problem. It is not entirely necessary to
count T the total number of values in each
batch as this can be derived from the sum of
U, O and W. It is however convenient to
have T available and to test for T=0 to tell
whether or not to finish.

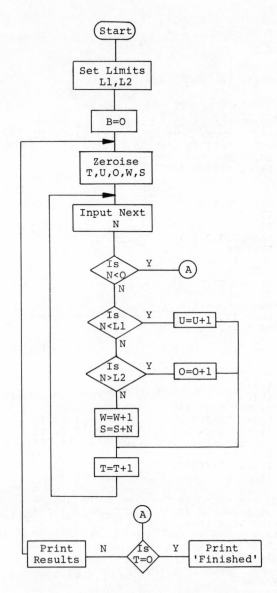

Stop

Below are two BASIC programs both of which are
solutions to the problem. Note that while
both programs are solutions to the same problem one has fewer BASIC statements than the
other. Note that where we test the converse
logical relationship to less than, in the
second solution it is greater than or equal to
and the converse of greater than is less than
or equal to. Note also the use of RESTORE

Study the flow chart and the two programs
carefully. They are almost right. Can you
spot any errors?

```
10   REM SOLUTION 1
20   L1=10
30   L2=50
40   B=0
50   T=0
60   U=0
70   O=0
80   W=0
90   S=0
100  INPUT N
110  IF N<0 THEN 240
120  IF N<L1 THEN 140
130  GOTO 160
140  U=U+1
150  GOTO 220
```

```
160 IF N>L2 THEN 180
170 GOTO 200
180 O=O+1
190 GOTO 220
200 W=W+1
210 S=S+N
220 T=T+1
230 GOTO 100
240 IF T=O THEN 290
250 PRINT "BATCH NO.";B,"TOTAL COUNT";T
260 PRINT "OVER LIMIT";O,"UNDER LIMIT";U
270 PRINT "WITHIN LIMITS";W,"MEAN VALUE";S/W
280 GOTO 50
290 PRINT "FINISHED"
300 END

10  REM SOLUTION 2
20  L1=10
30  L2=50
40  DATA 0,0,0,0,0
50  RESTORE
60  READ T,U,O,W,S
70  INPUT N
80  IF N<O THEN 190
90  IF N>=L1 THEN 120
100 U=U+1
110 GOTO 170
120 IF N<=L2 THEN 150
130 O=O+1
140 GOTO 170
150 W=W+1
160 S=S+N
170 T=T+1
180 GOTO 70
190 IF T=O THEN 240
200 PRINT "BATCH NO.";B,"TOTAL COUNT",T
210 PRINT "OVER LIMIT";O,"UNDER LIMIT";U
220 PRINT "WITHIN LIMITS";W,"MEAN VALUE";S/W
230 GOTO 50
240 PRINT "FINISHED"
250 END
```

Well, the error is that the Batch Number B is
not incremented as we loop through for each
batch. To correct this, add B=B+1 to the
operation box in the flow chart 'zeroise T,
U,O,W,S'. In the programs, the correction
may be made by:

Solution 1 - add the statement 95 B=B+1
Solution 2 - add the statement 65 B=B+1

9.7.   BASIC STATEMENTS 3

We considered earlier the concept of arrays
both one dimensional and multi-dimensional.
We may tell the computer the number of
dimensions in an array and the number of elements of each dimension by the use of the DIM
statement.

DIM

The computer can recognise array variables by
the brackets enclosing the subscript(s) and
can detect the number of dimensions by the
commas separating the subscripts within the
brackets. If we want an array of a specific
size we may indicate this in a DIM statement,
eg, an array the upper most element of which
is 5.

DIM A(5). This causes an array named A of
6 elements to be created. (Remember the
first element of any array is element zero.)
DIM H(20,6). Will set up a two dimensional
array named H comprising of 147 elements
arranged as 21 rows and 7 columns, O-20 and
O-6. We may specify the size of more than
one array in a single DIM statement and the
arrays may be of different types, eg,
DIM A(5),B(10,20),I%(100),R$(23). Remember

% indicates whole numbers (integers) and $
indicates letters and symbols (strings).
There may be more than one DIM statement in a
program and the specification of subscripts
may be by an arithmetic expression, eg,
100 INPUT I,J
110 DIM A(I,J),B(I,2*J)
Note however that an array once dimensioned
may not be redimensioned within the program.
If we use an array within a program without
previously having specifically defined it in
a DIM statement the computer assumes each
subscript to have been dimensioned 10.

REM

The REMARK statement is used only as a note
for the programmer and is ignored by the
computer during execution of the program. It
has the form:

```
10 REM THIS IS A REMARK STATEMENT
20 REM ANY CHARACTER MAY APPEAR AFTER REM
30 REM *-SRETCARAHC YNA +/$
```

The liberal use of REM statements makes a
program more easily understood, although not
executed by the computer they do occupy
memory space.

Note if we make use of the multiple statement
on one line number facility, no statements
may follow a REM as the : separator will be
taken as part of the REMARK. We may however
make a REM statement the last on the line, eg,
100 C1=C1+1:C2=C2+1:REM INCREMENT COUNTERS 1
      and 2.

STOP

This statement causes the computer to stop
execution of the program and display the line
number at which it has stopped.

END

This statement causes the computer to stop
execution of the program, no line number is
displayed.

The program may also be stopped by pressing
the 'CTRL' key and the 'C' key together. If
the program is waiting for input it will be
necessary to also press the 'RETURN' key
after CTRL-C.

After a program has been stopped by any of
the above three means it may be continued
from the next statement, note not the next
line number, by typing CONT.

9.8.   PROGRAMMING EXERCISE 3

We will continue to develop the example we
have used and include the use of arrays with
the DIM statement and the REM statement. Let
us assume that instead of data in batches we
are to deal with the data from five machines
operating on a shop floor and calculate mean
values within the same truncation limits for
each machine. We will print results for each
machine as follows.

Machine Number
Total Count
Over Limit
Under Limit
Within Limits
Mean Value
And
Total Sample for all Machines

The input data will be presented as pairs of values. The first value will be the machine number and the second the measurement. The data input will be terminated by zero machine number with a dummy zero measurement.

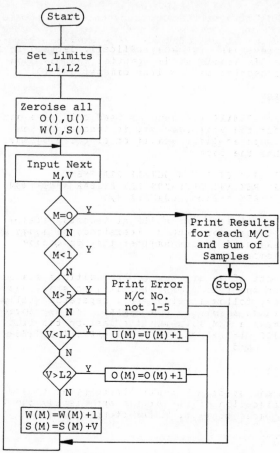

```
10   REM PROGRAM TO ACCEPT PAIRS OF VALUES:
     1ST IS M/C NO. 1-5, 2ND IS READING TAKEN
20   REM DATA ENTRY IS TERMINATED BY ENTERING
     0,0
30   REM
40   REM SET UP ARRAYS FOR 5 MACHINES
50   REM
60   REMO(),U() OVER AND UNDER LIMITS COUNT
70   REM W() WITHIN LIMITS COUNT
80   REM S() SUM OF VALUES WITHIN LIMITS
90   REM
100  DIM O(5),U(5),W(5),S(5)
110  REM LOWER AND UPPER LIMITS
120  DATA 10,20
130  READ L1,L2
140  REM ZEROISE COUNTERS
150  I=0
160  I=I+1
170  O(I)=0
180  U(I)=0
190  W(I)=0
200  S(I)=0
210  IF I<5 THEN 160
220  REM INPUT DATA
230  INPUT M,V
240  IF M=0 THEN 380
250  IF M<1 THEN 360
260  IF M>5 THEN 360
270  IF V>=L1 THEN 300
280  U(M)=U(M)+1
290  GOTO 230
300  IF V<=L2 THEN 330
310  O(M)=O(M)+1
320  GOTO 230
330  W(M)=W(M)+1
```

```
340  S(M)=S(M)+V
350  GOTO 230
360  PRINT "ERROR M/C NO. NOT 1-5"
370  GOTO 230
380  I=0
390  C=0
400  I=I+1
410  C=C+U(I)+O(I)+W(I)
420  PRINT "M/C NO. ";I,"TOTAL=";U(I)+O(I)+W(I)
430  PRINT "OVER LIMIT ";O(I),"UNDER LIMIT "U(I
440  PRINT "WITHIN LIMITS ";W(I),"MEAN VALUE=";
     S(I)/W(I)
450  IF I 5 THEN 400
460  PRINT
470  PRINT "TOTAL SAMPLES FOR ALL M/CS=";C
480  END
```

9.9.   BASIC STATEMENTS 4

FOR   NEXT

In the previous example we wanted to do a sequence of program steps 5 times. Once for each machine. We did this by using a counter I and adding 1 each time round the loop until we had done it 5 times. Because this is a programming operation done frequently for various sizes of loops BASIC has a statement pair to achieve this.

These are the 'FOR' and 'NEXT' statements. If we wanted to execute a sequence of program statements five times we may write

```
FOR I=1 to 5
The Statements to be Executed
NEXT I
```

The statements between FOR and NEXT will be executed 5 times with I taking the values 1 through 5. We may even nest these loops, eg,

```
100 FOR I=1 TO 10
110 FOR J=1 TO 5
120 A(I,J)=0
130 NEXT J
140 NEXT I
```

This would zeroise the elements of a two dimensional array 1-10 and 1-5, ie, 5 by 10 = 50 elements. It is equivalent to the 50 statements A(1,1)=0:A(1,2)=0:A(1,3)=0:A(1,4)=0; A(1,6)=0 A(2,1)=0:A(2,2)=0:A(2,3)=0 . . . A(10,1)=0:A(10,2)=0:A(10,3)=0:A(10,4)=0: A(10,5)=0. Note that the inner J FOR loop is completely bracketed by the outer I FOR loop. We may nest several loops within one another or more than one loop in succession within an outer loop but the range of loops may not overlap.

```
100 FOR I=1 TO 10
110 FOR J=5 TO 20
120 REM SOME STATEMENTS HERE
130 NEXT J
140 FOR J=2 TO 5
150 REM SOME STATEMENTS HERE
160 FOR K=P TO Q
170 REM MORE STATEMENTS HERE
180 NEXT K
190 NEXT J
200 NEXT I
```

Note above we have used P and Q, ie, variables to define the start and end values of the loop We can also increment the loop by a value other than 1 by the use of the STEP statement, eg, 100 FOR I=-3 TO 5 STEP 2
     110 PRINT I;",";
     120 NEXT I
Would Print:- -3,-1,1,3,5. We may even step backwards, eg,

```
100 FOR I=5 TO -3 STEP -1.5
110 PRINT I;",";
120 NEXT I
```
Would print:- 5,3.5,.5,-1,-2.5. Note that the
next step brings us through the limit to -4
and so is not executed. Thus we need not end
exactly on a limit.

GOSUB RETURN

We have used the GOTO statement to jump to a
specific statement number. We may also use
the GOSUB statement to jump to a statement
number. The difference however is that the
computer remembers the next statement which
would have been executed in sequence had the
GOSUB statement not broken the flow and when
it encounters a RETURN statement a jump is
made back to that remembered statement.
Sections of program which are jumped to in
this way are called subroutines. Consider
the following example in which, at various
points in a program we wish to print the value
of a variable squared.

```
100 X=11
110 GOSUB 1000
120 X=27
130 GOSUB 1000
140 X=15
150 GOSUB 1000
160 INPUT X
170 GOSUB 1000
180 END
190 REM SUBROUTINE TO PRINT X AND X SQUARED
1000 PRINT "X= ";X,"X SQUARED= "; X*X
1010 RETURN
1020 END
```

The statements above will be executed in the
following order: 100, 110, 1000, 1010, 120,
130, 1000, 1010, 140, 150, 1000, 1010, 160,
170, 1000, 1010, 180.

ON

The ON statement may be used in conjunction
with the GOTO or GOSUB statements. This
statement allows us to choose between a
number of different GOTO or GOSUB destinations
depending on the value of an expression. The
general form of the statement is: ON
'Expression' GOTO 'Statement number', . . . ,
'Statement Number' or ON 'Expression' GOSUB
'Statement number', . . . , 'Statement Number',
eg,
ON a GOTO 100,500,600,1000,200,300.
This is equivalent to the statements
```
IF A=1 GOTO 100
IF A=2 GOTO 500
IF A=3 GOTO 600
IF A=4 GOTO 1000
IF A=5 GOTO 200
IF A=6 GOTO 300
ON 3*Z/2+1 GOSUB 5000,4000,7000,9000.
```

If the value of the expression is 0 or exceeds
the count of statement numbers then execution
of the program continues with the next statement. If the value of the expression is less
than 0 or greater than 255 an error will
result.

9.10 PROGRAMMING EXERCISE 4

Let us consider again our example to calculate
statistics for five machines, but this time in
addition to calculating the mean we will also
calculate the variance and standard deviation.
In addition instead of printing the machine
numbers 1-5 we will print the serial numbers

which are:-

1. B/397-8
2. A/271-5
3. D/791-10
4. A/272-5
5. C/191-9

In order to calculate the additional statistics we must accumulate the sum of the square
of the numbers.

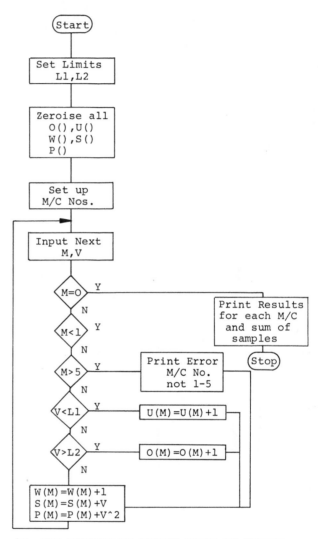

```
10   REM PROGRAM TO ACCEPT PAIRS OF VALUES:
     1ST IS M/C NO. 1-5, 2ND IS READING TAKEN
20   REM DATA ENTRY IS TERMINATED BY ENTERING
     0,0
30   REM
40   REM SET UP ARRAYS FOR 5 MACHINES
50   REM
60   REM O(),U() OVER AND UNDER LIMITS COUNT
70   REM W() WITHIN LIMITS COUNT
80   REM S() SUM OF VALUES WITHIN LIMITS
90   REM P() SUM OF SQUARES OF VALUES WITHIN
     LIMITS
100  DIM O(5),U(5),W(5),S(5),P(5)
110  REM LOWER AND UPPER LIMITS
120  DATA 10,20
130  READ L1,L2
140  REM MACHINE SERIAL NUMBERS
150  DATA B/397-8,A/271-5,D/791-10,A/272-5,
     C/191-9
160  DIM MC$(5)
170  REM ZEROISE COUNTERS AND SET UP M/C SERIAL
     NUMBERS
180  FOR I=1 TO 5
```

```
190 O(I)=O:U(I)=O:W(I)=O:S(I)=O:P(I)=O
200 READ MC$(I)
210 NEXT I
220 REM INPUT DATA
230 INPUT M,V
240 IF M=O THEN 390
250 IF M<1 THEN 370
260 IF M>5 THEN 370
270 IF V>=L1 THEN 300
280 U(M)=U(M)+1
290 GOTO 230
300 IF V<=L2 THEN 330
310 O(M)=O(M)+1
320 GOTO 230
330 W(M)=W(M)+1
340 S(M)=S(M)+V
350 P(M)=P(M)+V*V
360 GOTO 230
370 PRINT "ERROR M/C NO. NOT 1-5"
380 GOTO 230
390 C=O
400 FOR I=1 TO 5
410 GOSUB 1000
420 NEXT I
430 PRINT
440 PRINT "TOTAL SAMPLES FOR ALL M/CS=";C
450 END
990 REM SUBROUTINE TO CALCULATE AND PRINT
    RESULTS
1000 C=C+U(I)+O(I)+W(I)
1010 PRINT "M/C NO. ";MC$(I),"TOTAL="; U(I)+
     O(I)+W(I)
1020 PRINT "OVER LIMIT ";O(I),"UNDER LIMIT ";
     U(I)
1030 PRINT "WITHIN LIMITS ";W(I),"MEAN VALUE=";
     S(I)/W(I)
1040 REM COMPUTE VARIANCE
1050 V=(W(I)*P(I)-S(I)*S(I))/W(I)/(W(I)-1)
1060 PRINT "VARIANCE=";V,"STD.DEV.=";V^.5
1070 RETURN
1080 END
```

9.11. BASIC STATEMENTS 5

A number of functions are available in BASIC
to carry out various commonly used mathematical
and trigonometric operations. These include:
ABS(EXPRESSION) Determines the absolute value
   of the expression
EXP(EXPRESSION) Raises the constant, E
   (2.71828183), to the power of the computed
   expression
INT(EXPRESSION) Gives the largest integer
   value less than the value of the expression
SQR(EXPRESSION) Computes the square root of a
   positively valued expression
SIN(EXPRESSION) Determines the sine of an
   expression
COS(EXPRESSION) Determines the cosine of an
   expression
TAN(EXPRESSION) Determines the tangent of an
   expression
ATN(EXPRESSION) Determines the arctangent of
   an expression
Angles are assumed to be in radians.

DEF

In addition to the functions provided by BASIC
we may define our own functions with the DEF
statement. This takes the form -
DEF FN 'NAME' ('REAL VARIABLE')='ARITHMETIC
EXPRESSION')

We may then use this defined function in a
program as we would an intrinsic BASIC function by entering A=FN 'NAME'('ARITHMETIC
EXPRESSION').

For example if BASIC does not provide an
inverse sine function, we may define it from

the relationship ARCSINE=ATN(X/SQR(-X*X+1)).

The rules for naming functions are the same
as for variables thus we may define our function calling it 'AS' DEF FN AS(X)=ATN(X/SQR
(-1*X+1)).

When we wish to use the function we would
enter A=FN AS(C/7.5).

The computer will substitute the arithmetic
expression in brackets for the dummy variable
X used in the function definition and the
value of A will be set to the result of the
evaluated function.

Functions may be used as elements of expressions thus if we have previously defined
functions T,P1 and G we might enter the
expression A(I,INT(FN T(Q)))=R+FN P1(63*S+FN
G(X)).

9.12. PROGRAMMING EXERCISE 5

Amend the previous example to allow for zero
count of values in calculating the mean and
zero or one value in calculating variance.

9.13. DOCUMENTATION

Description

Write an accurate description of the problem
to be solved and detail any special error conditions or computational techniques used.

Flowcharting

Draw at least a general flow chart showing
the solution and if necessary expand boxes in
this general chart to greater detail on other
more detailed charts.

Program

Write a program numbering lines in stages of
10 or more and start numbering at say 100
rather than 10. Many computer systems provide some form of renumbering utility which
may be employed after the program has been
developed to produce a program numbered from
10 in steps of 10, which is the usual final
presentation of a completed BASIC program.

Collect together in a group as far as possible
statements such as DIM and DEF. Prefix all
subroutines with an END statement. This will
prevent accidental entry to a subroutine by
'Falling through' from the statement above
during program debugging and testing. Group
all subroutines together as a program block.
Use REM statements within the program
wherever appropriate.

Testing

The program should be fed test data to which
the answers are known and all error cases
such as negative, zero values, etc, should
be tried.

Revision

Any subsequent revisions to a program should
be documented together with the reason for
the revision and the error if any corrected.

9.14 OPERATING MODES

To 'get into' BASIC on the Apple, press the
RESET key on the keyboard, followed by the

CONTROL (CTRL) and B keys simultaneously, and
then the RETURN key. A prompt character (>)
and a blinking square cursor will appear on
the monitor (or TV) display.

You may now: 1. Type in and edit programs
2. Introduce BASIC commands
3. Use the Apple as a simple desk calculator.

To generate a BASIC program (for example, one
of those discussed earlier in this chapter),
the typed commands NEW and LIST provide for
storing statements, and listing them. To
execute the program, type RUN. Comprehensive
editing facilities are provided, with the aid
of the cursor. As a simple desk calculator,
the Apple provides answers to questions posed,
by typing PRINT followed by the arithmetic
operation required, followed by RETURN. This
calculate mode operates only with integers.

Programs may be written to and loaded from
tape cassette units and floppy disc storage
units, where these peripherals form part of
the computer system.

When an error is detected, BASIC prints out an
error message, and the message meanings are
listed in the computer handbook.

Similar operating procedures apply to other
small computers. The Apple is mentioned as
a popular example of a modern microprocessor
(6502) based computer. Before using an
unfamiliar computer for the first time, ensure
that you are aware of special features and
differences, preferably by consulting the
computer user's handbook.

9.15. REFERENCES

1. Kemeny, J.G., and Kurtz, T.E., BASIC
    Programming, (John Wiley & Sons, 1971).

2. Apple II BASIC Programming Manual, (Apple
    Computer Inc., 1978).

Glossary of terms

Acknowledgment: Many of the definitions given here have been extracted from 'A Glossary of Computing Terms' (3rd Edition) published by the British Computer Society. Permission to use them is gratefully acknowledged.

Access time	Time between providing an address to a memory device and having the addressed data available.
Accumulator	A register that acts as a source and as a destination for data and results for arithmetic and logical operations.
Acknowledge, ACK	Response to a data transfer or to a request to transfer data.
Address	is the identification of a store location.
Address field	is the part of a machine code instruction which specifies the address of the data to be operated upon.
Algorithm	is a finite set of rules giving a sequence of operations for solving a specific type of problem.
Applications Package, also Package	is a set of specialised programs and associated documentation to carry out a particular application (such as Stock Control).
Analogue	Continuously variable signal or representation of a quantity or parameter.
Architecture	The arrangement of components and systems within a computer or microprocessor and the communications and control connections between them.
Argument	is an input parameter to a subprogram, usually a function.
Array	is a set of storage locations referenced by a single identifier.
ASCII	is a standard code to facilitate the exchange of data between systems (American Standard Code for Information Interchange.
Assembler	is a program, usually provided by the computer manufacturer, to translate a program written in assembly language to machine code. In general, each assembly language instruction is changed into one machine-code instruction. Also called an Assembly Program.
Assembly Language	is a low-level programming language, generally using symbolic addresses, which is translated into machine code by an assembler.
Asynchronous	Without reference to overall timing control - irregular operation.

BASIC	Beginners' All-purpose Symbolic Instruction Code.
Baud	One binary level per second – used as a measure of data transmission rate
Binary-coded Decimal (BCD)	is a numeric coding system in which each decimal numeral is represented by a group of four binary digits.
Binary Notation	is the system using base two and the digits 0 and 1.
Bipolar	Semiconductor technology based on the interaction of positive and negative charge carriers to control current.
Bit	(BInary digiT) is one of the digits used in binary notation, ie, 0 or 1. It is also the smallest unit of storage.
Bubble memory	Solid state device wherein information is stored as microscopic domains (bubbles) of magnetic polarisation.
Bug	is an error in a program or a fault in equipment.
Bus	A physical highway (electrical circuits) for transfer of data within a computer system using parallel lines.
Byte	A group of bits (usually 8) taken together and handled as a unit in a computer.
Card Punch	is an output device which punches holes into cards.
Card Reader	is an input device which reads punched cards.
Carry Bit	is the value which is carried forward from one stage to the next in a binary addition.
Cassette	A package of magnetic tape enclosed in a plastic housing
Central Processing Unit (CPU)	The section of a computer that controls the systems operation by interpreting and executing the program's instructions.
Character	is one of the set of symbols that may be represented in a computer. These can be letters, digits, spaces, punctuation marks, etc.
Chip (silicon chip)	A small piece of silicon on which is fabricated semiconductor devices capable of digital or analogue functions.
Chip Select	A signal or connection whereby an individual packaged chip (integrated circuit) is selected, usually to facilitate a data transfer.
Clock	is an electronic unit for synchronising related pieces of equipment by generating pulses at a constant rate.
COBOL	Common Business Oriented Language.
Code	is a set of program instructions.
Core Store	is a storage device consisting of a matrix of ferrite rings (called cores) with an interlacing system of sensing and

energising wires. Each core can be energised in either of two directions, to represent a single bit of data.

CP/M (Control Program Monitor)	is an operating system for microcomputers which are based on the Z80 microprocessor chip.
Current loop	Serial data connections defined by current levels, eg, binary '0' is zero current, binary '1' is 20 mA.
Data	Information.
Data channel	Interfacing structure using a bus separate from the memory bus.
Data transfer	Movement of data between registers or to and from peripheral equipment.
Decoder	A device that interprets coded inputs to produce unencoded outputs.
Digital	Having only discrete levels, quantized into a set of distinct levels.
Diode	An electronic component which allows current to flow in only one direction.
Direct Access	is the process of storing or retrieving data items without the necessity of reading any other stored data first. Also called Random Access.
Direct Addressing	is where the address specified in the instruction is the address of the location to be used.
Disc (disk)	A magnetic surface for data storage - the circular area is divided into tracks and sectors. Flexible discs are called floppy discs.
Discrete component	A packaged component with a single function, eg, a resistor, diode or transistor.
Dot Matrix	A row and column arrangement of marks or spots to print or display characters or graphic symbols.
Dynamic	Loses memory contents unless they are re-established - 'refreshed'.
Editor	is a program which enables the user to inspect and alter his program or data.
Enable	Permit a device to provide data output or perform a data transfer.
EPROM	Erasable Programmable Read Only Memory (usually erasable by exposure to ultraviolet light).
Executive Program	is a control program which schedules the use of the hardware required by the program being run. Also called Monitor, Supervisor Program.
Field	is a predetermined section of a record.

Field effect	A transistor mechanism where current flow is controlled by an electric field resulting from a voltage applied to the device 'gate'.
File	is an organised collection of related records.
Firmware	Computer programs implemented or 'embedded' in read only memory.
Flipflop	A digital logic circuit with two stable states. It can be switched from one state to the other.
Floating-point Notation	is a form of notation in which numbers are expressed as a fractional value (mantissa followed by an integer exponent of the base). This increases the range of numbers which can be represented. Generally the advantage of the extra range available when working in floating-point notation is gained at the expense of processing time and precision.
Flowchart	is a graphical representation of the operations involved in a data processing system. Symbols are used to represent particular operations or data, and flow lines indicate the sequence of operations or the flow of data.
FORTRAN	FORmula TRANslation.
Game Paddle	is a general name for a hand-held control device used for computer games.
Gate	A digital circuit or element where the output binary code depends on the inputs according to a logic rule.
Graphical Display Unit	is an output device, incorporating a cathode ray tube, on which both line drawings and text can be displayed. It is usually used in conjunction with a light pen to input or re-position data.
Handshake	Response to acknowledge a data transfer.
Hardware	Physical electronic devices and other equipment which form a computer system.
Hexadecimal Notation	is the system using base sixteen and the digits 0, 1, 2, 3 ... 9, A, B, C, D, E, F.
High-level Programming Language	is a problem-oriented language, in which instructions may be equivalent to several machine-code instructions and which may be used on different computers by using an appropriate compiler.
High Resolution Graphics	is a term generally applied to graphical display units capable of fine definition by plotting around 300 or more distinct points in the width of a domestic TV screen.
Immediate Addressing	is where the address field itself is used to hold the data which is needed for the operation. Although the **address** field cannot hold numbers as large as a full storage location, this method is particularly convenient for loading constant data into the accumulator.

Index Addressing	is one method of indirect addressing in which the actual address is found by adding a modifier held in a special register (the index register) to the address in the instruction.
Indexed Addressing	is where the (direct or indirect) address is further modified by the addition of a number held in a special-purpose register, called an Index Register.
Indirect Addressing	is where the address specified in the instruction is that of a location which in turn contains the required address.
Information	is the meaning given to data by the way in which it is interpreted.
Instruction	A set of bits that defines a computer operation.
Integrated Circuit	A complete electronic circuit comprising the equivalent of a large number of functional devices, on a single silicon chip.
Interface	A system of electronic circuits, often with related programs, to connect peripheral equipment (eg, a printer) to a computer.
Interpreter	is a program which translates and executes a source program one statement at a time.
Interrupt	is a signal, generated by a source such as an input or output device, which causes a break in the execution of the current routine. Control passes to another routine in such a way that afterwards the original routine may be resumed.
I/O (Input/Output)	Generic term for equipment and procedures used to transfer data and programs to and from a computer.
Job Control Language	(JCL) is a special language used to identify a job and describe its requirements to the operating system.
K	2^{10} or 1024 (approximately 1000) – a unit of memory.
Keyboard	A set of keyswitches for data and program entry.
Large Scale Integration (LSI)	Electronics comprising more than the equivalent of 100 gates on a single integrated circuit.
Library	is a set of programs which is available to computer users as part of the software of the computer.
Light Emitting Diode (LED)	A semiconductor device that emits light.
Logic	A system in which binary conditions at the inputs provide related binary signals at the outputs.
Low-Level Programming Language	is a machine-oriented language in which each program instruction is close to a single machine-code instruction.

Macro Instruction	is an instruction in a programming language which causes several instructions of the same language to be generated, and which is replaced by those instructions in the program.
Mainframe	is a computer with a variety of peripheral devices, a large amount of backing store and fast CPU. The term is generally used in comparison to a smaller or subordinate computer.
Mark	The state on a serial data communications link representing binary '1'.
Maskable Interrupt	An interrupt that the computer can disable.
Memory	is that part of a computer where data and instructions are held.
Memory Map	The plan of memory areas in a computer system, delineated by storage addresses.
Microcomputer	is a computer whose CPU is a microprocessor. Generally this is a cheap and relatively slow computer with a very limited immediate access store, a simple instruction set and only elementary backing store (eg, cassette tapes, floppy disks).
Microelectronics	Electronic components, devices and circuits fabricated to very small dimensions and the related technology.
Microinstruction	One of the sequence of control signals for control processing unit operation.
Micro-orders	Control signals for computer operation.
Microprocessor	The central processing unit of a small computer on a single LSI integrated circuit, sometimes with additional memory or functions.
Microprogram	A program written at the central processing unit control level.
Minicomputer	is a computer whose size speed and capabilities lie between those of a mainframe and a microcomputer. The term referred originally to a range of computers cheaper and less well equipped than contemporary mainframe machines. With the advent of even cheaper microcomputers, the term is becoming more vague.
Mnemonic	is the name given to a memorising aid which uses a rational 'sounds like what it means' basis, eg, LDA represents LoaD Accumulator.
Modem	MOdulator/DEModulator, a device that converts data into and from a form suitable for transmission over a telephone connection.
MOS	Metal-oxide semiconductor - the technology which uses field effect transistor action.

Multiplexer | A device that selects one of several inputs to be placed on an output bus.

Multiprogramming | is a method of benefiting from the speed of a CPU compared to a slower peripheral device, by allowing two or more programs to be processed apparently simultaneously but actually in bursts, controlled by an operating system. For example, while one program is waiting for an input or output operation to be performed, another may have access to the CPU.

Nonmaskable interrupt | An interrupt that the computer cannot disable.

Object Program | is the translated version of a program that has been assembled or compiled.

Octal Notation | is the system using base eight and the digits 0, 1, 2, 3 ... 7.

Operand | The part of an instruction that is operated upon - the data which is processed.

Operating System | is an advanced form of control program which allows a number of programs to be run on the computer without the need for operator intervention.

Operation Code (Op Code) | The part of an instruction that defines the operation to be performed next.

Overflow | occurs when arithmetic operations produce results which are too large to store.

Paper-tape Punch | is an output device which punches data into paper tape.

Paper Tape Reader | is an input device which reads punched paper tape.

Parallel | Data transmission in which more than one bit is transferred simultaneously.

Parameter | is a name or value made available to a subprogram (eg, subroutine or procedure) from a calling program, or vice versa.

Pascal | after Blaire Pascal, a mathematician.

Peripheral Device | is the term used to describe any input, output, or backup storage device which can be connected to the central processing unit.

Peripheral Interface Adaptor (PIA) | A specialised chip that controls input/output operations in a microprocessor system.

Printer | is an output device producing characters or graphic symbols on paper. There are many methods of printing and of organising the operation of a printer.

Program	is a complete set of program statements structured in such a way as to specify an algorithm.
Program counter	A register that holds the address of the next instruction to be extracted from memory.
Programming Language	is an artificial language constructed in such a way that people and programmable machines can communicate with each other in a precise and intelligible way.
PROM	Programmable Read Only Memory - a type of memory permanently programmed.
Protocol	is an agreed set of operational procedures governing the format of data being transferred, and the signals initiating controlling and terminating the transfer.
RAM	Random Access Memory - memory which can be written to or read from (read/write memory).
Real Number	(in a computing context) is any number with a fractional part. In FORTRAN and some other high-level languages, 'real' is used to indicate floating-point storage.
Record	is a collection of related items of data, treated as a unit (eg, one line of an invoice may form a record). This is called a logical record where necessary to distinguish it from the record as held in computer storage, which may also include control information (the physical record).
Register	is a location, which is sometimes protected, used for specific purposes only, eg, accumulator, control register.
Reset	A signal that starts a computer system in a known state.
ROM	Read Only Memory - memory with fixed contents which can only be read.
Run	is the act of executing a program.
Semiconductor	Material used to fabricate electronic systems, with electrical conductivity between that of conductors and insulators.
Serial	Signal transmission one bit at a time.
Software	Generic term for the programs used in a computer or microprocessor system.
Software Package	is a fully documented program, or set of programs, designed to perform a particular task.
Source Language	is the language in which the source program is written.
Space	The state on a serial data communications link representing binary '0'.
Stack	is a list where items are added to or deleted from the same end of the list.

Static	Retains memory contents unless acted upon by external signals (unlike dynamic memory).
String	is textual data in the form of a list of characters.
Strobe	A one-bit signal used for timing or to clock or enable a register.
Subprogram/ Subroutine	is a set of program instructions performing a specific task, but which is not a complete program. It must be incorporated into a program in order to be used; variously known as a subroutine, routine, procedure or function.
Symbol Table	is the table maintained by a compiler or assembler relating names to machine addresses. Also called a Name Table.
Sync	Timing signal.
Synchronise	Operate in time with an overall source or clock.
Systems Program	is one of the programs which control the performance of a computer system (eg, Compiler or Monitor).
Tape	Magnetic material in the form of a strip.
Teletypewriter	is an input/output device consisting of a keyboard and a typewriter-like printer, often combined with a paper tape punch and reader. It can be used either for direct communication with the computer or for the preparation of punched paper tape for subsequent input.
Terminal	is the term used to describe any input/output device which is used to communicate with the computer from a remote site.
Time-Sharing	is a means of providing multi-access to a computer system. Each user is, in turn, allowed a time slice of the system's resources, although each appears to have continuous use of the system.
Time slice	is the predetermined maximum length of time during which each program is allowed to run during multiprogramming.
Transistor	A semiconductor device in which the current flow between two terminals is controlled by the voltage or current at another terminal.
Translator	is a computer program used to convert a program from one language to another, usually from a low-level language to machine code.
Tri-state	Logic outputs with three possible states – high, low and inactive (high impedance). The inactive state can be combined with other similar outputs in a bus arrangement.
Truth table	A listing of inputs and corresponding outputs for a logic device or system.

TTL	Transistor-Transistor-Logic - a digital logic device family based on transistor structures implemented as integrated circuits.
Variable	is the identifier associated with a particular storage location.
Visual Display Unit (VDU)	is a terminal device, incorporating a cathode ray tube, on which text can be displayed. It is usually used in conjunction with a keyboard.
Vectored interrupt	An interrupt that provides a code to identify the appropriat interrupt service routine.
VLSI	Integrated circuits with the equivalent of over 1,000 gates on a single chip.
Volatile	Loses memory contents when power supply removed.
Winchester disc	A hard disc system with non-removable storage media.
Word	is a collection of bits treated as a single unit by the central processor.
Word length	The number of bits in the computer word.

Index